TOPOLOGICAL DYNAMICS

TOPOLOGICAL DYNAMICS

An International Symposium

Editors

JOSEPH AUSLANDER
University of Maryland

WALTER H. GOTTSCHALK
Wesleyan University

W. A. Benjamin, Inc.

New York   Amsterdam

1968

TOPOLOGICAL DYNAMICS
AN INTERNATIONAL SYMPOSIUM

Library of Congress Catalog Card Number 68-8615
Manufactured in the United States of America
12345K321098

*The manuscript for this volume was received January 25, 1968;
this volume was published October 14, 1968*

W. A. Benjamin, Inc.
New York, New York 10016

Frank J. Hahn   1929-1968

This volume of the papers presented at the Colorado Symposium on Topological Dynamics is dedicated to Frank J. Hahn. He played an active role in the organization of the symposium. In spite of his illness, the dangers of which he was well aware and which led to his death on January 14, 1968, he participated with all the energies at his command in the symposium itself thereby contributing greatly to its spirit and success. His interests spanned much of the work presented there and many of those mathematicians with whom he had worked closely and collaborated in research were present.

Preface

Topological dynamics is an active field of research both in its own right and in its connections with other branches of mathematics.

In August 1967 a symposium on topological dynamics was held at Colorado State University. Over seventy mathematicians from the United States and several foreign countries—England, France, Germany, Israel, Italy, Mexico—participated.

This volume consists of papers presented at the symposium. Included are invited addresses, mainly of an expository nature, by a number of distinguished mathematicians, as well as contributed papers, in which new results are presented.

Invited speakers whose reports appear here are Professors Andrew Avez, Robert Ellis, F. Brock Fuller, Walter H. Gottschalk, Leon Green, G. A. Hedlund, and George Mackey.

In addition to topological dynamics, these papers touch on ergodic theory, ordinary differential equations, almost periodic functions, differental geometry, differential topology, and topological groups. This volume should be of interest to research workers in all of these fields. It should serve, as well, as a supplementary reading to students in advanced graduate courses.

The five-day conference was sponsored by the Air Force Office of Scientific Research through contract F 44620-67-C-0012 with the University of Maryland. Travel grants for many of the participants were made through this contract. Additional funds for travel were made available by a grant from Wesleyan University.

The organizing committee for the symposium consisted of Professors Joseph Auslander (University of Maryland), Donald W. Bushaw (Washington State University), Ervin R. Deal (Colorado State University), Walter H. Gottschalk (Wesleyan University), the late Frank J. Hahn (Yale University), and Dr. Robert J. Pohrer (Air Force Office of Scientific Research).

We would like to express our thanks to Dr. Pohrer, to Professor Hedlund, who assisted in the preparation of these proceedings, and to the Office of Conference Services of Colorado State University for making the facilities of the campus available, thereby providing an ideal setting for the symposium.

Joseph Auslander
Walter H. Gottschalk

July 1968

Table of Contents

Contents

Biography of Frank J. Hahn

Frank J. Hahn was born in New York City on April 14, 1929, the son of Margarata and the late Karl H. Hahn. He graduated from the University of Rochester with a B.A. in mathematics in 1951. After graduation, he served in the United States Navy, being detached in June 1954, with the rank of Lieutenant, j.g.

Hahn entered the graduate school of the University of Illinois in the fall of 1954, earning an M.A. in 1956 and a Ph.D. in 1959. He was a student of Professor W. J. Trjitzinsky who aroused his interest in topological dynamics, the topic in which his dissertation was written (2, 3*). He held a National Science Foundation postdoctoral fellowship at the Institute for Advanced Study during 1959–60 and continued his work on the topological aspects of transformation groups (4, 5).

The following year, 1960–61, Hahn came to Yale as an instructor. This marked an important point in his development as a mathematician. The National Science Foundation sponsored a conference on Analysis in the Large that year at Yale, and a number of distinguished visitors were present. Hahn, with his talent for collaboration, plunged avidly into the work, and played a major role in ensuring the success of the conference.

This work resulted in several papers (6, 7, 8) and in the monograph "Flows on Homogeneous Spaces" (10). This volume is an intensive study of the topological and measure theoretic properties of flows associated with Lie groups. A one parameter subgroup of a Lie group G acts on a homogeneous space G/D of G to produce a coset flow. This includes, as special cases, the classical work of Hopf and Hedlund on horocycle and geodesic flows on compact surfaces of constant negative curvature. In the case that G/D is a nilmanifold, that is, G is nilpotent, an infinite number of minimal, distal,

*See list of publications that follow this biography.

nonequicontinuous flows are produced. These were the first examples of this phenomenon; indeed, it had been conjectured that minimal distal flows were necessarily equicontinuous.

"Distal" was a recurring theme in Hahn's work. Another class of distal systems which he studied were the transformations with quasi-discrete spectrum (12, 19). These include the skew product transformations studied in paper 13. In paper 18, a minimal distal homeomorphism of the two dimensional torus is constructed which admits uncountably many invariant ergodic measures; this has consequences in the theory of C* algebras.

Another notion which interested Hahn was the interrelation between algebras of functions on groups, and the spaces on which these groups act (9, 13, 14). This is connected with almost periodic functions and various generalizations.

We mention two further results. In paper 11, ergodic properties of affine transformations of the torus are used to obtain an elegant proof of Weyl's theorem on equidistribution modulo one. (It is interesting that the Weyl theorem was applied in paper 12 in the study of quasi-discrete spectrum.) In paper 16, examples of uniquely ergodic minimal sets with arbitrarily large entropy are constructed.

Hahn's mathematical contribution extended beyond his distinguished research. He played an important role in mathematical life at Yale. (He was promoted to Assistant Professor in 1961, to Associate Professor in 1966, and to Professor in January 1968.) He was a superb teacher on both the undergraduate and graduate levels, and was most generous with his time to students and younger colleagues.

Frank married Elizabeth Jacobson in 1951. They had four children, Karl, Nancy, Catherine, and Amy. He had a warm and outgoing personality, and had a large number of friends. Certainly, his influence will be felt for many years to come.

Publications of Frank J. Hahn

1. Isolated points in a Banach space. Amer. Math. Monthly 67, 570-571 (1960).
2. Recursion of set trajectories in a transformation group. Proc. Amer. Math. Soc. 11, 527-532 (1960).
3. Some embeddings, recurrence properties and the Birkhoff-Markov theorem for transformation groups. Duke J. Math. 27, 513-525 (1960).
4. On the action of a locally compact group on E_n. Pacific J. Math. 11, 221-223 (1961).
5. Nets and recurrence in transformation groups. Trans. Amer. Math. Soc. 99, 193-200 (1961).
6. (with L. Auslander and L. Markus) Topological dynamics on nilmanifolds. Bull. Amer. Math. Soc. 67, 298-299 (1961).
7. (with L. Auslander and L. Green) Flows on some three dimensional homogeneous spaces. Bull. Amer. Math. Soc. 67, 494-497 (1961).
8. (with L. Auslander) Discrete transformations on tori and flows on solvmanifolds. Bull. Amer. Math. Soc. 68, 614-615 (1962).
9. (with L. Auslander) Real functions coming from flows on compact spaces and concepts of almost periodicity. Trans. Amer. Math. Soc. 106, 415-426 (1963).
10. (with L. Auslander and L. Green) Flows on homogeneous spaces. Annals of Math. Study No. 55, Princeton University Press vii, 107 (1963).
11. Affine transformations of compact Abelian groups. Amer. J. Math. 85, 428-446 (1963); errata, Amer. J. Math. 86, 463-464 (1964).
12. (with W. Parry) Minimal dynamical systems with quasi-discrete spectrum. Proc. London Math. Soc. 40, 309-323 (1965).
13. Skew product transformations and the algebras generated by $\exp(p(n))$. Illinois J. Math. 9, 178-190 (1965).
14. (with J. Auslander) Point transitive flows, algebras of functions and the Bebutov system. Fund. Math., LX, 117-137 (1967).
15. A fixed point theorem. Math. Systems Theory I, 1, 55-57 (1967).
16. (with Y. Katznelson) On the entropy of uniquely ergodic transformations. Trans. Amer. Math. Soc. 126, 335-360 (1967).
17. (with E. Effros) Locally compact transformation groups and C^* algebras, Bull. Amer. Math. Soc. 73, 222-226 (1967).
18. (with E. Effros) Locally compact transformation groups and C^* algebras, Memoirs Amer. Math. Soc. No. 75 (1968).
19. (with W. Parry) Some characteristic properties of dynamical systems with quasi-discrete spectrum, Math. Systems Theory, 2, 179-190 (1968).

UNIVERSAL AND QUASI-UNIVERSAL FLOWS

R. D. Anderson

(Louisiana State University)

1. INTRODUCTION

The results cited in this paper are, for the most part, included in [1, 2], but the point of view here is somewhat more general. In [4] Baayen and in [5] Baayen and deGroot have also obtained a number of results like those represented here. In addition, they have generalizations of the method of linearization given below which give interesting results for types of topological groups other than discrete flows. The argument below for Theorem 3.3 is considerably simplified from that given in [1]. All spaces under consideration are understood to be separable metric. By a _map_ or _mapping_ is meant a continuous transformation.

1

A <u>transformation</u> <u>group</u> is a triple (G, Y, a)
where G is a topological group, Y is a separable
metric space and, a is a map from G x Y onto Y such
that (1), for g_1, $g_2 \in G$ and $y \in Y$, $a(g_1g_2, y)$
$= a(g_1, a(g_2, y))$, and (2), if e is the identity of
G, then for any $y \in Y$, $a(e, y) = y$.

A flow is a transformation group (G, Y, a)
in which G is isomorphic to either the additive
group Z of integers or the additive group R of
reals (with the group G usually written multipli-
catively). In the former case we call the flow
<u>discrete</u>, in the latter <u>continuous</u>.

For any continuous flow (R, X, a), there is
an <u>induced</u> discrete flow (Z, X, a) where Z is regarded as a subset of R and a is appropriately
restricted to the domain Z x X. Any discrete flow
(Z, Y, a) can be considered to be generated by a
homeomorphism g of Y onto itself; thus, $g(y)$
$= a(1, y)$. Also any such homeomorphism generates
a discrete flow with $a(n, y) = g^n(y)$.

For any flow (G, Y, a) and any $Y' \subset Y$ for
which $a(G \times Y') = Y'$, we say that (G, Y', a) is a
subflow of (G, Y, a). If Y' is also a closed
subset of Y we say that (G, Y', a) is a closed

subflow of (G, Y, α).

The flow (G, X, β) is raised by f to the flow (G, Y, α) if f is a map of Y onto X such that the following diagram is commutative.

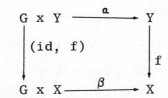

If (G, X, β) and (G, Y, α) are discrete flows generated by the homeomorphisms g_X and g_Y, respectively, then this condition is equivalent to the condition that $g_X f = fg_Y$.

Remark. If the flow (G, W, γ) is raised by f_1 to the flow (G, X, β) and the flow (G, X, β) is raised by f_2 to the flow (G, Y, α) then (G, W, γ) is raised by $f_1 f_2$ to (G, Y, α).

A flow (G, Y, α) is said to be (closed) quasi-universal with respect to a class χ of spaces if for any $X \in \chi$, any flow (G, X, β) can be raised by a mapping h to a (closed) subflow of (G, Y, α). A flow is universal if it is quasi-universal and the mapping h may be specified to be a homeomorphism.

A flow (G, X, β) can be <u>embedded</u> in a flow (G, Y, α) if (G, X, β) can be raised by a homeomorphism to a subflow (G, Y', α) of (G, Y, α). If also $C\ell \ Y' = Y$, then (G, X, β) is said to be <u>densely</u> <u>embedded</u> in (G, Y, α).

<u>Remark</u>. Any flow to which a quasi-universal flow can be raised is itself quasi-universal and any flow in which a universal flow can be embedded is itself universal.

2. UNIVERSAL DISCRETE FLOWS

The basic theorem on universal discrete flows is due to the method of linearization of de Groot [7] as used by Copeland and de Groot in [6].

An <u>infinite</u> <u>product</u> <u>space</u> is a space Y which is homeomorphic to the countable infinite product of a space Y* by itself. Clearly, by refactoring and regrouping such a product, we may write Y as $\Pi_{-\infty < i < \infty} \ Y_i$ where for each i, there is a homeomorphism g_i of Y_i onto Y. We call this latter product, together with the associated homeomorphisms g_i, a <u>canonical</u> product. We shall be

primarily concerned with four infinite product
spaces:

(A)   the Hilbert cube, I^∞, the countable
infinite product of closed intervals;

(B)   the space s, the countable infinite
product of open intervals (or lines);

(C)   the Cantor Set, C, the countable
infinite product of two-point sets;

(D)   the space M of irrationals in s, that is,
the countable infinite product of the space of
irrationals on the line by itself.
It is known [8] that M is homeomorphic to the space
of irrationals on the line.

The infinite shift σ of any infinite product
space Y regarded as a canonical product is the
homeomorphism obtained by carrying each point
$(y_i)_{-\infty < i < \infty}$ to the point $(x_i)_{-\infty < i < \infty}$ where for each
i, $g_{i+1}(y_{i+1}) = g_i(x_i)$.   For any space of types (A)
to (D) above we label the infinite shift as σ_A,
σ_B, σ_C, or σ_D.   Notice that the infinite shift σ_C
is not the same as the well-known ordinary shift σ_0
of the Cantor set in which C is regarded as a
product of two-point spaces.   We may note that σ_0
has exactly two fixed points while σ_C has infinitely

many fixed points.

THEOREM 2.1 (METHOD OF DE GROOT). For any infinite
product space Y, the infinite shift σ generates a
(closed) universal discrete flow with respect to
the class of all spaces which have (closed) embeddings in Y.

Outline of proof. Let $\Pi_{-\infty<i<\infty} Y_i$ be a canonical
product for Y with, for each i, g_i a homeomorphism
of Y_i onto Y. Let f_o be a (closed) embedding of a
space X in Y and let h be a homeomorphism of X onto
itself. Let f be the function of X into Y defined
for each $x \in X$, by

$$f(x) = (y_i)_{-\infty<i<\infty}$$

where for each i

$$y_i = g_i^{-1} f_o h^i(x)$$

Then it may easily be verified that f is a
homeomorphism of X into Y with the property that
$fh = \sigma f$ or, equivalently, $hf^{-1} = f^{-1}\sigma$. Thus f^{-1} is
the desired homeomorphism of a subset of Y onto X.
For the closed flow case, we may also easily verify

that $f(X)$ is closed if and only if $f_o(X)$ is closed.

Since, as is well known, any separable metric space can be embedded in the Hilbert cube or in s and since any zero-dimensional separable metric space can be embedded in the Cantor Set or in the space of irrationals on the line, we immediately get two corollaries.

COROLLARY 2.2. The infinite shifts on the Hilbert cube and on s generate universal discrete flows with respect to the class of all separable metric spaces.

COROLLARY 2.3. The infinite shifts on the Cantor set and on the space of irrationals generate universal discrete flows with respect to the class of all zero-dimensional separable metric spaces.

From Corollary 2.2 we know that we can embed any discrete flow on any separable metric space in a flow on a compact metric space, namely I^∞. Indeed, the discrete flows on compact metric spaces are precisely those which can be embedded as closed subflows of the flow generated by σ_A. Also, since σ_A is a homeomorphism, we know that for any subflow

(Z, Y', a) of the flow generated by σ_A, $C\ell$ Y' in
I^∞ is compact and $a(Z \times C\ell Y') = C\ell Y'$. Thus we
have established the following theorem about
compactifications. (A metric <u>compactification</u> of
a separable metric space X is a compact metric space
containing a dense homeomorphic image of X.)

THEOREM 2.4. Any discrete flow on a separable
metric space X can be densely embedded in a discrete flow on some metric compactification of X.

<u>Remark</u>. The compactification of X identified in
Theorem 2.4 is by no means unique. There may be
many different possible such compactifications.
Each metric compactification of X which admits a
flow on which the flow on X can be densely embedded, can be obtained by the process of linearization since any such compactification of X
could itself be embedded by f_0 in the space Y of
the outline of the proof of Theorem 2.1. Then the
flow on the compactification could be embedded in
the flow on I^∞.

The discussion above answers certain
questions about closed universal flows and about

closed embeddings of flows for the class of compact metric spaces. For noncompact spaces we need some more definitions. An <u>absolute-G_δ</u> space is a (separable metric) space which may be considered to be a G_δ-subset of some compact metric space Y (that is, its complement in Y is a countable union of compact sets).

In [3, Corollary 5.6] it is shown that for any subset K of s such that K is the countable union of compact sets, s\K is homeomorphic to s.

We are now in a position to give an easy argument for the following theorem.

THEOREM 2.5. A separable metric space X is embeddable as a closed set in s if and only if X is an absolute-G_δ.

<u>Proof</u>. I. Suppose X is an absolute-G_δ and let f be an embedding of X in a compact space Y with, by hypothesis, $K = Y \setminus f(X)$ being a countable union of compact sets. Let g be an embedding of Y in s. But by [3, Corollary 5.6], there is a homeomorphism h of $s \setminus g(K)$ onto s and thus hgf is a closed embedding of X in s.

II. Suppose ϕ is a closed embedding of X in s and consider s as canonically embedded in I^∞ (the closed interval factors of I^∞ being the closures of the open interval factors of s). Then $C\ell\ \phi(X)$ in I^∞ is compact and $C\ell\ \phi(X)\backslash\phi(X)$ is a countable union of compact sets (since $I^\infty\backslash s$ is a countable union of compact sets). Hence X is an absolute-G_δ.

From Theorems 2.1 and 2.5 we get the following corollary.

COROLLARY 2.6. The infinite shift σ_B of s generates a closed universal discrete flow on s with respect to the class of all absolute-G_δ separable metric spaces.

Since every absolute-G_δ, zero-dimensional, nowhere locally compact, separable metric space is homeomorphic to the space M of irrationals [8], it is not difficult to prove the following theorem.

THEOREM 2.7. The infinite shift σ_D of M generates a closed universal discrete flow on M with respect to the class of all absolute-G_δ zero-dimensional separable metric spaces.

3. QUASI-UNIVERSAL DISCRETE FLOWS

In this section we shall prove the following theorem. The method is different from and easier than that used in [1, 2].

THEOREM 3.1. The infinite shift σ_C on the Cantor set is a quasi-universal discrete flow with respect to the class of all separable metric spaces.

Proof. By Corollary 2.2, every discrete flow on a separable metric space can be raised to (in fact, embedded in) a subflow of the flow on I^∞ generated by σ_A. Thus in order to prove Theorem 3.1 it suffices to prove the following theorem.

THEOREM 3.2. The flow generated by the infinite shift σ_A on the Hilbert cube can be raised to the flow generated by the infinite shift σ_C on the Cantor set.

Proof. Let $\Pi_{-\infty<i<\infty}C_i$ and $\Pi_{-\infty<i<\infty}I_i^\infty$ be canonical products for C and I^∞, respectively, with, for each i, g_i a homeomorphism of C_i onto C and g_i' a homeomorphism of I_i^∞ onto I^∞. Let f_0 be a map of C_0 onto

I_o^∞ and let f be the map of C onto I^∞ defined (co-ordinatewise) as

$$f((y_i)_{-\infty < i < \infty}) = (x_i)_{-\infty < i < \infty}$$

where for each i,

$$x_i = g_i'^{-1} g_o' f_o g_o^{-1} g_i (y_i)$$

It is easy to verify that f raises the flow on I^∞ generated by σ_A to the flow on C generated by σ_C.

As an almost immediate corollary of Theorem 3.1 we get a theorem proved with some difficulty in [1] and used in [2] to prove a theorem like Theorem 3.1.

THEOREM 3.3. For any homeomorphism h of a compact metric space X onto itself there exists a map ϕ of the Cantor set C onto X and a homeomorphism g of C onto itself such that $\phi g = h\phi$.

Proof. By Theorem 3.1 we raise the flow generated by h to a subflow (Z, C', α) of the flow generated by σ_C. But C' must be compact since X is compact.

Now define (Z, C' x C, $\overline{\alpha}$) by

$$\overline{\alpha}: Z \times (C' \times C) = \overline{\alpha}: (Z \times C') \times C$$

$$= (a: Z \times C', \text{ identity}: C)$$

and clearly the flow generated by h can be raised
to $(Z, C' \times C, a)$. Since $C' \times C$ is homeomorphic
to C the theorem follows.

4. QUASI-UNIVERSAL CONTINUOUS FLOWS

Let (Z, C, a^*) denote the discrete flow
generated by σ_C on C. Using this discrete flow,
there is an easy way to produce a quasi-universal
continuous flow.

Let Y denote the space $C \times I$ where I is the
closed interval $[0, 1]$. Let Y^* denote the image of
$C \times I$ under a map which is one-to-one except on
$(C \times \{0\}) \cup (C \times \{1\})$ and is two-to-one there,
identifying each point $(c, 1)$ with the point
$(\sigma_C(c), 0)$. Since Y is one-dimensional, so is Y*.
Let $(Z, Y*, \beta*)$ denote the discrete flow on Y*
generated by the homeomorphism f which for each t
$(0 \le t < 1)$ carries (c, t) onto $(\sigma_C(c), t)$. But
using the parametrization of t from zero to one,
there is a naturally defined continuous flow
$(R, Y*, \beta)$ for which $(Z, Y*, \beta*)$ is the induced
discrete flow. Furthermore, any continuous flow

(R, X, α) can be raised to a subflow of (R, Y*, β) by first raising the induced discrete flow (Z, X, α) to a subflow of (Z, Y*, β*). We have thus indicated a proof of the following theorem.

THEOREM 4.1.   There is a one-dimensional compact metric space Y* and a continuous flow on Y* which is quasi-universal with respect to the class of all separable metric spaces.

The following theorem is proved explicitly in [9]. We only state it here.

THEOREM 4.2.   Let I^2 be the closed 2-cell with boundary $B(I^2)$ and let $\tilde{C}$ be any topological Cantor set contained in $I^2 \backslash B(I^2)$.   Then any homeomorphism f of $\tilde{C}$ onto itself can be extended to a homeomorphism F of I^2 onto I^2 such that $F \big| B(I^2)$ = identity $\big| B(I^2)$.

For our final theorem we let f be the infinite shift on $\tilde{C}$ (using notation as in Theorem 4.2). Let $W = I^2 \times [0, 1]$ and let W* be the image of W under a map which is one-to-one except on $(I^2 \times \{0\})$ $\cup (I^2 \times \{1\})$, and is two-to-one there, identifying each point (x, 1) with the point (F(x), 0).   Now

W* is a solid torus since F is the identity on

$B(I^2)$. Proceeding as indicated above we may

describe a continuous flow on W* in which (R, Y*, β)

may be embedded and in which each longitudinal

circle on the boundary B(W*) of W* is carried onto

itself. Letting V* be a slightly larger solid

torus containing W* in its interior, we may, in

$C\ell$ V*\W*, scale the flow down from (R, B(W*), β)

on B(W*) to a flow keeping each point of B(V*)

fixed. Thus we have the following theorem.

THEOREM 4.3. There exists a continuous flow on the

solid torus which is quasi-universal with respect

to the class of all separable metric spaces and

which leaves the boundary of the torus pointwise

fixed.

REFERENCES

1.   Anderson, R. D., On Raising Flows and Mappings,
Bull. Am. Math. Soc., 69 (1963), pp. 259-264.
2.   Anderson, R. D., Quasi-Universal Flows and
Semi-Flows, Fund. Math., 57 (1965), pp. 1-8.
3.   Anderson, R. D., Topological Properties of the

Hilbert Cube and the Infinite Product of Open
Intervals, Trans. Am. Math. Soc., 126 (1967), pp.
200-216.

4.   Baayen, P. C., Universal Morphisms, Mathematical
Centre Tracts 9, Mathematical Centre, Amsterdam,
1964.

5.   Baayen, P. C., and de Groot, J., Linearization
of Locally Compact Transformation Groups in Hilbert
Space.   Submitted to Math. Systems.

6.   Copeland, Jr., A. H., and de Groot, J.,
Linearization of a Homeomorphism, Math. Ann., 144
(1961), pp. 80-92.

7.   De Groot, J., Every Continuous Mapping is
Linear (Abstract), Notices Am. Math. Soc., 6 (1959),
p. 844.

8.   Knaster, B., and Urbanik, K., Sur les espaces
complets separables de dimension 0, Fund. Math.,
40 (1953), pp. 194-202.

9.   Oxtoby, J. C., and Ulam, S. M., Measure-
Preserving Homeomorphisms and Metrical Transitivity,
Ann. Math. 2, No. 42 (1941), pp. 874-920.

ANOSOV DIFFEOMORPHISMS[1]

A. Avez

(Faculte des Sciences, Paris,

and University of Minnesota)

In recent years Anosov [1, 2] introduced an interesting class of diffeomorphisms, the so-called C-diffeomorphisms, and announced several new results concerning their structural stability and their ergodic properties. In my report I shall give a short presentation of results already known concerning these diffeomorphisms and I shall present some new results of mine related to their topological classification. Let us begin with an example.

---

[1]This work was partially supported by the United States Air Force under Contract No. F 44620-67-0012.

1. EXAMPLE (THOM, SMALE)

Let us consider the diffeomorphism φ of the two-dimensional torus $T^2 = \{(x, y) \bmod 1\}$

$$\varphi : \begin{pmatrix} x \\ y \end{pmatrix} \longrightarrow \begin{pmatrix} 1 & 1 \\ 1 & 2 \end{pmatrix}\begin{pmatrix} x \\ y \end{pmatrix} (\bmod 1)$$

In the chart (x, y), the differential $d\varphi_m$ of φ at $m \in T^2$ is the linear mapping

$$\begin{pmatrix} 1 & 1 \\ 1 & 2 \end{pmatrix}$$

Hence, $d\varphi$ has two real propervalues, λ_1 and λ_2

$$0 < \lambda_2 < 1 < \lambda_1$$

with corresponding properdirections X_m and Y_m. Now let $\|u\|$ be the length of a tangent vector u of T^2 with respect to the Riemannian metric $ds^2 = dx^2 + dy^2$.   Then

(a) the tangent space $T(T^2)_m$ at m splits into the direct sum $X_m \oplus Y_m$

(b) $\|d\varphi(u)\| = \lambda_1\|u\|$ for $u \in X_m$

$\|d\varphi(u)\| = \lambda_2\|u\|$ for $u \in Y_m$

This means that X_m is dilating and Y_m contracting. This is a typical example of the C-diffeomorphisms.

2.   DEFINITION (ANOSOV [1])

A diffeomorphism φ of a compact connected smooth manifold M onto itself is called a C-diffeomorphism if there exist two fields of tangent planes X_m and Y_m and a Riemannian metric g on M such that:

(a)   the tangent space TM_m at m is the direct sum $X_m \oplus Y_m$, where dim $X_m \neq 0$, dim $Y_m \neq 0$;

(b)   if $d\varphi$ is the differential of φ and $||u||$ is the Riemannian length of a tangent vector $\vec{u}$, then, for any positive integer n, we have

$$||d\varphi^n(\vec{u})|| \geq a\lambda^n||u|| \quad ||d\varphi^{-n}(u)|| \leq b\lambda^{-n}||u||$$
$$\text{for} \quad u \in X_m$$
$$||d\varphi^n(u)|| \leq b\lambda^{-n}||u|| \quad ||d\varphi^n(u)|| \geq a\lambda^n||u||$$
$$\text{for} \quad u \in Y_m$$

with some constants a, b > 0, λ > 1 independent of n and u. X_m is called the dilating space and Y_m the contracting space.

Example 1 is a C-diffeomorphism

$$a = b = 1 \quad \lambda = \lambda_1$$

Although these conditions seem to depend on the choice of the metric g, one sees immediately that

the inequalities hold for any metric g', possibly
with other constants a' and b'. In fact, since M
is compact there exist two positive constants A and
B such that

$$A||u||' \leq ||u|| \leq B||u||' \quad \text{for every} \quad u \in TM$$

Hence, if the above inequalities hold for g with
constants a and b, they still hold for g' with
constants a' = A/Ba and b' = B/Aa.

3.   ELEMENTARY PROPERTIES

The following properties are easily checked:

3.1.   The subspaces X_m and Y_m are uniquely determined
and depend continuously on m (they are, respectively, the "most dilating" and the "most contracting"
subspaces of TM_m).

3.2.   The integers dim X_m and dim Y_m do not depend
on m (they are continuous functions of m with
integer values on the connected space M).

3.3.   The dilating and the contracting fields X_m

and Y_m are invariant under φ

$$X_m = d\varphi(X_\varphi - 1_m) \qquad Y_m = d\varphi(Y_\varphi - 1_m)$$

(apply the definition and the uniqueness).

3.4 POWERS OF φ. Let $N \neq 0$ be an integer, then (M, φ^N) is a C-diffeomorphism.

<u>Proof</u>. If $N > 0$, just change λ into λ^N. If $N = -1$, just exchange X_m and Y_m:

$$X_m' = Y_m \qquad Y_m' = X_m$$

3.5 PRODUCT. Let (M_i, φ_i), $i = 1, 2$, be two C-diffeomorphisms. We regard $M_1 \times M_2$ as the Riemannian product of M_1 and M_2 and we define $\varphi_1 \times \varphi_2: M_1 \times M_2 \rightarrow M_1 \times M_2$ by

$$(\varphi_1 \times \varphi_2)(m_1, m_2) = (\varphi_1 m_1, \varphi_2 m_2)$$

Then $(M_1 \times M_2, \varphi_1 \times \varphi_2)$ is a C-diffeomorphism.

<u>Proof</u>. Using the notations of Section 2, we find that

$$X_{(m_1, m_2)} = X_{m_1} \oplus X_{m_2} \qquad Y_{(m_1, m_2)} = Y_{m_1} \oplus Y_{m_2}$$

$$a = \min(a_1, a_2) \quad b = \max(b_1, b_2)$$
$$\lambda = \min(\lambda_1, \lambda_2)$$

Thus, studying C-diffeomorphisms reduces to studying the irreducible ones.

We turn now to some deeper results.

4.   FURTHER PROPERTIES

4.1   (ARNOLD-SINAI [5]).   The dilating and the contracting fields X and Y are invariant under φ and they are completely integrable.

Hence, there exist two foliations X and y which are invariant under φ. The foliation X is tangent to the dilating field X and the foliation y is tangent to the contracting field Y.

Each leaf of both these foliations is a smooth submanifold of M, but the foliations need not be differentiable: a leaf passing through m does not need to depend smoothly on m. However, if dim M = 2 (and then dim X_m = dim Y_m = 1) then X_m and Y_m have continuous derivatives with bounded variations.

4.2   (ARNOLD-SINAI [5]).   The C-diffeomorphisms on

a prescribed manifold M form an open set in the space of diffeomorphisms for the C^1-topology.

Both of the above statements are proved in full generality in [4, 6].

4.3 (ANOSOV [1, 3]). Every C-diffeomorphism is structurally stable.

A very lucid proof can be found in J. Moser [12].

5. C-DIFFEOMORPHISMS WHICH POSSESS AN INVARIANT MEASURE

Now, let us assume that there exists a smooth measure $\mu > 0$ which is invariant under the C-diffeomorphism φ; for example, $d\mu = dx \cdot dy$ in Example 1.

5.1 (ANOSOV-SINAI [2]). (M, μ, φ) is ergodic.

Since, according to 3.5, (M x M, φ x φ) is still a C-diffeomorphism with invariant measure μ x μ, the Cartesian square (M x M, μ x μ, φ x φ) is ergodic and the mixing theorem (see Halmos [9, p. 39]) implies that (M, μ, φ) is weakly mixing.   In fact, Anosov proved more:

5.2   (ANOSOV [2]).   (M, μ, φ) is a K-system.

In particular this system is strongly mixing, has Lebesgue spectrum and positive entropy.

Let us call m $\in$ M a periodic point if it is a fixed point of some iterate φ^n, n $\in$ Z^+.

5.3   (ANOSOV [1]).   The set of the periodic points of φ is dense in M.

Proofs of the above results will be found in the forthcoming paper of Anosov [3].

Quite recently K. R. Meyer [11] proved the following counterpart of 5.3:

Let $N_n(\varphi)$ be the number of fixed points of φ^n, then there exists a constant k>0 such that

$$N_n(\varphi) \leq k^n \quad \text{for} \quad n \in Z^+$$

6.   SOME PROBLEMS

Let M be a compact, connected, orientable surface which admits a C-diffeomorphism.   By 3.1, we see that M admits two continuous fields of tangent directions X_m and Y_m.   Thus, the Euler-

Poincaré number $\chi(M)$ is zero and M is homeomorphic to the torus T^2.

More generally, let us consider a C-diffeomorphism (M, φ), the dilating (or contracting) spaces of which are odd-dimensional. Then, by a theorem of Samelson-Willmore, we see easily that $\chi(M) = 0$ (Avez [6, t.2, p. 90]).

These examples lead to the following problems.

6.1 (AVEZ [6], SMALE [18]). Which compact manifolds M admit C-diffeomorphisms? Must M be covered by Euclidean space?

6.2 (SMALE [18]). Find all C-diffeomorphisms of compact manifolds, up to topological conjugacy.

What follows is mainly devoted to these problems.

7. C-DIFFEOMORPHISMS WITH A CONTRACTING FOLIATION
   OF CODIMENSION 1

In this section, we consider C-diffeomorphisms $\varphi : M \rightarrow M$ whose contracting (or dilating) foliations (see Section 4) have codimension 1.

7.1   THEOREM.   Let $\varphi : M \to M$ be a C-diffeomorphism.
Let us assume that dim M $\neq$ 4 and that the contracting (or dilating) foliation y is C^2-differentiable.
If Y_m has codimension 1, then M is homeomorphic to
a torus.   If dim M = 2, the theorem reduces to a
remark of Section 6.   If dim M = 3, the theorem is
due to H. Rosenberg and J. Sondow [16, Corollary 2].
Let us assume dim > 4, the theorem is a direct
consequence of the following lemmas.

7.2   LEMMA.   Let $\varphi : M \to M$ be a C-diffeomorphism.
Then, each leaf of the contracting or dilating
foliation is diffeomorphic to Euclidean space.

Proof (Communicated to me by V. Arnold).   To fix
the ideas, let us consider a contracting leaf y_m.
It is a complete Riemannian submanifold of M for
some Riemannian metric on M.   Let K $\subset y_m$ be a
compact subset.   The invariance of the foliation
y implies that $\varphi^n K$, $n \in Z$, is a compact subset of
the leaf $y_{\varphi^n m}$.   But there exists $\epsilon > o$ such that
any compact subset K' of M, whose diameter δ is
smaller than ϵ, is covered by a ball B.   Hence, if
n is large enough, that is

$$\delta(\varphi^n K) \leq b\lambda^{-n} \cdot \delta(K) < \epsilon$$

$\varphi^n K$ is covered by a ball B' of $y_{\varphi^n m}$ belonging to B. The counterimage $\varphi^{-n}(B')$ is a ball of y_m which covers K. Thus, y_m is a paracompact manifold such that every compact subset is covered by a ball. Then, y_m is diffeomorphic to Euclidean space (Brown [8], Stallings [19]).

7.3 LEMMA (NOVIKOV [13], ROSENBERG [15]). Let M be a compact n-dimensional manifold with a foliation of class C^2 each of whose leaves is R^{n-1}. Then M is covered by R^n and $\pi_1(M)$ is free Abelian.

The final "lemma" was communicated to me by C. T. Wall.

7.4 LEMMA. If a compact manifold M is covered by R^n and if $\pi_1(M)$ is free Abelian, then M is homeomorphic to the torus T^n if $n > 4$.

After this theorem, one can hope that any compact manifold which admits a C-diffeomorphism is homeomorphic to a torus. This turns out to be false, as Smale proved by exhibiting nontoral diffeomorphisms.

8. AN EXAMPLE OF SMALE [18]

Let H be the nilpotent group of the matrices
of the form:

$$\begin{pmatrix} 1 & x & y \\ 0 & 1 & z \\ 0 & 0 & 1 \end{pmatrix} \qquad x, y, z \in R$$

The group G = H x H is the space of matrices

$$\begin{pmatrix} A & 0 \\ 0 & B \end{pmatrix}$$

A, B each of the above form.

Let Γ be the subgroup of G, whose matrices
are of the form

$$\begin{pmatrix} 1 & a & b & & & \\ & 1 & c & & & \\ & & 1 & & & \\ & & & 1 & \overline{a} & \overline{b} \\ & & & & 1 & \overline{c} \\ & & & & & 1 \end{pmatrix}$$

where a, b, c $\in Z(\sqrt{3}) = \{m + n\sqrt{3} \quad m, n \in Z\}$ and
$\overline{a} = m - n\sqrt{3}$ if a = m + n$\sqrt{3}$.

It is easily checked that:

  (a) Γ is nilpotent, non–Abelian, and discrete

  (b) $M = \{g^\Gamma \mid g \in G\} = G/\Gamma$ is compact

Since G is diffeomorphic to R^6 and then simply
connected, the first homotopy group $\pi_1(M)$ is
isomorphic to Γ and non–Abelian. In particular M
is nonhomeomorphic to T^6. Now, we set $\lambda = 2 + \sqrt{3}$,
$\nu = (2 - \sqrt{3})^2$, $\mu = \lambda\nu = 2 - \sqrt{3}$. Any element of
G is identified with $(x, y, z, X, Y, Z) \in R^6$, and
we define a mapping $\widetilde{\varphi} : G \to G$ by:

$$\widetilde{\varphi}(x, y, z, X, Y, Z) = (\lambda x, \mu y, \nu z, \overline{\lambda}X, \overline{\mu}Y, \overline{\nu}Z)$$

  It is an automorphism of G because $\mu = \lambda\nu$.
On the other hand, $\widetilde{\varphi}\Gamma = \Gamma$, and we define a diffeo-
morphism of $M = G/\Gamma$ by setting $\varphi : g^\Gamma \longrightarrow \widetilde{\varphi}(g)\,\Gamma$.
We are going to prove that $\varphi : M \to M$ is a C-diffeo-
morphism. First we define a Riemannian metric on M.
The Lie algebra of G is:

$$(TG)_e = \left\{ \begin{pmatrix} 0 & a & b & & & \\ & 0 & c & & & \\ & & 0 & & & \\ & & & 0 & A & B \\ & & & & 0 & C \\ & & & & & 0 \end{pmatrix} \right\}$$

The following metric on TG_e

$$ds^2 = da^2 + db^2 + dc^2 + dA^2 + dB^2 + dC^2$$

defines a right invariant metric on G and, consequently, a Riemannian metric on M.

The tangent space TG_e is the direct sum
$X \oplus Y$, where:

$$X = \left\{ \begin{pmatrix} 0 & a & 0 \\ & 0 & 0 \\ & & 0 \\ & & & 0 & 0 & B \\ & & & & 0 & C \\ & & & & & 0 \end{pmatrix} \right\} \qquad Y = \left\{ \begin{pmatrix} 0 & 0 & b \\ & 0 & c \\ & & 0 \\ & & & 0 & A & 0 \\ & & & & 0 & 0 \\ & & & & & 0 \end{pmatrix} \right\}$$

By right translations the splitting is imposed on
the tangent space of G at g, $TG_g = \tilde{X}_g \oplus \tilde{Y}_g$, and is
right invariant under Γ. Thus, this defines a
splitting $X_m \oplus Y_m$ of TM_m. Since $\lambda > 1$, $0 < \mu$,
$\nu < 1$, it is easily checked that $d\varphi : X_m \longrightarrow X_{\varphi m}$ is
dilating and $d\varphi : Y_m \longrightarrow Y_{\varphi m}$ is contracting.

9.   UNIVERSAL COVERING

    Although the Smale example is nontoral, the

space M is covered by the Euclidean space R^6 = G.
This fact is general as far as we assume there
exists a continuous measure $\mu > 0$ which is invariant
under the C-diffeomorphism.

9.1 THEOREM. Let φ be a C-diffeomorphism of a
compact manifold M, which possesses a continuous
invariant measure $\mu > 0$. Then, the universal
covering $\tilde{M}$ of M is a Euclidean space. The proof
depends on the subsequent lemmas.

　　　Let $\pi : \tilde{M} \longrightarrow M$ be the natural projection. The
diffeomorphism φ lifts to a diffeomorphism
$\tilde{\varphi} : \tilde{M} \longrightarrow \tilde{M}$, $\pi\tilde{\varphi} = \varphi\pi$, which is defined up to an
element of $\pi_1(M)$. Of course, $\tilde{\varphi}$ is a C-diffeo-
morphism. In particular, it possesses two in-
variant foliations $\tilde{X}$ and $\tilde{Y}$ which are, respectively,
the lifts of the dilating and the contracting
foliations of φ.

9.2 LEMMA. Each leaf of $\tilde{X}$ (or $\tilde{Y}$) is diffeomorphic
to a Euclidean space.

Proof. This is just a rephrasing of Lemma 7.2.
According to 5.3, φ possesses some periodic point

m; $\varphi^N m = m$. The leaf X_m of X (or Y_m of Y) passing
through m is called a periodic leaf.

9.3 LEMMA. Let X_m (or Y_m) be a periodic leaf. Then,
$\pi^{-1} X_m$ is everywhere dense in $\widetilde{M}$ and any leaf of
$\pi^{-1} X_m \subset \widetilde{X}$ intersects all the leaves of $\widetilde{Y}$.

Proof. It is sufficient to prove that X_m is dense
in M and cuts all the contracting leaves. The
uniform transversality (M compact) of the foliations
X and Y implies that the union of the contracting
leaves which intersect X_m is an open set Ω (Reeb [14,
p. 106]). On the other hand, X_m and Y are invariant
under φ^N, because $\varphi^N m = m$. Hence, Ω is invariant
under φ^N. But φ^N is a C-diffeomorphism (see 3.4)
which possesses an invariant measure μ; thus, φ^N
is ergodic (see 5.1) and, consequently, $\mu(M - \Omega) = o$.

Let x be a point of Ω. The contracting leaf
Y_x passing through x cuts X_m. We denote by $f(x)$
the Riemannian distance in Y_x of x to $X_m \cap Y_x$. Of
course $f(x)$ is greater than the Riemannian distance
$d(x)$ of x to X_m, counted in M. Let us consider the
dynamical system (Ω, μ, φ^N) and the function $d(x)$.
From the very definition of C-systems, we have

$$\frac{d(x) + \ldots + d(\varphi^{Nk}x)}{k}$$

$$\leq \frac{f(x) + \ldots + f(\varphi^{Nk}x)}{k}$$

$$\leq b \cdot f(x) \cdot \frac{1 + \lambda^{-N} + \ldots \lambda^{-Nk}}{k}$$

$$\leq b \cdot f(x) \cdot \frac{1}{k(1 - \lambda^{-N})}$$

Thus, the time mean $\overset{*}{d}(x)$ of $d(x)$ vanishes on Ω. The Birkhoff ergodic theorem implies

$$\int_\Omega d(x) \cdot d\mu(x) = 0$$

But $\mu(M - \Omega) = 0$, therefore

$$\int_M d(x) \cdot d\mu(x) = 0$$

and $d(x) \equiv 0$ because $d(x)$ is continuous and non-negative. This means precisely that X_m is dense in M.

It follows at once that X_m cuts all the leaves of y.

9.4 LEMMA. Two leaves of $\widetilde{X}$ and $\widetilde{y}$, which are, respectively, the lifts of a periodic dilating leaf

X_m ($\varphi^N m = m$) and a periodic contracting leaf y_m,
intersect only in one point.

Proof. By the preceding lemma their intersection
is not empty. Let us assume they intersect in two
distinct points $\tilde{a}$ and $\tilde{b}$. Then, X_m and y_m intersect
in two distinct points $a = \pi\tilde{a}$ and $b = \pi\tilde{b}$, such that
there exists a closed curve $a\beta$ which bounds a disk
D, with $a \subset X_m$, $\beta \subset y_m$, and $\partial a = -\partial\beta = b - a$. We
can even select the curves a and β such that D be
a smooth surface, because X_m and y_m are smooth
submanifolds.

The foliation y induces on D [or at least on
a disk bounded by $\varphi^{-Nk}(a\beta)$, k large] a continuous
and free-of-singularity field of directions. This
field must be tangent to a and transverse to β,
whence contradiction.

9.5 LEMMA. Let X_m be a periodic leaf ($\varphi^N m = m$) and
a and b two points of $\pi^{-1}X_m$. There are two
dilating leaves $\tilde{X}_a$ and $\tilde{X}_b$ passing through a and b
and which are some lifts of X_m. By the preceding
lemma, a leaf $\tilde{y}_m \subset y$, which is a lift of the
periodic leaf y_m, intersects $\tilde{X}_a$ in a' and $\tilde{X}_b$ in b'.

Let $\delta(a', b')$ be the Riemannian distance (in $\widetilde{y}_m$) of a' to b', and $d(a, b)$ be the Riemannian distance (in $\widetilde{M}$) of a to b. Then

$$\delta(a', b') \leq C \cdot d(a, b)$$

where C is a constant independent of the particular lift $\widetilde{y}_m$ of y_m.

Proof. It is a direct consequence of the axioms of C-diffeomorphisms if one observes that we may assume $\pi(a) = \pi(b) = m$ and, therefore

$$d(\widetilde{\varphi}^{Nk}a, \widetilde{\varphi}^{Nk}b) = d(a, b)$$

while

$$\delta(\widetilde{\varphi}^{Nk}a', \widetilde{\varphi}^{Nk}b') \leq b \cdot \lambda^{-Nk} \cdot \delta(a', b')$$

9.6 PROOF OF THEOREM 9.1. Let m be a periodic point $\varphi^N m = m$, with periodic leaves X_m and y_m. We select definitively a lift $\widetilde{X}_m \subset \widetilde{X}$ of X_m and a lift $\widetilde{y}_m \subset \widetilde{y}$ of y_m, and we set

$$A = \widetilde{X}_m \cap \pi^{-1}y_m \qquad B = \widetilde{y}_m \cap \pi^{-1}X_m$$

Let us define a mapping $f : A \times B \to \widetilde{M}$. If $(a, b) \in A \times B$, then $f(a, b)$ is the unique point

of intersection of the contracting leaf of $\tilde{y}$ passing
through a with the dilating leaf of $\tilde{X}$ passing
through b. Lemma 9.5 shows that f is an homeomorphy
of the subspace A x B of the Riemannian product
$\tilde{X}_m$ x $\tilde{y}_m$ onto f(A x B). This lemma proves also that
the oscillation of f vanishes at every point of the
closure $\overline{A \times B}$. Since $\tilde{M}$ is a complete Riemannian
space, according to a theorem of Lavrantiev (for
example, Kuratowski [10, p. 336]), f can be extended
to an homeomorphy f* of $\overline{A \times B}$ into $\tilde{M}$. But the
transversality of $\tilde{X}$ and $\tilde{y}$ and the density of
$\pi^{-1}y_m$ and $\pi^{-1}X_m$ imply

$$\overline{A} = \tilde{X}_m \qquad \overline{B} = \tilde{y}_m \qquad \overline{f(A \times B)} = \tilde{M}$$

Thus, we have

$$\tilde{M} = \overline{f^*(A \times B)} = f*(\overline{A \times B}) = f^*(\overline{A} \times \overline{B})$$
$$= f^*(\tilde{X}_m \times \tilde{y}_m)$$

and $\tilde{M}$ is homeomorphic to $\tilde{X}_m$ x $\tilde{y}_m$. This concludes
the proof because $\tilde{X}_m$ and $\tilde{y}_m$ are homeomorphic to
Euclidean spaces.

Now, we turn to the more difficult problem
of the topological classification of the C-diffeomorphisms.

10.   TOPOLOGICAL CLASSIFICATION OF THE C-DIFFEO-

       MORPHISMS

    Let us begin with an example.

10.1 ERGODIC AUTOMORPHISMS OF THE TORUS T^2. Let

φ be an ergodic automorphism of the torus T^2

$= \left\{ (x, y) \mod 1 \right\}$

$$\varphi : \begin{pmatrix} x \\ y \end{pmatrix} \longrightarrow \begin{pmatrix} A & B \\ C & D \end{pmatrix} \begin{pmatrix} x \\ y \end{pmatrix} \quad (\mod 1)$$

$$A, B, C, D \in Z \quad AD - BC = 1 \quad (or\ -1)$$

We already know (Section 1) that φ is a C-diffeo-

morphism which preserves the measure $d\mu$ = dxdy.

It is readily checked that the following quadratic

form is invariant under φ

$$ds^2 = C\ dx^2 + (D - A)\ dxdy\ - B\ dy^2$$

This form is indefinite because φ is ergodic:

$$1 - \left(\frac{D + A}{2} \right)^2 < 0$$

Thus an ergodic automorphism φ of T^2 is an isometry

for some Lorentzian metric ds^2 whose isotopic

directions at m are the dilating space X_m and the

contracting space Y_m of φ.

This situation is quite general.

10.2 THEOREM.[2] Let φ be a C-diffeomorphism of a smooth, compact, connected, and orientable surface M. Let us assume there exists a smooth (C^2) positive measure μ, which is invariant under φ. Then, (M, φ) is topologically conjugate to an ergodic automorphism of T^2.

The proof depends on the subsequent lemmas.

10.3 LEMMA. The surface M admits a Lorentzian metric g, whose isotropic directions at $m \in M$ are X_m and Y_m, whose area element is $d\mu$, and which possesses continuous derivatives $\partial_\alpha g_{\beta\gamma}$ with bounded variations.

Proof. According to Arnold and Sinai (see 4.1) X_m and Y_m possess continuous derivatives with bounded variations. Since M is orientable, this allows one to construct two vector fields u and v, the deriva-

―――――――――

[2]Since this paper was written, Smale communicated to me that J. Franks relaxed the existence of μ.

tives $\partial_\alpha u_\beta$ and $\partial_\alpha v_\beta$ of which are continuous with bounded variations, and such that

$$0 \neq u_m \in X_m \qquad 0 \neq v_m \in Y_m$$

Let $(u_m{}^*, v_m{}^*)$ be the dual basis of (u_m, v_m) in $T(M)_m$. Then, $h = u^* \oplus v^* + v^* \oplus u^*$ is a metric which possesses continuous derivatives with bounded variations.

This metric is indefinite and its isotropic directions at m are X_m and Y_m because

$$h(u, u) = 2 < u^*, u > \cdot < u^*, v > = 0$$
$$h(v, v) = 2 < u^*, v > \cdot < v^*, v > = 0$$

The metric we require is

$$g = \frac{\mu}{|\operatorname{Det} h|^{\frac{1}{2}}} \cdot h$$

10.4 LEMMA. The diffeomorphism φ is an isometry of (M, g).

Proof. The metric g_m and its image $\varphi^* g_m$ under φ possess the same isotropic directions and the same area element, because X_m, Y_m, and μ are invariant under φ. Since dim $M = 2$, we have $\varphi^* g_m = g_m$ for all m $\in$ M.

10.5 LEMMA.   The Lorentzian manifold (M, g) is
flat.

Proof.   Let us assume, which is not the case a
priori, that g is C^2-differentiable.   Then, the
Gaussian curvature R of g exists and is continuous,
and we may resort to the following argument:

. The Gaussian curvature $\overset{*}{R}(m)$ of φ^*g at m is
nothing but $R(\varphi m)$, as proves a local computation.
Since $\varphi^*g = g$, we have $R(\varphi m) = R(m)$.   Hence, R is
invariant under φ.   But φ is ergodic (see 5.1) and
R is continuous; thus, R = constant.   On the other
hand, the Gauss-Bonnet formula still holds for
Lorentzian metrics (see Avez [7]) and the Euler-
Poincaré number $X(M)$ vanishes (see Section 6);
thus, R = 0.

In fact we only know that the metric g has
continuous derivatives with bounded variations.
This implies that the geodesics of (M, g) exist
and that

$$\left| \hat{A} + \hat{B} + \hat{C} - \pi \right| \leq K \cdot \mu(ABC) \qquad (10.6)$$

for any simply connected geodesic triangle ABC,

where $\widehat{A}$, $\widehat{B}$, $\widehat{C}$ are the Lorentzian angles of ABC and

K is a constant independent of ABC.

Let G be the set of the simply connected

geodesic triangles of M, with nonisotropic sides.

It is clear that these triangles form a basis of

the σ-algebra M of the μ-measurable sets of M.

Consequently, the set L of the finite disjoint

unions of elements of G is dense in M in the sense

of the metric

$$\mu(A \cup B - A \cup B) \qquad A, B \in M$$

Now we define an absolutely continuous addi-

tive function f on L. If $P = \sum_i G_i$, $G_i \in G$, we set

$$f(P) = \sum_i f(G_i) \qquad \text{where} \qquad f(ABC)$$
$$= \widehat{A} + \widehat{B} + \widehat{C} - \pi$$

The following properties of f are easily checked:

(a) $f(P)$ is independent of the decomposition

$\sum_i G_i$;

(b) f is additive;

(c) f is absolutely continuous (consequence

of 10.6).

Thus, f can be extended to an absolutely continuous additive function f^* on M. By the Radon-Nikodym theorem, there exists an integrable function $r : M \to R$ such that

$$f^*(V) = \int_V r \cdot d\mu \quad \text{for any} \quad V \in M$$

In particular, we have

$$\int_{ABC} r \cdot d\mu = \widehat{A} + \widehat{B} + \widehat{C} - \pi \quad \text{for any}$$

$$ABC \in G \tag{10.7}$$

The isometry φ preserves the angles, hence, we have

$$\int_{ABC} r(m) \cdot d\mu(m) = \int_{ABC} r(\varphi m) \cdot d\mu(m)$$

But the elements ABC of G form a basis of M, consequently $r(\varphi m) = r(m)$ a. e. and the ergodicity of φ implies: $r = $ constant a. e.

Now, let $M = \sum_i A_i B_i C_i \quad A_i B_i C_i \in G$, be a finite triangulation of M. By relation 10.7 we have:

$$r = \int_M r \cdot d\mu = \sum_i \int_{A_i B_i C_i} r d\mu = \sum_i (\widehat{A}_i + \widehat{B}_i + \widehat{C}_i -$$

On the other hand, let n_s, n_a, n_f be, respectively, the number of vertices, edges, and triangles of the triangulation; we have, of course,

$$3n_f = 2n_a \qquad n_s - n_a + n_f = \chi(M) = 0$$

It follows that

$$\sum_i (\widehat{A}_i + \widehat{B}_i + \widehat{C}_i - \pi) = 2\pi n_s - \pi n_f = 0$$

and $r = 0$ a. e. By relation 10.7 we have $\widehat{A} + \widehat{B} + \widehat{C} = \pi$ for any geodesic triangle of G. (Q.E.D.)

10.8 PROOF OF THEOREM 10.2. Let $\widetilde{M}$ be the universal covering of M and $\pi : \widetilde{M} \to M$ be the natural projection. The preceding lemma shows that $(\widetilde{M}, \varphi^* g)$ is flat; it is the Minkowsky plane. Thus, any lift $\widetilde{\varphi} : \widetilde{M} \to \widetilde{M}$ of the isometry φ is an inhomogeneous Lorentzian transformation because it is an isometry of $(\widetilde{M}, \varphi^* g)$. The C-diffeomorphism φ does not reduce to a translation and then we can select the lift $\widetilde{\varphi}$ to be an homogeneous Lorentzian transformation of the Minkowsky plane $\widetilde{M}$. Thus, $\widetilde{\varphi}$ is a linear mapping of $\widetilde{M}$, which possesses a fixed point $\widetilde{o}$. Since (M, g) is flat, a fundamental domain of M is a parallelogram $\widetilde{P}$ and we can select $\widetilde{P}$ to have a vertex coin-

ciding with $\tilde{o}$.   Thus, we see that φ is an automorphism of the torus $M = \pi\tilde{P}$.

10.9 REMARK.   Theorem 10.2 implies the analyticity
of φ as a consequence of the existence of a smooth
invariant measure.   This makes probable that
general C-diffeomorphisms do not have such an
invariant measure.

10.10 THE GENERAL C-DIFFEOMORPHISMS.   Let us try
to adapt the proof of Theorem 10.2 to general
C-diffeomorphisms.

    It is clear that a C-diffeomorphism possesses
an invariant metric[3] only if it possesses an invariant measure, namely the volume element of the
metric.   Therefore, in the future, we assume that
$\varphi : M \longrightarrow M$ is a C-diffeomorphism which possesses a
C^2-differentiable invariant measure $\mu > o$ identified
with its density.   Now, we ask for a generalization
of Lemma 10.4:   Does φ admit an invariant metric g?

---

[3]A metric is a field of symmetric and nondegenerate
bilinear forms on M.

10.11 LEMMA. If g is a piecewise continuous invariant metric of φ, then, at each point m $\in$ M, we
have

$$g(\xi, \xi) = o \quad \text{for} \quad \xi \in X_m \cup Y_m$$

Proof. It is sufficient to check the lemma at a
periodic point, because the set of the periodic
points of φ is dense in M (see 5.3) and g is piecewise continuous. Let m be a periodic point,
$\varphi^N m = m$, N > 0. The differential $d\varphi^{kN}$ of any
iteration of φ^N maps the contracting space Y_m onto
itself. The invariance of g implies that

$$g_m(\xi, \xi) = g_m(d\varphi^{kN}\xi, \ d\varphi^{kN}\xi)$$

for any k $\in$ Z and any $\xi \in Y_m$.

Now, let $||u||$ be the length of a tangent
vector in some Riemannian metric of M. Since M is
compact there exists a constant K such that

$$|g(u, u)| \le K \cdot ||u||^2 \quad \text{for any} \quad u \in TM$$

Hence, we have (see Definition 2)

$$|g_m(\xi, \xi)| \le K||d\varphi^{kN} \cdot \xi||^2 \le Kb^2 \cdot \lambda^{-2kN} \cdot ||\xi||^2$$

for any k > o. Consequently, $g_m(\xi, \xi) = 0$
(for $\xi \in X_m$ take k $\rightarrow$ $- \infty$).

10.12 LEMMA. A piecewise continuous invariant
metric g of φ can be canonically identified with a
piecewise continuous field $\widehat{g}$ of isomorphisms
$\widehat{g}_m : X_m \longrightarrow Y_m^*$ of X_m onto the dual Y_m^* of Y_m.

Proof. Any $\xi \in TM_m$ can be written in a unique way:

$$\xi = x + y \quad x \in X_m \quad y \in Y_m$$

By 10.11, we have

$$\widehat{g}_m (\xi, \xi) = 2g_m(x, y)$$

The required isomorphism g_m is defined by

$$2 < \widehat{g}_m(x) \quad y > = g_m(\xi, \xi)$$

Lemma 10.11 shows that, in general, a C-diffeomorphism does not admit an invariant metric g. In
fact, we must have dim X_m = dim Y_m, and the
isotropic cone of g must be contained in $X_m \cup Y_m$.
To overcome this difficulty we introduce the
"twisted square" (M x M, μ x μ, φ x φ^{-1}) of
(M, μ, φ).

10.13 LEMMA. $\varphi \times \varphi^{-1} : M \times M \to M \times M$ is a C-diffeo-morphism which possesses a C^2-differentiable in-variant measure $\mu \times \mu > o$.

Proof. Direct consequence of 3.4 and 3.5.

The dilating and the contracting spaces at (m, m') are, respectively,

$$X_{(m, m')} = X_m \oplus Y_{m'}, \qquad Y_{(m, m')} = X_{m'} \oplus Y_m$$

Their dimensions are equal to $n = \dim M$.

10.14 LEMMA. $M \times M$ possesses a piecewise continuous metric g such that the isotropic space of g at (m, m') is

$$X_{(m, m')} \cup Y_{(m, m')}$$

Proof. Since the dilating and the contracting fields are integrable, any point $(m, m') \in M \times M$ belongs to a local chart (Ω, h), $h : \Omega \to R^{2n}$, such that the dilating leaves of $\varphi \times \varphi^{-1}$ have equations $x^{n+1} = $ constant, ..., $x^{2n} = $ constant, and the contracting leaves $x^1 = $ constant, ..., x^n = constant. The counterimage $h^* 1$ of the metric

$$1(\xi, \; \xi) = 2(\xi^{1} \cdot \xi^{n+1} + \ldots + \xi^{n} \cdot \xi^{2n})$$

of R^{2n} is a continuous metric on Ω, the isotropic space of which at (m, m') is $X_{(m, \; m')} \cup Y_{(m, \; m')}$. The required metric is obtained by selecting a finite covering $\{\Omega\}$ of M and piecing together the corresponding metrics $h^{*}1$.

10.15 THEOREM. There exists a continuous metric g on M x M, which is invariant under $\varphi \; x \; \varphi^{-1}$ and the volume element of which is μ x μ.

A proof of this result would be out of place here. However, the main points can be made quite clearly.

We introduce the vectorial space L of the piecewise continuous fields of linear mappings

$$f_{(m, \; m')} : \; X_{(m, \; m')} \to Y^{*}_{(m, \; m')}$$

We turn L into a normed space by setting

$$||f|| = \sup_{(m, m')} |f_{(m, \; m')}|$$

where

$$|f_{(m, \; m')}| = \sup_{\substack{x \in X_{(m, \; m')} \\ ||x|| < 1}} ||f_{(m, \; m')}x||$$

By 10.12, the nonempty set of the metrics g described in 10.14 is identified with a subset H of
L of piecewise continuous fields $\hat{g}$ of isomorphisms.

The C-diffeomorphism $\varphi \times \varphi^{-1}$ induces an
invertible linear mapping $\Phi : L \to L$ by:

$$< \Phi f_{(m, m')}x, \ y > \ = \ < f_{(\varphi m, \ \varphi^{-1}m')} d(\varphi \times \varphi^{-1})x,$$
$$d(\varphi \times \varphi^{-1})y >$$

for all $x \in X_{(m, m')}, \ y \in Y_{(m, m')}$.

The required invariant metrics g are those
which satisfy $\Phi\hat{g} = \hat{g}$. We establish the existence
of such a fixed point in H by showing that the
closure of the convex hull of H contains a weakly
compact convex subset which is invariant under Φ
(see [17]). The piecewise continuous invariant
metric g we obtain is continuous because $\varphi \times \varphi^{-1}$
is ergodic.

The ergodicity of the isometry $\varphi \times \varphi^{-1}$ of
(M x M, g) is still used to prove that (M x M, g)
is an homogeneous space $G/\Gamma = \{h\Gamma | h \in G\}$. Then,
according to Smale [18], G is nilpotent. We deduce
at once that M x M, and so M, is covered by
Euclidean space, which provides another proof of
Theorem 9.1.

REFERENCES

1. Anosov, D. V., Dokl. Akad. Nauk., 145 (1962),
pp. 707-709.

2. Anosov, D. V., Dokl. Akad. Nauk., 151 (1963),
pp. 1250-1253.

3. Anosov, D. V., Trudy Instituta Steklova (to be
published).

4. Arnold, V. I., and Avez, A., Problemes
ergodiques de la mecanique classique, Gauthier-
Villars, Paris, 1967.

5. Arnold, V. I., and Sinai, Y., Dokl. Akad. Nauk.,
144 (1962), pp. 695-698.

6. Avez, A., Ergodic Theory of Dynamical Systems,
2, lecture notes, University of Minnesota, 1967.

7. Avez, A., C. R. Acad. Sci. Paris, 255 (1962),
pp. 2049-2051.

8. Brown, M., Proc. Am. Math. Soc., 12 (1961),
pp. 812-814.

9. Halmos, P. R., Lectures on Ergodic Theory,
Math. Soc. Japan, 1956.

10. Kuratowski, C., Topologie, 1, Warsaw, 1948.

11. Meyer, K. R., Bull. Am. Math. Soc., 73, No. 5
(1967), pp. 615-617.

12. Moser, J., On a Theorem of Anosov (to be published).

13. Novikov, S. P., Trudy Mosk. Math. Obaces. Va., t 14, n°513.83.

14. Reeb, G., Proprietes topologiques des varietes feuilletees, Hermann, Paris, 1952.

15. Rosenberg, H., Comment. Math. Helv. (1966), pp. 36-44.

16. Rosenberg, H., and Sondow, J., Foliations by Planes (to be published).

17. Ryll-Nardzewsky, Proceedings of the Topological Dynamics Symposium, Berkeley, 1965.

18. Smale, S., Bull. Am. Math. Soc., 73 (1967).

SOME REMARKS ON P-LIMIT POINT STABILITY

J. D. Baum

(Oberlin College and Birkbeck College,
University of London)

The notion of P-limit point stability discussed here is a generalization of the notion of
"stability" due to Friedlander [2, Section 12].
The reference for the fundamental definitions is
[3]. Besides the natural extension of Friedlander's
results [2, Section 13] we prove some further
theorems, perhaps the most interesting of which is
that P-limit point stability is inherited from
syndetic subgroups to the ambient group, but, in
general, not vice versa. A number of examples from
symbolic dynamics is given.

We assume throughout that X is a compact
Hausdorff space, hence is a uniform space, and
that the uniformity agrees with the original
(Hausdorff) topology of X. We make the assumption

of compactness in order to guarantee that for $x \in X$, the P-limit set of x, P_x, is nonempty. We also assume that the phase group T is Abelian throughout. Not every theorem requires the full use of these hypotheses.

DEFINITION. X is $\{$P-limit point stable at x$\}$ $\{$P-limit point stable at x with respect to $Y \subset X\}$ if and only if for each index a of X there is an index β of X so that $\{y \in x\beta\}$ $\{y \in x\beta \cap Y\}$ implies $P_y \subset P_x a$ and $P_x \subset P_y a$. We also say that x is $\{$P-limit point stable$\}$ $\{$P-limit point stable with respect to Y$\}$.

DEFINITION. If $Z \subset X$, Z is $\{$P-limit point stable$\}$ $\{$P-limit point stable with respect to $Y \subset X\}$ if and only if each $x \in Z$ is $\{$P-limit point stable$\}$ $\{$P-limit point stable with respect to Y$\}$. We also say Z is pointwise $\{$P-limit point stable$\}$ $\{$P-limit point stable with respect to Y$\}$.

Remark. Let $C = \{F \,|\, F \subset X,\ F \text{ closed}\}$. Let $a \in U$, the uniformity of X, and define $a^* =$ $\{(F,\ G) \,|\, F,\ G \in C,\ F \subset Ga \text{ and } G \subset Fa\}$, then define

$U^* = \{a^* \mid a \in u\}$. It is easily verified that U^* is
a uniformity base for C. We designate the uniformity
on C thus generated by U^* as well. Now to say that
X is P-limit point stable at x is to say that the
function $\varphi : X \to C$, defined by $\varphi(x) = P_x$, is continuous on (X, U) to (C, U^*) at the point x. Further
to say that X is P-limit point stable at x with
respect to $Y \subset X$ is to say that $\varphi|Y$, that is, the
restriction of φ to Y, is continuous at x.

THEOREM 1. Let P be a replete semigroup in T, let
$x \in X$ be P-limit point stable, then xt is P-limit
point stable for each $t \in T$.

Proof. Let a be an index of X, β the index of X
determined by the P-limit point stability of x,
that is, $y \in x\beta$ implies $P_y \subset P_x a$ and $P_x \subset P_y a$.
Let $z = xt$, then there exists γ, and index of X, so
that $w \in z\gamma = xt\gamma$ implies $wt^{-1} \in zt^{-1}\beta = x\beta$, whence
$P_w = P_{wt^{-1}} \subset P_x a = P_{xt} a = P_z a$, and similarly $P_z \subset P_w a$.
This completes the proof.

THEOREM 2. Let P be a replete semigroup in T, S a
syndetic subgroup in T, then there exists $K \subset T$,

K compact, such that $T = SK$, and $(P \cap S)_x K = P_x$.

Proof. Without loss of generality we may assume that K is chosen so that $T = SK$ and $K^{-1} \subset P$, for by definition there is a K_1, compact, such that $T = SK_1$, and there is a $p \in T$ so that $pK_1 \subset P^{-1}$. Let K $= p^{-1}K_1^{-1}$, then $T = SK$ and $K^{-1} \subset P$.

Now let $p \in P$, $p = sk$ for some $s \in S$ and $k \in K$, $K^{-1} \subset P$. Then $s = pk^{-1} \in P$. Let a be an index of X, then $y \in (P \cap S)_x$ implies $y \in xsq\alpha$ for some $q \in P \cap S$. Thus $y \in xp(qk^{-1}) \alpha$, where $qk^{-1} \in P$, since $K^{-1} \subset P$, whence $y \in \overline{xpP}$ for each $p \in P$. Thus $y \in P_x$ and $(P \cap S)_x \subset P_x$, and since P_x is invariant, $(P \cap S)_x K \subset P_x K \subset P_x$.

On the other hand, let a be an index of X, then select β, an index of X, so that, using [3, Section 1.20]

$$xK\beta \subset x\alpha K \tag{*}$$

Then each of the following statements implies the next: $z \in P_x$; for all $p \in P$ there is a $q \in P$ such that $z \in xqp\beta$; for all $p \in P \cap S$ there is a $q \in P$ such that $z \in xpq\beta$; for all $p \in P \cap S$ there is a $q \in P$ such that $z \in xpsk\beta$, where $q = sk$, for some

$s \in S$, $k \in K$, whence $s = qk^{-1} \in P \cap S$, since $K^{-1} \subset P$;

for all $p \in P \cap S$, there is an $s \in P \cap S$ such that

$z \in xps\alpha K$ by $(*)$ above; $z \in (P \cap S)_x K$. Thus

$P_x \subset (P \cap S)_x K$ and, finally, $(P \cap S)_x K = P_x$. This

completes the proof.

THEOREM 3. Let S be a syndetic subgroup of T. Let

x be $(P \cap S)$-limit point stable in S, then x is

P-limit point stable in T.

Proof. Let α be an index of X; by $[3,\ \text{Section } 1.20]$

there is β, an index of X, such that $z \in (P \cap S)_x$

implies $z\beta K \subset zK\alpha$. Then there exists an index γ of

X so that $y \in x\gamma$ implies $(P \cap S)_y \subset (P \cap S)_x \beta$,

since x is $(P \cap S)$-limit point stable. Now using

Theorem 2 above, we have

$$P_y = (P \cap S)_y K \subset (P \cap S)_x \beta K \subset (P \cap S)_x K\alpha = P_x \alpha$$

Similarly $P_x \subset P_y \alpha$. This completes the proof.

The converse of the above theorem is false;

that is, x can be P-limit point stable, yet not

$(P \cap S)$-limit point stable, as is shown by the

following:

EXAMPLE. Let X be the usual bisequence space [3,
Chapter 12]; let m, n, and k be integers, and let
$a \in X$ where

$$a(k) = 1 \quad \text{for} \quad k = 10n$$
$$a(k) = 0 \quad \text{for} \quad k \neq 10n$$

For n > 0 let $\beta_n \in X$, where

$$\beta_n(k) = a(k) \quad \text{for} \quad |k| \leq 10n$$
$$= 0 \quad \text{for} \quad |k| > 10n \quad k \neq 10m - 1$$
$$= 1 \quad \text{for} \quad |k| > 10n \quad k = 10m - 1$$

Let Y be the union of the orbit closures of a,
β_n, n > 0, and let $P = Z^+ = \{n \mid n \text{ a positive}$
integer$\}$. Then $P_a = aT$, the orbit of a, $P_{\beta_n} = aT$,
since for sufficiently large k, $\beta_n(k) = a(k - 1)$.
Thus a is P-limit point stable in (Y, T). Now let
$S = \{n \mid n = 10m, \text{ m an integer}\}$, then $(P \cap S)_a$
$= a$, $(P \cap S)_{\beta_n} = a\sigma^{-1}$ where σ is the shift transformation; and if ρ is the metric in X, $\rho(a, a\sigma^{-1}) =$
$\frac{1}{2}$, whence a is not (P ∩ S)-limit point stable.

THEOREM 4. If x is P-Liapunov stable with respect
to Y [that is, for each index a of X there exists
an index β of X so that $y \in x\beta \cap Y$ implies

(xp, yp) $\in$ α for all p $\in$ P] and if Y contains some neighborhood U of x, then x is P-limit point stable; in fact, for a suitably chosen neighborhood V of x, V $\subset$ U, y $\in$ V implies $P_x = P_y$.

Proof. Let α be an index of X. Select γ an index of X so that $\gamma^2 \subset \alpha$, and β an index of X so that x$\beta \subset$ U $\subset$ Y, and according to the Liapunov stability of x, that is, so that y $\in$ xβ implies (xp, yp) $\in \gamma$ for all p $\in$ P. Let z $\in P_x$ and let p $\in$ P, then z $\in \overline{xpP}$, whence there exists q $\in$ P such that z $\in$ xpqγ. Now y $\in$ xβ implies (xqp, yqp) $\in \gamma$; thus y $\in$ xβ implies z $\in$ ypq$\gamma^2 \subset$ ypqα, and since α was arbitrary, z $\in \overline{ypP}$; and since p $\in$ P was arbitrary, z $\in P_y$, whence $P_x \subset P_y$. Similarly $P_y \subset P_x$, whence $P_x = P_y$. This completes the proof.

COROLLARY. If x is P-Liapunov stable with respect to Y, then x is P-limit point stable with respect to Y.

The converse of the preceding theorem is not correct, namely, P-Liapunov stability relative to a set Y which contains a neighborhood of the point in question is strictly stronger than P-limit point stability as is shown by the following:

EXAMPLE. Let X be the usual bisequence space [3, Chapter 12], let n and k be integers, and let $a \in$ X, where

$$a(k) = 0 \quad \text{for all} \quad k$$

Let $a_n \in$ X, where

$$a_n(k) = 0 \quad \text{for} \quad k \neq n$$
$$a_n(k) = 1 \quad \text{for} \quad k = n$$

Let Y be the union of the orbit closures of a and a_n, n an integer. Let $P = Z^+ = \{n \mid n$ a positive integer$\}$. We observe that $P_{a_n} = \{a\}$ for all n, whence a is P-limit point stable. However, a is not P-Liapunov stable with respect to any set Z which contains any neighborhood U of a; in fact, a is not pP-Liapunov stable with respect to any such Z for any $p \in$ P, for let $\epsilon < \frac{1}{2}$, $\delta > 0$ so that $U \supset \{\gamma \mid \rho(\gamma, a) < \delta\}$, $p \in$ P, then select $n > p$ so that $1/n < \delta$. Then $\rho(a_n, a) < \delta$, so that $a_n \in$ U, $a(n) = 0$, $a_n(n) = 1$, $n \in$ pP, and $\rho(a\sigma^n, a_n\sigma^n) = \frac{1}{2} > \epsilon$, where ρ is the metric in X and σ is the shift transformation. Thus a is not pP-Liapunov stable with respect to any Z containing U.

One might suppose that if x is P-limit point stable and y is P-asymptotic [0] to x that then y would be P-limit point stable. Such however, is not the case, as is shown by the following:

EXAMPLE. Let X be the usual bisequence space [3, Chapter 12], let m, n, and k be integers, and let $a_{mn} \in X$, where m < n - 1 and

$$a_{mn}(k) = 0 \quad \text{for} \quad m < k < n$$
$$= 1 \quad \text{for} \quad k \leq m \quad \text{and} \quad k \geq n$$

Let $\beta_{mn} \in X$, m < n where

$$\beta_{mn}(k) = 0 \quad \text{for} \quad k \neq m \quad \text{or} \quad n$$
$$= 1 \quad \text{for} \quad k = m \quad \text{or} \quad k = n$$

Let $\delta_n \in X$, where $\delta_n(k) = 0$ for $k \neq n$, $\delta_n(n) = 1$. Let $a \in X$, where $a(k) = 1$ for all k; and $\beta \in X$, where $\beta(k) = 0$ for all k. Let Y be the union of the orbit closures of the points a_{mn}, β_{mn}, δ_n, a, and β above, and let $P = Z^+ = \{k \mid k$ a positive integer$\}$. Note that:

(a) δ_0 and β are P-asymptotic;

(b) δ_0 is P-limit point stable since $P\delta_0$
= $\{\beta\}$ and any neighborhood of δ_0 of
sufficiently small radius contains only
points of the form β_{0n} or β_{m0} for m
and n with $|m| > N$ and $|n| > N$ for
suitably large positive N. Clearly
$P_{\beta_{0n}} = \{\beta\}$ and $P_{\beta_{m0}} = \{\beta\}$ as well;

(c) β is not P-limit point stable, for no
matter how small a neighborhood of β is
chosen, there exist points of the form
α_{mn} in the neighborhood, and $P_\beta = \{\beta\}$
while $P_{\alpha_{mn}} = \{\alpha\}$.

THEOREM 5. Let P be a replete semigroup in T, let
$x \in P_y$ for some $y \in X$, and let x be P-limit point
stable, then

$$P_x = P_y \qquad\qquad\qquad (1)$$

x is P-recurrent [1] $\qquad\qquad (2)$

$$P_x = \overline{xT} \qquad\qquad\qquad (3)$$

Proof. (1) Since P_y is closed and invariant and
$x \in P_y$, $P_x = \bigcap_{p \in P} \overline{xpP} \subset P_y$. Let α be an index of
X, then since x is P-limit point stable there is an
index β of X such that $z \in x\beta$ implies $P_z \subset P_x \alpha$.

Since $x \in P_y = \bigcap_{p \in P} \overline{ypP}$, there exists $q \in P$ such that $yq \in x\beta$; thus $P_{yq} \subset P_x a$, and since $P_y = P_{yq}$, we have $P_y \subset P_x a$ for each index a of X. Since X is regular (that is, T_3 and T_2) we have that $P_y \subset P_x$. Thus $P_y = P_x$.

(2) $x \in P_y = P_x$ by (1) above, hence by [1, Lemma 1], x is P-recurrent.

(3) $P_x \subset \overline{xT} \subset P_y = P_x$ by (1) above, thus equality holds throughout and $P_x = \overline{xT}$. This completes the proof.

Remark. We observe that the preceding theorem guarantees that if T is Abelian and X is compact Hausdorff, then there is a P-recurrent point in X. In view of [3, Section 4.06] this is not surprising; however, the interesting aspect of the remark is that [3, Section 4.06] involves the axiom of choice (or extremum law) whereas this remark does not.

THEOREM 6. Let M be a P-limit set, say $M = P_z$ for some $z \in X$, then (M, T) is minimal if and only if M is pointwise P-limit point stable.

Proof. If M is minimal, let $x \in M$, then since P_x is closed, nonempty, and invariant, $M = P_x$.

Similarly if $y \in M$, $P_y = M$, whence $P_x = P_y$ for any x, $y \in M$, and clearly M is P-limit point stable at x for any $x \in M$.

Conversely, if M is pointwise P-limit point stable, then if $x \in M$, $M = \overline{xT}$ by Theorem 5 above, whence M is minimal. This completes the proof.

COROLLARY. Let M be a P-limit set, say $M = P_z$ for some $z \in X$, then M is minimal if and only if M is pointwise P-limit point stable with respect to M.

THEOREM 7. Let P be a replete semigroup in T, let $x \in P_y$ for some $y \in X$, and let x be P-limit point stable. If z is such that $x \in P_z$, then z is P-limit point stable.

Proof. Let a be an index of X, let $\beta^2 \subset a$; select γ open and symmetric according to the P-limit point stability of x, that is, so that $x' \in x\gamma$ implies $P_x \subset P_{x'}\beta$ and $P_{x'} \subset P_x\beta$.

If $x \in P_z$, then for all $p \in P$, $x \in \overline{zpP}$; thus, there exists $q \in P$ so that $zpq \in x\gamma$ whence, since $x\gamma$ is open, there is an index δ of X so that $zpq\delta \subset x\gamma$. Now if $w \in zpq\delta \subset x\gamma$ we have

$$P_w \subset P_x \beta \quad \text{and} \quad P_x \subset P_w \beta \quad \text{since} \quad w \in x\gamma$$

and

$$P_x \subset P_{zpq} \beta \quad \text{and} \quad P_{zpq} \subset P_x \beta \quad \text{since} \quad zpq \in x\gamma$$

It follows that

$$P_w \subset P_{zpq} \beta^2 \subset P_{zpq} \alpha \quad \text{and} \quad P_{zpq} \subset P_w \alpha$$

Thus zpq is P-limit point stable, whence by Theorem 1 above, z is P-limit point stable. This completes the proof.

Finally the author would like to thank the Governors of Birkbeck College (University of London) and more specifically Professor C. H. Dowker of that college for the facilities of the college and encouragement during the preparation of this paper.

REFERENCES

0. Baum, J. D., Asymptoticity in Topological Dynamics, Trans. Am. Math. Soc., 77 (1954), pp. 506-519.

1. Baum, J. D., P-Recurrence in Topological Dynamics, Proc. Am. Math. Soc., 7 (1956), pp.

1146-1154.

2. Friedlander, F. G., On the Iteration of a
Continuous Mapping of a Compact Space into Itself,
Proc. Cambridge Phil. Soc., 46 (1950), p. 46.

3. Gottschalk, W. H., and Hedlund, G. A., Topological Dynamics, Providence, 1955.

ENTROPY OF TORUS AUTOMORPHISMS[1]

Kenneth R. Berg

(University of Maryland)

I wish to discuss the calculation of the entropy of a group automorphism of the n-dimensional torus X^n. X^n can be described as the quotient group R^n/Z^n ($Z = \{0, \pm 1, \ldots\}$, R = real numbers). If A is an endomorphism of R^n which preserves the integer lattice Z^n then A defines, in a natural way, an endomorphism T of X^n. This correspondence between endomorphisms of R^n preserving Z^n and endomorphisms of X^n is bijective, and the automorphisms T of X^n are characterized by the relation det $A = \pm 1$ for the corresponding transformation

[1]The author wishes to acknowledge partial support by the National Science Foundation under Grant No. GP-5252 and GP-3752 during the time this work was carried out and presented.

A of R^n. It is convenient to restrict our discussion to automorphisms, although the results obtained carry over to the case of endomorphisms.
Thus, in this talk, T will denote an automorphism
of X^n, A will denote the corresponding automorphism
of R^n, $\lambda_1, \ldots, \lambda_n$ will denote the eigenvalues of
A, and $||A||$ will be the norm of A, calculated by
$||A|| = \sup_{v \neq 0} \frac{|Av|}{|v|}$ where $|v|$ is the Euclidean length of
a vector v in R^n.

We let μ denote Haar measure on X^n. We use
μ also to denote Lebesgue measure on R^n. An automorphism of an Abelian group preserves the Haar
measure, so (X^n, μ, T) is a measure space with
measure preserving transformation. (The measure
algebra is, of course, the Borel algebra.)

THEOREM. With the notation above, the metric
entropy and the topological entropy of T are equal
and the value is given by the formula $-\Sigma \log|\lambda_i|$
where the summation is carried out over those λ_i
satisfying $|\lambda_i| \leq 1$. In case the λ_i are repeated,
they are to be counted with their multiplicity in
the characteristic polynomial of A. ($|\lambda|$ denotes
the modulus of the complex number λ.)

Today we will outline a proof for the metric case, and indicate the modifications necessary for the topological case (for metric read measure-theoretic).

The metric case has received the most attention in the literature. In the two-dimensional case, the formula was established by Ja. G. Sinai in [9]. In the same paper, he asserted that the result was true in n dimensions, providing the eigenvalues were real and distinct. A. L. Genis [6] stated that the formula held in n dimensions with no restrictions on the eigenvalues, but he offered no proof. L. M. Abramov [1] pointed out several errors in the paper of Genis, but asserted that the formula for the entropy was correct. D. Z. Arov [3] gave a proof for the formula in 1964. The proof which I will outline today was done independently of Arov's work, and the technique is somewhat different. I believe that the techniques I use can be applied to compute entropy in a more general setting.

We briefly review the notions from entropy theory which we will need. For further details, consult P. Billingsley [5], W. Parry [8], and K. Jacobs [7]. Let (X, F, μ) be a probability space and let T be

a measure preserving transformation of X into itself. Let a be a finite partition of the space X
into measurable subsets $A_1, \ldots, A_k$. By $H(a)$ we
mean $-\Sigma_{i=1}^{k} \mu(A_i) \log \mu(A_i)$. We call $H(a)$ entropy of
the partition a. If we let $a(x)$ be that element of
a such that x is in $a(x)$, then we can express $H(a)$
by the formula $H(a) = -\int \log \mu(a(x)) \, dx$. We define
$a^{(p)}$ to be $a \vee T^{-1}a \vee \cdots \vee T^{-p+1}a$, where $\beta_1 \vee \beta_2$
denotes the common refinement of partitions β_1 and
β_2. It can be shown that $\lim_{p \to \infty} 1/p \, H(a^{(p)})$ exists,
and this limit is denoted $h(a, T)$. Finally, $h(T)$
$= \sup h(a, T)$ where the supremum is taken over all
finite partitions a; $h(T)$ is the (metric) entropy
of the transformation T. It is known that if a_q is
a sequence of partitions such that (1) a_{q+1} refines
a_q, and (2) (almost) every two distinct points are
eventually separated by $\{a_q\}$, then $h(T, a_q) \to h(T)$
as $q \to \infty$.

We return to the specific case $X = X^n$, where
μ is equal to Haar measure, T is an automorphism of
X^n. Let $\nu_1, \ldots, \nu_k$ be distinct positive numbers such
that for every λ_i we have $\lambda_i = \nu_j$ for some j, and
vice versa. That is, the ν_i are the moduli of the
λ_j. It is not hard to show that R^n can be written

as the direct sum $R^n = \bigoplus_{i=1}^{k} L_i$ such that (1) each L_i is invariant under A, $(A \sim T)$, (2) $A_i = A\big|_{L_i}$ is a transformation such that every eigenvalue of A_i has modulus ν_i. For X in R^n we let $x = \sum_{i=1}^{k} x_i$, x_i in L_i, and we let $S_i(x_i, \delta)$ be the sphere in L_i of radius δ centered at x_i. We let $S(x, \delta)$ consist of all x' in R^n such that x'_i is in $S_i(x_i, \delta)$ $[S(x, \delta)$ is the intersection of k cylinders with spherical sections; in case all eigenvalues are distinct, $S(x, \delta)$ is a parallelepiped$]$.

Let us say that a partition a of X^n is in the class $S(\delta)$ if it consists of the atoms of the Boolean algebra generated by the projection (from R^n) of a finite covering by sets $S(x_1, \delta_1)$, $S(x_2, \delta_2),\ldots,S(x_k, \delta_k)$, where $\delta_i \leq \delta$ for $i = 1, 2,\ldots,k$. It is not difficult to see that there is a sequence of partitions a_q in $S(\delta)$ which converge monotonically to the unit partition. We will show that if δ is sufficiently small, then $h(T, a) = -\Sigma_{|\lambda_i| \leq 1} \log|\lambda_i|$. In view of the preceding remarks, this implies that $h(T)$ $= -\Sigma_{|\lambda_i| \leq 1} \log|\lambda_i|$.

We choose δ small enough so that $S(x, \delta)$ is contained in a box $B(x, \delta')$, centered at x of edge length δ', where $\delta' < \min(\frac{1}{2}, \dfrac{1}{2||A^{-1}||})$.

We wish to deal with projections of sets

$S(x_1, \delta)$, $S(s_2, \delta)$,...,$S(x_j, \delta)$. The fact that

each $S(x_i, \delta)$ is enclosed in a box of side length

at most one half implies that if $S(s_i, \delta)$ intersects

$S(s_j, \delta)$, then $S(x_i, \delta)$ does not intersect any non-

trivial translate (by Z^n) of $S(s_j, \delta)$. Let π be

the projection of R^n into X^n. It follows that

$$\bigcap_{i=1}^{k} \pi(S(x_i, \delta_i)) = \pi \bigcap_{i=1}^{k} (S(y_i, \delta_i))$$

where y_i is an appropriate translate (by Z^n) of x_i.

The fact that $\delta < \dfrac{1}{2||A^{-1}||}$ means that the same argument

can be applied to intersecting sets $S(x_i, \delta_i)$ and

$A^{-1}(S(x'_i, \delta'_i))$. We observe that

$$S(x, \delta) \cap A^{-1}S(x', \delta') \cap A^{-2}(S(x'', \delta''))$$
$$= S(x, \delta) \cap A^{-1}[S(x', \delta') \cap A^{-1}(S(x', \delta''))]$$

and

$$S(x', \delta') \cap A^{-1}(S(x', \delta'')) \subset S(x', \delta')$$

From such observations it can be seen that

$$\bigcap_{i=1}^{p-1} T^{-i}\pi(S(x_i, \delta_i)) = \pi \bigcap_{i=0}^{p-1} A^{-i}S(y_i, \delta_i)$$

where y_i is an appropriate translate of x_i. (The object of the foregoing rather tedious discussion is to lift the calculations from X^n to R^n. The problem is that portions of sets which are disjoint in R^n may project into the same image in X^n. This is remedied by choosing the sets sufficiently small.)

Each element of a is contained in some set $S(x, \delta)$. It follows from the foregoing that a set of $a^{(p)} = a \vee \cdots \vee T^{-p+1}a$ is contained in the projection of a set of the form

$$\overset{p-1}{\underset{i=0}{\cap}} A^{-i}S(y_i, \delta_i) \subset S(y_1, \delta_1) \cap A^{-p+1}S(y_{p-1}, \delta_{p-1})$$

The measure of the set $S(y_1, \delta_1) \cap A^{-p+1}S(y_{p-1}, \delta_{p-1})$ is bounded by the product of the measures of the projections of that set into the spaces L_i. In L_i, A_i alters the measure of a set by the factor $\nu_i^{\dim L_i}$ (A_i is its own Jacobian and $\det A_i$ is the product of the eigenvalues). We can thus estimate the measure of $S(y_1, \delta_1) \cap S(y_{p-1}, \delta_{p-1})$ by $\Pi_{\nu_i \leq 1}(\nu_i^{\dim L_i})^{-p+1}$. This quickly leads to the inequality

$$h(T, a) \geq -\Sigma_{\nu_i \leq 1}(\dim L_i) \log \nu_i$$

$$= -\Sigma_{|\lambda_i| \leq 1} \log |\lambda_i|$$

To obtain the reverse inequality, we estimate sets of $a^{(p)}$ from the inside by projections of sets of the form $\bigcap_{i=0}^{p-1} A^{-i}S(x_i, \delta_i)$. The basic obstacle is that $a(x)$ may intersect $(T^{-1}a)(x)$ only in points near the boundary of $a(x)$ and $(T^{-1}a)(x)$, and so the sets $S(x_i, \delta_i)$ would have to be chosen very small. We resolve this difficulty with some lemmas:

LEMMA 1.   Let $d_j(x)$ be the distance of $T^j x$ from the boundary of $a(T^j x)$.   Then $\lim_{j \to \infty} d_j(x)^{1/j} = 1$ a.e.

The proof is an indirect application of the Birkhoff ergodic theorem.

LEMMA 2.   If $\{a_j\}$ is a sequence of positive numbers such that $a_j^{1/j} \to \ell$ and if $b_p = \max_{j=1}^{p-1} a_j$, then $b_p^{1/p} \to \max\{1, \ell\}$.

The proof is elementary.

LEMMA 3.   Let $d_j(x)$ be as in Lemma 1.   Then

$$\lim_{p \to \infty} (1/p) \int_{X^n} \log \min_{j=0}^{p-1} d_j(x) = 0$$

The proof of Lemma 3 uses the results of Lemmas 1 and 2, together with the dominated ergodic theorem.

The following estimate on the size of $a^{(p)}(x)$ is tedious but direct:

$$\mu(a^{(p)}(x)) \geq \sigma \prod_{i=1}^{k} \left[(\tfrac{1}{R}) C_i^{(p)} \min_{j=0}^{p-1} d_j(x) \right]^{\dim L_i}$$

where

(1)   k is the number of subspaces L_i

(2)   R is a constant such that $S(x, \epsilon)$ is contained in the sphere of radius R centered at x

(3) $\sigma = \mu(S(x, 1))$ (which is independent of x)

(4) $C_i^{(p)} = \min_{j=0}^{p-1} \dfrac{1}{\|A_i^{\ j}\|}$ $(i = 1, \ldots, k)$

From the above, and from the formulas

$$H(a^{(p)}(x)) = -\int \log \mu(a^{(p)}(x)) \ dx$$

and

$$h(T, a) = \lim_{p \to \infty} \left(\tfrac{1}{p}\right) H(a^{(p)}(x))$$

we obtain

$$h(T, a) \leq \lim_{p \to \infty} \sup \log(\frac{R}{\sigma})^{n/p}$$

$$+ \sum_{i=1}^{k} \lim_{p \to \infty} \sup(\frac{1}{p}) \log(C_i^{(p)})^{-\dim L_i}$$

$$+ \lim_{p \to \infty} \sup(\frac{-n}{p}) \int \log \min_{j=0}^{p-1} d_j(x)$$

In this expression, n is the dimension of X^n. The first term obviously goes to zero. The third term goes to zero as a consequence of the lemmas. The second term can be calculated. Since all eigenvalues of A_i are of modulus ν_i, it follows that $||A_i^p||^{1/p} \to \nu_i$ as $p \to \infty$. An application of Lemma 2 yields the desired result that

$$\lim_{p \to \infty} \sup(\frac{1}{p}) \log(C_i^{(p)})^{-\dim L_i} \longrightarrow (-\dim L_i) \log$$
$$(\max(\frac{1}{\nu_i}, 1))$$

and so

$$h(T, a) \geq - \sum_{\nu_i \leq 1} \log \nu_i = \sum_{|\lambda_i| \leq 1}^{-} \log|\lambda_i|$$

The formula for metric entropy is established.

For the definition and basic properties of topological entropy, see [2]. Let $h(T, \beta)$ be the entropy of T with respect to an open covering β. It suffices to compute $h(T, \beta)$ where β is an open covering by sets of the form $S(x, \delta')$ with $\delta' < \cdot \delta$ (the notation has the same meaning as before). We can estimate the measure of a member of $\beta^{(p)}$ as before. This gives a lower bound on the number of sets from $\beta^{(p)}$ needed to cover X^n. This establishes the inequality

$$h(T, \beta) \geq \sum_{|\lambda_i| \leq 1} \log |\lambda_i|$$

Now let F_i be the projection of $[0, 1]^n$ into L_i. There are constants K_i such that, for all $r < 1$, the space F_i can be covered by $K_i (1/r)^{\dim L_i}$ spheres of radius r. For each integer p, we cover F_i by $K_i \left[\dfrac{1}{\delta' C_i^{(p)}} \right]^{\dim L_i}$ spheres of radius $\delta' C_i^{(p)}$ [$C_i^{(p)}$ has the same meaning as before]. We let γ be the following covering of $[0, 1]^n$. Each member of γ is the intersection of k (= number of L_i) cylinders over the above-mentioned spheres. One can show that each set of γ is contained upon projection into X^n in some member of $\beta^{(p)}$. It follows that the minimum number of sets from $\beta^{(p)}$ needed to cover X^n is at most the cardinality of γ. But that cardinality is at most

$$\prod_{i=1}^{k} K_i \left[\frac{1}{\delta' C_i^{(p)}} \right]^{dim\ L_i}$$

From here on, the analysis parallels that of the metric case, to show that $h(T, \beta) \leq -\Sigma_{|\lambda_i| \leq 1} \log |\lambda_i|$.

The details of the proofs outlined above can be found in Chapter 1 of [4].

REFERENCES

1. Abramov, L. M., Correction of a Note of Genis, R Z Mat., 1963, No. 8, p. 439 (Russian).

2. Adler, R. L., Konheim, A. L., and McAndrew, M. H., Topological Entropy, TAMS, 114 (1965), pp. 309-319.

3. Arov, O. Z., The Computation of Entropy for One Class of Group Endomorphisms, Zap. Mat. Otd. Fiz.-Mat. Fak. i. Har'kov. Mat. Obsc., 30 (4), (1964), pp. 48-69.

4. Berg, K. R., Thesis: On The Conjugacy Problem for K-Systems, University of Minnesota, 1967.

5. Billingsley, P., Ergodic Theory and Information, John Wiley, New York, 1965.

6. Genis, A. L., Metric Properties of the Endomorphisms of the n-Dimensional Torus, Sov. Math.

Dok., 1, 2 (1961), pp. 750-752.

7. Jacobs, K., Lecture Notes on Ergodic Theory, Yale University, 1962-63.

8. Parry, W., Entropy and Generators in Ergodic Theory, Yale University, 1966.

9. Sinai, Ja. G., On the Concept of Entropy of a Dynamical System, Dokl. Akad. Nauk., 124 (1959), pp. 768-771 (Russian).

SEMIDYNAMICAL FLOW NEAR A COMPACT INVARIANT SET [1]

Nam P. Bhatia

(Case Western Reserve University)

0. INTRODUCTION

Kimura and Ura [1] obtained the following result on the flow in a neighborhood of a compact invariant set of a dynamical system (X, R, π) defined on a locally compact space X.

0.1 THEOREM. Let $M \subset X$ be a nonempty compact invariant set. Then one of the following four conditions holds:

(0.2) M is positively asymptotically stable;

(0.3) M is negatively asymptotically stable;

[1]This research was partially supported by the National Science Foundation under Grant No. NSF-GP-7447.

(0.4)   every neighborhood of M contains a complete

trajectory not contained in M;

(0.5)   there exist points x, y $\notin$ M such that

$\Lambda^+(x) \neq \phi$, $\Lambda^-(y) \neq \phi$ and $\Lambda^+(x) \subset M$,

$\Lambda^-(y) \subset M$.

Here for any $x \in X$, $\Lambda^+(x)$ $[\Lambda^-(x)]$ denotes the positive or omega [negative or alpha] limit set.

This beautiful result was for some reason not

emphasized in [1] and I rediscovered it last year

(see [2]) using a property of weak attractors [3],

thus obtaining an alternate and perhaps simpler

proof of Theorem 0.1.   In [4] we obtained the

generalization of the needed property of weak

attractors for semidynamical systems ([4], [5], [6]),

and the purpose of this note is to announce a gener-

alization of Theorem 0.1 for semidynamical systems.

1.   NOTATION

Let X be a locally compact Hausdorff space.

Let R be the set of real numbers and R^+ the set of

nonnegative real numbers.   A (positive) semidynamical

system is the triple (X, R^+, π), where π is a mapping

of X x R^+ into X satisfying

(1.1) $x \pi 0 = x$ for all $x \in X$

(1.2) $(x \pi t) \pi s = x \pi (t + s)$ for all $x \in X$

and $t, s \in R^+$

(1.3)   the map π is continuous

Here $x \pi t$ denotes the image under π of the point $(x, t) \in X \times R^+$.

Note that if in the above definition R^+ is replaced by R, then we get the usual definition of a dynamical system.

Given a (positive) semidynamical system on X and a point $x \in X$, one may define the positive semi-trajectory $\gamma^+(x)$, the positive limit set $\Lambda^+(x)$, the positive prolongation $D^+(x)$, and the positive prolongational limit set $J^+(x)$ just as it is done in dynamical systems (see, for example, [7]).   Thus

$$\gamma^+(x) = \left\{ x \pi t : t \in R^+ \right\} \tag{1.4}$$

$$\Lambda^+(x) = \cap \left\{ \overline{\gamma^+(y)} : y \in \gamma^+(x) \right\} \tag{1.5}$$

$$D^+(x) = \cap \left\{ \overline{\gamma^+(U)} : U \text{ is a neighborhood} \right.$$
$$\left. \text{of } x \right\} \tag{1.6}$$

and

$$J^+(x) = \cap \left\{ D^+(y) : y \in \gamma^+(x) \right\} \tag{1.7}$$

Here, as in what follows, given a map

$\phi:X \rightarrow P(X)$ $[P(X)$ is the class of all subsets of $X]$
and $M \subset X$, we write $\phi(M) = \cup\{\phi(x): x \in M\}$. Moreover, $\overline{M}$, $\partial(M)$, $C(M)$, and $\text{Int}(M)$ will, respectively,
denote the closure, boundary, complement, and
interior of the set M.

2. NEGATIVE SEMITRAJECTORIES

One of the basic differences between a dynamical system and a semidynamical system is the possible
existence of more than one negative semitrajectory
through a given point in the latter. Since the
image $x\pi t$ is not defined for $t< 0$, to arrive at a
concept of negative semitrajectory, we proceed as
follows:

Given a semidynamical system (X, R^+, π) and
a point $x \in X$, we define the set $F(x)$ by

$$F(x) = \{y \in X: \exists\, t \in R^+ \quad \text{with} \quad y\pi t = x\}$$
$$\equiv \{y \in X: x \in \gamma^+(y)\} \qquad (2.1)$$

and call this set the negative funnel through x.

If for every $y \in X$ and $t > 0$, $y\pi t \neq x$, then
the point x is called a start point. Note that if
x is a start point, then $F(x) = \{x\}$. However, the

converse does not hold.

2.2 DEFINITION. For any $x \in X$, a set $\theta \subset X$ will be called a negative semitrajectory whenever the three following conditions hold:

(2.3)   if y, $z \in \theta$, then either $y \in \gamma^+(z)$ or
        $z \in \gamma^+(y)$;

(2.4) $\theta \subset F(x)$; and

(2.5)   if $\varphi \supset \theta$, and φ has the properties 2.3 and
        2.4, then $\varphi = \theta$.

The set $F(x)$ may now be identified as the union of all negative semitrajectories through x.

The following theorem [4] gives a classification of the negative semitrajectories.

2.6 THEOREM. Let θ be a negative semitrajectory through x. Then one of the following holds:

(2.7) x is a start point so that $\theta = \{x\}$;

(2.8)   there is a start point $y \in X$ and a $t > 0$
        such that $y\pi t = x$ and $\theta \equiv y\pi[0, t]$;

(2.9) $t_x = \sup\{t > 0$: for some $y \in \theta$, $y\pi t = x\} < +\infty$,
        but θ contains no start point; and

(2.10) the supremum t_x in 2.9 is $+\infty$.

In dynamical systems a negative semitrajectory

is always of the type 2.10. This latter type is also most important as only for this type one may define a negative limit set. Such a negative semi-trajectory will therefore be called a principal negative semitrajectory.

It may be pertinent to remark that in 2.7 the negative semitrajectory is a point but is not a rest point. In 2.8 the negative semitrajectory is compact but is not periodic (it is homeomorphic to a segment).

We now introduce the definition of a negative limit set of a principal negative semitrajectory θ_x through a point x.

2.11 DEFINITION. Let θ_x be a principal negative semitrajectory through x. Then the negative limit set $\Lambda^-(\theta_x)$ of θ_x is the set

$$\Lambda^-(\theta_x) = \{ y \in X : \exists \{y_n\} \text{ in } \theta_x \text{ and } \{t_n\} \text{ in } R^+ \text{ such that } y_n \pi t_n = x, \ t_n \to +\infty, \text{ and } y_n \to y \} \qquad (2.12)$$

2.13 NOTE. One may theoretically define a negative limit set for a negative semitrajectory θ_x through

x which is of the type 2.9 by requiring the sequence
$\{t_n\}$ to be such that $0 \leq t_n < t_x$ and $t_n \to t_x$, where
t_x is defined in 2.9. But in this case the set
$\Lambda^-(\theta_x)$ always happens to be empty so that nothing
is gained by defining this concept.

The definition of a negative semitrajectory
leads to the concept of weak negative invariance.

2.14 DEFINITION. A set $M \subset X$ will be called weakly
negatively invariant if for each $x \in M$ there is a
negative semitrajectory θ_x through x which is contained in M.

Before pointing out some important properties
of the limit sets and the prolongational limit sets,
we introduce also the concepts of positive invariance,
negative invariance, and invariance.

2.15 DEFINITION. A set $M \subset X$ is called positively
invariant [negatively invariant or invariant] whenever $\gamma^+(M) = M$ $(\gamma^+(C(M)) = C(M))$
$[\gamma^+(M) = M \quad$ and $\quad \gamma^+(C(M)) = C(M)]$

2.16 THEOREM ([4]). Let (X, R^+, π) be a semidynamical system on a locally compact space X. Then for

any $x \in X$, $\Lambda^+(x)$ and $J^+(x)$ are closed positively invariant and weakly negatively invariant sets which contain no start points. If, moreover, either $\Lambda^+(x)$ or $J^+(x)$ is compact, then the only negative semitrajectories in them are of the principal type, and the sets are connected.

2.17 THEOREM. Let θ_x be a principal negative trajectory through x. Then the negative limit set $\Lambda^-(Q_x)$ is a closed positively invariant and weakly negatively invariant set which contains no start points. If $\Lambda^-(Q_x)$ is compact, then it is also connected, and the only negative semitrajectories contained in it are of the principal type.

3. ATTRACTION AND STABILITY

Attraction and stability properties of a set point, indeed, to particular kinds of flows in the neighborhood of a given set. We therefore describe these first.

Let $M \subset X$ be a compact set. We say that M is:

(3.1) <u>stable</u>, if given any neighborhood U of M, there is a neighborhood V of M such that

$\gamma^+(V) \subset U;$

(3.2)   a weak attractor, if the set

$$A_\omega(M) = \left\{ x \in X: \Lambda^+(x) \cap M \neq \phi \right\}$$

is a neighborhood of M;

(3.3)   an attractor, if the set

$$A(M) = \left\{ x \in X: \Lambda^+(x) \neq \phi \quad \text{and} \quad \Lambda^+(x) \subset M \right\}$$

is a neighborhood of M;

(3.4)   a uniform attractor, if the set

$$A_u(M) = \left\{ x \in X: J^+(x) \neq \phi \quad \text{and} \quad J^+(x) \subset M \right\}$$

is a neighborhood of M; and lastly

(3.5)   asymptotically stable, if it is stable and is
attracting.

For any $M \subset X$, the set $A_\omega(M)$ $[A(M), A_u(M)]$ is
called the region of weak attraction [attraction,
uniform attraction] of M. Whenever any one of these
sets is a neighborhood of M, the same is open and
invariant.

We are now in a position of stating the
following generalization of a theorem on weak
attractors [3].

3.6 THEOREM. Let (X, R^+, π) be a semidynamical
system on a locally compact space X, and let $M \subset X$
be nonempty and compact. If M is a weak attractor,
then $D^+(M)$ is a compact asymptotically stable set
with $A_\omega(M) = A(D^+(M))$. Moreover, $D^+(M)$ is the
smallest asymptotically stable set containing M.

4.   SEMIDYNAMICAL FLOW NEAR A COMPACT INVARIANT SET

A look at Theorem 0.1 shows that the concept
of negative asymptotic stability, which for dynamical
systems is defined normally using negative semitrajectories and their limit sets, makes little or
no sense for (positive) semidynamical systems. We
therefore would like to define the concept of negative asymptotic stability in terms of positive semitrajectories if possible.

Let (X, R, π) be a dynamical system defined
on a locally compact space X. Then the following
proposition holds:

4.1 PROPOSITION. Let $M \subset X$ be a compact negatively
invariant set. Then M is negatively asymptotically
stable if and only if there exists a relatively

compact open neighborhood U of M such that for each
x $\notin$ M, either $\Lambda^+(x) = \phi$ or $\Lambda^+(x) \cap C(U) \neq \phi$.

Since U is relatively compact, and C(M) is
positively invariant, it follows that in the above
proposition if for some x $\notin$ M, $\Lambda^+(x) = \phi$, then there
is a t > 0 such that $\gamma^+(x\pi t) \subset C(U)$. This shows
that the set C(U) has the property of a (positive)
weak attractor enunciated in Theorem 3.6. The
following corollary now becomes apparent.

4.2 COROLLARY. Let $X^* = X \cup \{\omega\}$ be the one-point
compactification of X, and let (X^*, R, π^*) be the
dynamical system on X^* obtained from a dynamical
system (X, R, π) on X by defining $x\pi t = x\pi^* t$ if
x $\in$ X, and $\omega\pi^* t = \omega$ for all t $\in$ R (see, for example,
[8]). Then a compact set M $\subset$ X is negatively
asymptotically stable if and only if there exists a
relatively compact neighborhood U of M in X such
that the complement of U in X^* is a positively
asymptotically stable set of the dynamical system
(X^*, R, π^*).

It is now clear that the following definition
makes sense in semidynamical systems. Let (X, R^+, π)
be a semidynamical system on a locally compact space X.

4.3 DEFINITION.   Let $M \subset X$ be a compact negatively invariant set.   We shall say that M is <u>completely unstable</u> (or negatively asymptotically stable) if and only if there is a relatively compact open neighborhood U of M such that for each $x \notin M$, either $\Lambda^+(x) = \phi$ or $\Lambda^+(x) \cap C(U) \neq \phi$.

We can now announce our generalization of Theorem 0.1 for semidynamical systems.

4.4 THEOREM.   Let $M \subset X$ be a nonempty compact invariant set of a semidynamical system (X, R^+, π) defined on a locally compact space X.   Then one of the four conditions holds:

(4.5) M is (positively) asymptotically stable;

(4.6) M is completely unstable;

(4.7)   every neighborhood U of M contains a point $x \notin M$ such that $\gamma^+(x) \subset U$ and a principal negative semitrajectory θ_x exists and is contained in U;

(4.8)   there exists a point $x \notin M$ such that $\Lambda^+(x) \neq \phi$ and $\Lambda^+(x) \subset M$, and there exists also a point $y \notin M$ such that a principal negative semitrajectory θ_y exists and $\Lambda^-(\theta_y) \neq \phi$ with $\Lambda^-(\theta_y) \subset M$.

We note that Theorem 0.1 is a corollary of the above theorem. The proof of the above theorem uses a combination of the weak attractor property and an idea of Kimura and Ura [1].

Remark. A systematic study of the properties of asymptotically stable sets and their regions of attraction is contained in the thesis of my student Mr. Paul Fallone [8].

CORRECTION. (i) The set $J^+(x)$ as introduced in (1.7) does not have, in general, the property claimed in Theorem 2.16. However, if $J^+(x)$ is defined by

$$J^+(x) = \left\{y: \exists \{x_n\}, \{t_n\}, \; x_n \to x, \; t_n \to +\infty, \right.$$
$$\left. \text{and} \quad x_n \pi t_n \to y\right\}$$

then this set has the desired property. For dynamical systems the two definitions are equivalent, that this is not the case in semidynamical systems can be shown on examples.

(ii) The definition of a negative trajectory in 2.2 does not yield the classification in Theorem 2.6. This discrepancy can be removed by replacing

(2.3) by:

(2..3') if y, $z \in \theta$ and $t_y = \inf\{t \geq 0: y\pi t_y = x\}$,
$t_z = \inf\{t \geq 0: z\pi t_z = x\}$, then either there
is a τ_y, $0 \leq \tau_y \leq t_y$, such that $y\tau_y = z$ or
there is a τ_z, $0 \leq \tau_z \leq t_z$, such that
$z\tau_z = y$.

The definition then reads: For any $x \in X$, a set
$\theta \subset X$ will be called a negative semitrajectory
through x whenever either $\theta \equiv \{x\}$ and x is a rest
point, or θ satisfies conditions (2.3), (2.4), and
(2.5).

For details see the author's forthcoming paper
"Local Semidynamical Systems" in joint authorship
with O. Hájek.

REFERENCES

1. Kimura, I., and Ura, T., Sur le courant
exterieur a une region invariante; Theoreme de
Bendixson, Comm. Math. Univ. Sancti Pauli, 8 (1960),
23-39.
2. Bhatia, N. P., Dynamical Systems, Lectures given
at the International Summer School on Mathematical
Systems Theory and Economics held in Varenna, Italy,

June 1-12, 1967.

3. Bhatia, N. P., Weak Attractors in Dynamical Systems, Bol. Soc. Mat. Mexicana, 11 (1966), 56-64.

4. Bhatia, N. P., Semi-Dynamical Systems, Lectures given at the International Summer School on Mathematical Systems Theory and Economics held in Varenna, Italy, June 1-12, 1967.

5. Hájek, O., Structure of Dynamical Systems, Comm. Math. Univ. Carolinae, 6 (1965), 53-72. Correction same journal, 6 (1965), 211-212.

6. Hájek, O., Local Dynamical Systems, unpublished notes of a seminar on Differential Equations and Dynamical Systems held at Western Reserve University, Cleveland, Spring, 1967.

7. Bhatia, N. P., and Szegö, G. P., Dynamical Systems: Stability Theory and Applications, Lecture Notes in Mathematics 35, Springer-Verlag, Berlin-Heidelberg-New York, 1967.

8. Fallone, P., Properties of Asymptotically Stable Sets and Their Regions of Attraction, thesis, Western Reserve University, 1967.

LOCALLY WEAKLY ALMOST PERIODIC
TRANSFORMATION GROUPS AND
FIBER BUNDLES[1]

Hsin Chu

(University of Maryland)

1. INTRODUCTION

In this talk, we outline certain relations
between compact transformation groups and noncompact
transformation groups. The notions of reducibility
and separability of transformation groups are
introduced. Several necessary and sufficient conditions are established: (1) a separable transformation group to be locally weakly almost periodic;
(2) a reducible and separable transformation group
to be a minimal, but not totally minimal, set; and
(3) a reducible and separable transformation group

[1]This work was supported in part by the National
Science Foundation under Grant No. GP-6167.

97

to be a coordinate bundle. For terminology and
notations we refer to [9, 10, 13] .

2. SEMIREDUCIBLE, REDUCIBLE, AND SEPARABLE
    TRANSFORMATION GROUPS

We may find the following definitions and
some elementary results related to them in [2, 9].

DEFINITION 1. Let (X, T, π) be a transformation
group. Let $x \in X$. We say that T is locally weakly
almost periodic at x if U is a neighborhood of x,
then there exist a neighborhood V of x and a compact
subset K of T such that $y \in V$ and $t \in T$ imply
$ytK \cap U \neq \phi$. We say the group T is locally weakly
almost periodic on X if T is locally weakly almost
periodic at every $x \in X$. Let (X, T, π) be a
transformation group where X is a uniform space.
We say that T is weakly almost periodic at X if a
is a uniform index of X, then there exists a compact
subset K of T such that for each $x \in X$ and $t \in T$
we have $xtK \cap (x)a \neq \phi$.

Remark. Every transformation group (X, T, π) with
T compact is always locally weakly almost periodic

as well as weakly almost periodic.

DEFINITION 2.   Let (X, T, π) be a transformation

group.   We say that (X, T, π) is semireducible if

there is a transformation group (X*, H, π*) where

X* is a nontrivial compact Hausdorff space and H

is a nontrivial compact group such that there is a

continuous homeomorphism f: T $\to$ H from T onto H and

a continuous map p: X $\to$ X* from X into X* and for

each t $\in$ T and each x $\in$ X, we have pπ(x, t)

= π*(p(x), f(t)).   We say that (X, T, π) is

reducible if it is semireducible such that X* = H

and π* is the multiplication in H.   We denote a

semireducible transformation group by

(X, T, π; X*, H, π*, p, f) and a reducible transfor-

mation group by (X, T, π; H, p, f), if necessary.

LEMMA 1.   Let (X, T, π; X*, H, π*, p, f) be a semi-

reducible transformation group.   Let Ker (f) = N.

Then N is a closed, normal, syndetic subgroup of

T and for each x $\in$ X, p(cl(π(x, N))) = p(x).

Proof.   Let t $\in$ N.   Then f(t) = e and p(π(x, t))

= π*(p(x), f(t)) = p(x).   Since p is continuous and

X^* is Hausdorff, we have $p(cl(\pi(x, N))) = p(x)$.

DEFINITION 3. A semireducible transformation group
$(X, T, \pi; X^*, H, \pi*, p, f)$ is called separable if
for any pair x, y in X such that $x \not\subseteq cl(\pi(y, N))$,
then $p(x) \neq p(y)$.

LEMMA 2. Let $(X, T, \pi; X^*, H, \pi*, p, f)$ be a
separable transformation group. Then for each
$x \in X$, $cl(\pi(x, N))$ is a minimal set under N in X.

Proof. Let $x \in X$. Suppose that $cl(\pi(x, N))$ is not
a minimal set. There exists $y \in cl(\pi(x, N))$ such
that $cl(\pi(y, N)) \subset cl(\pi(x, N))$ but they do not
coincide. There is an element $z \in cl(\pi(x, N))$ but
not in $cl(\pi(y, N))$. By the definition of separability, we have $p(z) \neq p(y)$. By Lemma 1, we have
$p(y) = p(x)$ and $p(z) = p(x)$. A contradiction!

THEOREM 1. Let (X, T, π) be a transformation group
where X is a locally compact Hausdorff space. Let
N be a closed, normal syndetic subgroup of T. If
the induced transformation group (X, N, π) is locally weakly almost periodic, then (X, T, π) is a

separable transformation group, the map p: X → X* is closed, and p^{-1}(x*), for every x* in X*, is compact. Conversely, if (X, T, π; X*, H, π*, p, f) is a separable transformation group, the map p is closed, and p^{-1}(x*), for every x* in X* is compact, then the reduced transformation group (X, N, π) is locally weakly almost periodic, where N = f^{-1}(e).

Proof. By Lemma 2 and some known results.

3. MINIMAL SETS

DEFINITION 4. Let (X, T, π) be a transformation group. Let N be a closed, normal syndetic subgroup of T. We say N has a property (A), if for every x ∈ X the group $\{t \in T \mid \pi(cl(xN), t) = cl(xN)\}$ is equal to N.

LEMMA 3. Let (X, T, π; H, p, f) be a reducible and separable transformation group. Then X is minimal, but not totally minimal, under T, and N = f^{-1}(e) has property (A).

Proof. By Lemmas 1 and 2, and the definition of separability.

LEMMA 4.   Let (X, T, π) be a transformation group.
Let X be a compact Hausdorff minimal set under T.
Let N be a closed syndetic, proper subgroup of T
with the property (A).   If X is not minimal under
N, then (X, T, π) is reducible and separable.

Proof.   By Theorem 1 and the fact that (X, N, π)
is weakly almost periodic.

LEMMA 5.   Let (X, T, π) be a transformation group
where T is an Abelian topological group.   Let X be
a compact Hausdorff minimal, but not totally
minimal, set under T.   Then T has a proper, closed,
syndetic subgroup with the property (A).

Proof.   By Theorem 1 and properties of a minimal,
but not totally minimal set.

THEOREM 2.   Let (X, T, π) be a transformation group
where X is compact Hausdorff.   Then X is minimal
under T but not minimal under a proper, closed,
normal subgroup having the property (A) if and only
if (X, T, π) is reducible and separable.

Proof.   It is a direct consequence of Lemmas 3 and 4.

COROLLARY.   Let (X, T, π) be a transformation group where X is compact Hausdorff and T is Abelian. Then X is minimal but not totally minimal if and only if (X, T, π) is reducible and separable.

Proof.   By Lemma 5 and Theorem 2.

4.   FIBER BUNDLES

By a fiber bundle we mean an equivalence class of coordinate bundles (see [13]).

LEMMA 6.   Let $(X, T, \pi; H, p, f)$ be a reducible and separable transformation group where T acts on X freely, X is compact Hausdorff, and $f: T \to H$ is a group covering.   Then (X, H, p) is a fiber bundle.

Proof.   By Lemma 3 and the definition of coordinate bundle.

LEMMA 7.   Let $(X, T, \pi; H, p, f)$ be a reducible and separable transformation group as in Lemma 6.   Then $\{T, f, H, N, N\}$ is the associated principal bundle of the fiber bundle $\{X, p, H, Y, N\}$

as constructed in Lemma 6.

Proof. It is a direct consequence of the definition
(see [13]) of associated principal bundle and the
way we constructed the coordinate neighborhoods
$\{V_i \mid i \in T\}$ and coordinate functions $\{\phi_i \mid i \in J\}$ in
the proof of Lemma 6.

LEMMA 8. Let $\left\{X, p, H, Y, N, \{V_i\}, \{\phi_i\}\right\}$ be a
fiber bundle, where X is a compact Hausdorff space,
H is a compact group, Y is a minimal set under N
with N acting on Y freely, and N is a discrete
group. Let $\widetilde{p}: T \to H$ be a group covering from T
onto H such that $\{T, \widetilde{p}, H, N, N\}$ is the principal
associated bundle of the given fiber bundle. Then
there exists an action π of the group T on X so
that (X, T, π; H, f, p) is a reducible and separable
transformation group and T acts on X freely.

Proof. It is more or less a straightforward but
rather long computation.

THEOREM 3. Let (X, T, π; H, p, f) be a reducible
and separable transformation group where X is a
compact Hausdorff space, T acts on X freely, and

f: T → H is a group covering.   Then $\{$X, p, H, Y, N$\}$ is a fiber bundle and $\{$T, f, H, N, N$\}$ is its principal associated bundle.   Conversely, if $\{$X, p, H, Y, N$\}$ is a fiber bundle, where X is a compact Hausdorff space, H is a compact group, Y is a minimal set under N, N acts on Y freely, and N is a discrete group.   Let f: T → H be a group covering from T onto H such that $f^{-1}(e) = N$ and $\{$T, f, H, N, N$\}$ is the principal associated bundle of the given fiber bundle.   Then there exists an action of the group T on X so that (X, T, π; H, p, f) is a reducible and separable transformation group and T acts on X freely.

Proof.   By Lemmas 6, 7, and 8.

REFERENCES

1.   Anderson, R. D., On Raising Flows and Mappings, Bull. Am. Math. Soc., 69 (1963), pp. 259-264.

2.   Chu, Hsin, On the Existence of Slices for Transformation Groups, Proc. Am. Math. Soc., 18 (1967), pp. 513-517.

3.   Chu, Hsin, On Universal Transformation Groups, Ill. J. Math., 6 (1962), pp. 317-326.

4.   Chu, Hsin, and Geraghty, M. A., The Fundamental
Group and the First Cohomology Group of a Minimal
Set, Bull. Am. Math. Soc., 69 (1963), pp. 377-381.

5.   Ellis, R., Global Sections of Transformation
Groups, Ill. J. Math., 8 (1964), pp. 380-394.

6.   Ellis, R., and Gottschalk, W. H., Homomorphisms
of Transformation Groups, Trans. Am. Math. Soc.,
64 (1960), pp. 258-271.

7.   Iwasawa, K., On Some Types of Topological
Groups, Ann. Math., 50 (1949), pp. 507-558.

8.   Gottschalk, W. H., Minimal Sets, Bull. Am. Math.
Soc., 64 (1958), pp. 336-351.

9.   Gottschalk, W. H., and Hedlund, G. A., Topological Dynamics, Am. Math. Soc. Colloq. Publ.,
36 (1955).

10.   Hu, S. T., Homotopy Theory, Academic Press,
New York, 1959.

11.   Milnor, J., Lectures on Characteristic Classes,
mimeographed notes, Princeton University, 1957.

12.   Schwartzman, S., Global Cross Sections of
Compact Dynamical Systems, Proc. Nat. Acad. Sci.,
U.S.A., 48 (1962), pp. 786-791.

13.   Steenrod, N., The Topology of Fibre Bundles,
Princeton University Press, Princeton, New Jersey, 19

ON CAUSAL DYNAMICS WITHOUT
METRIZATION[1]

Michael Cole

(Academic Industrial Epistemology,

London)

0. INTRODUCTION

This is a mathematical review of work that
has been more extensively discussed from the viewpoint of a physicist [1]. That work grew out of a
curiosity about the permissible content of topology
and set theory required for the construction of a
physical theory of dynamics and for the definition
of "causality," yet without presupposing the existence of either space or time, nor yet even of
the notion of metrizability. Some interesting and
unexpected results have been found, but, as one

[1]This work was supported in part by the USAF Office
of Scientific Research under Contract No. F44620-67-
C-0012 and

might expect, there have also arisen some problems
that seem rather tricky to solve.

1. SOME IMPORTANT CATEGORIES

The proposals of [1] assert that all the
notions contained in the general notion of "causal
dynamics" may be expressed in terms of certain
structures over an ordered set of events. Here we
recall that an ordered set may be considered as a
category in which the objects are the ordered
elements and the morphisms are the binary relations
between pairs of related elements.

The physicist's raw material is the "category
of physical events," E , of which the objects are
the elements of the set E of events apprehended by
observers, and with morphisms that are dynamical
changes between the events. Associated with E
are two other categories: the "category of physical conditions," C , with physical conditions (of
which an observer postulates that he has become
apprised through an event) as objects, and with
dynamical processes as morphisms; the "category of
measurements," F , of which objects are open subsets

of a space of measurement parameters, and of which
the morphisms are dynamical transitions between
those subsets. (The different terms for the
morphisms have been chosen merely to avoid ambi-
guity of reference to morphisms.)

We may now consider three functors between
these three categories:

(1) The functor P: $C \rightarrow F$ is called "the
measurement functor," mapping sets of objects of
C into objects of F, and mapping sets of dynamical processes into dynamical transitions.

(2) The "observation functor" O: $E \rightarrow F$
maps objects of E, into objects of F, and maps
dynamical changes into dynamical transitions.

(3) The functor R: $C \rightarrow E$ maps sets of
objects of C into objects of E, and maps sets of
dynamical processes onto dynamical changes.

We therefore obtain the following suggestive
diagram:

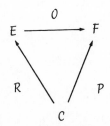

which makes it natural to ask if there exists a
unique R whenever both O and P are given. Such a
unique functor may be called the "universal behavior" of the physical theory specified by E , F ,
C , O, P, and the interpretive system to which they
belong.

2. BASIC CONSIDERATIONS

We must first assume that mappings of the
measurement functor correspond to measuring devices
that are able to assign parameters to restricted
classes of phenomena (that is, different techniques
are needed to measure different effects). Let us
call the object mappings p_i of P "measurement sub-
processes." Then we shall assume that it is possible to patch together several measurement sub-
processes to make a "measurement process" P, which
will have at least a connected range in F, and
possibly a connected domain in C.

In practice it is impossible to reduce errors
in a physical measurement process to zero, therefore
one must always say that a measurement process maps
a physical condition into a <u>neighborhood</u> of the

set F. If the measuring process is carried out
upon every (observationally) possible different
physical condition, then a set of neighborhoods
$0^{(P)} \equiv \{0_i\}$ will be generated as a covering of $F^{(P)}$,
that part of F determined by the measurement process
P.

One must consider F as a space which has a
topology generated on it by the measurement
processes. It is not legitimate to give as convenient a topology as one may desire. This latter
point has been disregarded by physicists to a considerable extent. By careful examination [1, (1)]
it is found that the following assumptions only are
the strongest that are valid:

ASSUMPTION 1. A measurement process defines open
sets, only, of the space of measurement parameter
values; closed sets may be specified by hypothesis
only.

ASSUMPTION 3. The topology endowed upon a parameter
space of measurement values by a measurement process
is no more than locally compact and Hausdorff.

ASSUMPTIONS 5, 6.   Measurement processes preserve
open sets and limit points.

ASSUMPTION 8.   The region of the space of physical
conditions which is accessible by a measurement
process has a locally compact, Hausdorff topology.

Dynamics is the study of the relationships
between the objects of E , the category of events,
as given by the structural content of the set of
morphisms of E.   Within a given semiotic, therefore,
dynamics must be formulated in terms of the relationships amongst the objects of F given by the
structural content of the morphisms of F .   Using
Assumptions 1, 3, 5, 6, and 8 above, we may attempt
to deduce the possible natures of C from the observed content and structure (and "permissible"
generalizations) of F .

Let F_1, $F_2 \subset F$ represent two successive sets
of measurement values, that is, they are objects of
F , and let π be an endomorphism of F such that
$\pi | F_1$ is the morphism $F_1 \rightarrow F_2$ of F ; π will be called
a dynamical transition just as $\pi | F_1$ is so-called.
The corresponding "physical" process $\tilde{\omega}$ (that is,
morphism of C), which gives rise to the dynamical

transition $F_1 \to F_2$, is a restriction of an endomorphism of C (and is called a <u>dynamical process</u>)
satisfying the commutative diagrams:

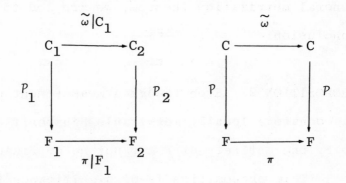

It may be argued that:

PROPOSITION 1. If a measurement process is open
(respectively, interior) then the morphisms of C
are open (respectively, interior) mappings [1, (1)].

Owing to the impossibility of carrying out an
infinite number of measurements in a finite time,
we may remark:

<u>Remark 1.</u> A measurement process endows F with a
locally finite covering. Furthermore, since the
presence of errors in physical measurements introduces a limiting degree of fineness into the
coverings that may be given to F, we must assume:

ASSUMPTION 9.   No space of measurement parameters
may be assumed to be paracompact.

Combining this assumption with Smirnov's
general metrization theorem, we are led to the
conclusion:

PROPOSITION 2.   Even though a measurement process
may donate a locally metrizable Hausdorff topology
to F, the entirety of F may not be metrizable.

This proposition is of significance to cosmo-
logical studies, for while distance measurements
may appear to satisfy the triangle inequality in
regions within which we can transport measuring
devices, the inability to define a paracompact
covering of 3-space (by means of measuring devices)
implies that our notions of distance may fail on
the large scale, in the sense that the triangle
inequality fails to hold.   The latter would imply
that invariance properties giving rise to conservation laws would break down in the large, even
though they might be locally valid.   One is therefore faced with the problem of finding some formulation of dynamics that is independent of such
vagaries associated with a more conventional

geometric description of dynamics.

3. CAUSAL DYNAMICS WITHOUT METRIZATION

Let us first notice that any ordering relation used to describe dynamical changes must be
transitive, otherwise a cause-effect chain of events
could never be constructed. Also, in order that
the maximum reduction in "subjectivity" in a
"physical" theory may be achieved, each observer's
experiences must be reproducible in all other
"physicists"; and this tacitly requires the following principle (which we shall call the PCA):

ASSUMPTION 10 (PRINCIPLE OF CORPORATE AGREEMENT).
There exists a theory language L satisfying the
following two conditions:

Condition 1. All physicists describe and inter-
relate their experiences within the semiotic L.

Condition 2. Each physicist believes all the other
physicists believe all the other physicists interpret
and use L in exactly the same way as he does.

We now suppose that each observer O_λ observes

a set of events $U_\lambda \subset E$, ordered by a relation R_λ,
and that these generate a set of neighborhoods
$0_\lambda^{(P_\lambda)} \equiv \{0_{(\lambda)i}\}$ in $F^{(P_\lambda)}$, with associated measurement process P_λ, everything being expressed in a
theory language L_λ. The ordered pair (U_λ, R_λ)
will be called the λth individual trajectory. The
morphisms of E corresponding to the ordering
mappings may be considered as dynamical ordering
operators, $\check{R}_\lambda$. These latter elements may now be
interpreted as elements of an ordering operator
groupoid, which we shall denote by $\check{R}$, using this
symbol to embody all the operations defined through
the activities of the set of observers. (In general, subscripts will refer only to particular members
of the set of observers, while their omission will
refer to the whole set.) L permits the introduction
of an equivalence relation between the individual
trajectories. When the observers compare records
of observations, they will find that, within
L-equivalence, only a subset of E can be put into
the same total order by all of them. In the spirit
of the PCA we now define:

DEFINITION 1. A set of events is causally ordered

with respect to a set of observers if each observer can assign to it a total order which gives a sequence of events that is totally ordered with respect to every other observer.

This definition also ensures that a causally ordered set of events is a set of physical events — within the context of the PCA. Further, the PCA requires that physical dynamical transitions are those upon which only <u>all</u> observers agree. It is therefore necessary to factor out from the ordering operator groupoid $\overset{\vee}{R}$ all those transitions that observers can neither agree upon in interpretation, nor put into a totally ordered sequence that all other observers can agree upon. Let us denote the set of such latter dynamical changes as $'\tilde{R}{}'$. Then the physical groupoid of causally ordered dynamical changes is the factor groupoid $\overset{\sim}{\overset{\vee}{R}} \equiv \overset{\vee}{R}/{}'\overset{\vee}{R}{}'$, which we shall denote as $\tilde{R}$ when no confusion can arise. Notice that $\tilde{R}$ can also be interpreted as a physical, dynamical ordering relation. We may summarize as follows:

PROPOSITION 3. The groupoid $\tilde{R}$ of causal, physical ordering operators corresponding to the groupoid of

physical dynamical processes has a quotient
structure defined by intermediate contributory
processes, and is free from unobservable ordering
operators.

Since we are concerned only with ordering
relations, we may denote any element of $\tilde{R}$ by $\tilde{R}$,
inverse elements by $\tilde{R}^{-1}$, and the composition of m
"forward" elements by $\tilde{R}^m$, and n "backward" elements
by $\tilde{R}^{-n}$. It may then be argued [1, (2)]:

PROPOSITION 4. If a set is totally ordered by a
relation $\tilde{R}$, then by considering $\tilde{R}$ as an operator
associating pairs of elements, it satisfies the
condition $[\tilde{R}^m, \tilde{R}^{-n}]_{(-)} \neq 0$.

This condition may be interpreted as the non-
contractibility of loops formed by the composition
of forward and backward elements of $\tilde{R}$. A representation of this condition, Proposition 4, may be
achieved in terms of Minkowski space in conjunction
with E. C. Zeeman's fine topology (consisting of
ϵ-balls of R^4 with the light cone removed and the
cone vertex restored). One considers the hyperbolic
metric as having an associated ordering operator
(a partial ordering) of which the "indistinguish-

ability" classes (namely, the sets of elements
equivalent with respect to the partial ordering)
are the light cones. It turns out [1, (2)] that
in order to be consistent one must use the Zeeman
fine topology, and that it is this very topology
which is also required to ensure the noncontracti-
bility of loops. The fine topology therefore
arises in a natural way, with no vestige of arti-
ficiality. This result is of particular physical
interest, owing to a move towards the viewpoint
that light cones are more important to retain in
any reformulation of relativity theory than specific
geometric notions.

It also appears likely that something like
the Zeeman fine topology will be a necessary
feature of all topologies endowed upon representation
spaces by realizations of operators satisfying the
condition of Proposition 4. A program of study has
now been begun upon this topic.

4. FUNDAMENTAL GROUPS

It is interesting to note that, in a crude
way, L-equivalence applied to the category $E^{\cdot}$,

having already given it the individual trajectory
structure, allows us to consider $(E^{\cdot}, L)$ as its
universal covering space. The ordering relation
which acts as the causal and physical ordering (in
the sense of the PCA) may then be viewed as the
fundamental group of the system of morphisms of
$E^{\cdot}$. These notions may also be carried over into
$F^{\cdot}$ and $C^{\cdot}$, of course. Under these circumstances
one may interpret $\tilde{R}$ as either being, or inducing,
the causal physical ordering relation/operator,
the fundamental group of the system of dynamical
processes, and the generator of intermediate
"virtual" dynamical processes. It is also related
to the dynamical invariants of the system. One
therefore begins to see that dynamics may be quite
comprehensively described by the homotopy properties of the system of dynamical transformations.

5. PLANTED STRUCTURES

In order to incorporate errors inherent in
any physical measurement process into a mathematical
model used for describing physical phenomena, we
define a generalized species of structure in the

following way $[1, (1)]$:

DEFINITION 2. Let U be a covering, with Lebesgue
number $d(U)$, of a topological space E which has a
complete atlas. Denote by $U_{L(-)}$ the set of elements
of $P(E)$, the power set of E, with diameter $< d(U)$;
denote by $U_{L(0)}$ the set of elements of $P(E)$ that
have diameter $d(U)$; and denote by $U_{L(+)}$ the set of
elements of $P(E)$ with diameter $> d(U)$. Now select
all elements of $P(E)$ satisfying the following
conditions:

Condition 0. Any subset $U^{(0)} \subset E$, $U^{(0)} \in U_{L(0)}$ is
called a Pip of E.

   For any two subsets U_i, $U_j \subseteq E$, we say:

Condition 1. U_i is U-identical to U_j if
$[U_i - (U_i \cap U_j)] \in U_{L(-)}$.

Condition 2. U_i is nominally U-distinct from U_j if
$[U_i - (U_i \cap U_j)] \in U_{L(0)}$.

Condition 3. U_i is strictly U-distinct from U_j if
$[U_i - (U_i \cap U_j)] \in U_{L(+)}$.

Condition 4. U_i is U-disjoint from U_j if

$(U_i \cap U_j) \in U_{L(-)}.$

The collection of all U-distinct elements of $P(E)$ is called the generalized U-planted structure on E, and will be denoted by E_U.

A U-planted structure E_U on E is therefore discrete in some way, although when viewed in the light of the finest topology of E it may appear to be fuzzy. This fuzziness, caused by the multiple identification of some subsets of E produces a "packing" problem: How can one take E_U to pieces and put it back together again? This Humpty Dumpty problem is best tackled by Čech homology theory, but in a modified form, as we shall see.

DEFINITION 3. Given two topological spaces E, F, and a covering V of F with Lebesgue number $d(V)$, a homomorphism $g_V: E \to F_V$ is called a speiromorphism of E into the V-planted structure F_V on F, and a homomorphism $h_V: F_V \to E$ is called an ekthamno- morphism of F_V into E.

DEFINITION 4. When $dV = 0$, $g_V: E \to F_V$ is called an embedding of E in F_V; when $d(V)$ is such that F_V consists of a single pip, g_V is called a burial of E in F.

A speirojection is a map $i_u : E \to E_u$, and an
ekthamnojection is a map $j_u :$ u $\to E_u$ A speiro-
morphism is defined in the obvious way, and it is
easy to rephrase the T_0, T_1, T_2 separation axioms
in terms of u-distinguished sets. Using the well-
known necessary and sufficient condition for a
mapping to be continuous, we can define speiron-
continuity in such a way that it reduces to ordinary
continuity when the covering has zero Lebesgue
number.

DEFINITION 5.   Given two topological spaces E, F,
with a planted structure F_v on F, together with a
speiromorphism $g_v : E \to F_v$, then g_v is said to be
speiron-continuous if for an arbitrary point x $\in$ E
and the pip $g_v(x) \in F_v$ there exist two subsets U$\subset$ E
and V $\subset F_v$ such that x $\in$ U and $g_v(x) \subset$ V, and such
that V is v-bidistinct from $g_v(U)$.

(Here we use the notion of U_i being u-bi-
distinct from U_j if both U_i and U_j are u-distinct
from each other.) The usual notions of open covering, compactness, open mappings, as well as the
simple mapping preservation properties, may be

easily translated into the language of U-dis-
tinguished sets. Planted structures are, therefore,
much like ordinary topological spaces (see [1, (1)]
for details of simple properties). However, the
notion of limit point does not go over in the same
way. All that one can do is use the following
definition:

DEFINITION 6. If a pip $x_U \in E_U$ is a limit pip of
E_U, then every (distinguished) subset of E containing x_U also contains another distinct E_U-pip.

Let us denote the nerve of a covering U of
E by $N(U)$. For planted structures we define the
nerve $N(U^{(E)})$ of a covering $U^{(E)}$ of E_U in the
obvious way, using distinguished sets of E'_U. One
may then define the (co-)homology structure by
means of Čech techniques. However, owing to the
fuzziness of E_U, one may introduce a form of "wild"
paracompactness into the theory of planted
structures; call a space E orthocompact if, for any
given covering U generating a homology structure
$H_*(E_U)$, one can find a locally finite refinement V
of U such that $H_*(E_V)$ is more complicated than
$H_*(E_U)$ [1, (1)]. This property offers the means

of introducing refinements to and extensions of
the structure of physical theories that are not
mere rephrasings. Instead one may add completely
new, extra structure to a theory to correspond to
new phenomenological structure revealed by more
accurate measurements.

6. DIFFERENTIATION IN PLANTED STRUCTURES

A physical theory may be constructed only by
patching together different pieces of information
obtained from experiment, therefore one may only
consider mathematical formalisms that are defined
in an operational manner. Since, in planted
structures, one may not define an arbitrarily small
"separation," but only a finite size pip, differentiation of functions must be modified. Let us see
how to adapt Fréchet differentiability. Consider
two Banach spaces E, F with coverings U, V having
Lebesgue numbers $d(U) = \varepsilon_E$, $d(V) = \varepsilon_F$, respectively.
Suppose the norms are $\|\ \|_E$, $\|\ \|_F$. Then we define
the differential of a linear map $\phi : E_U \to F_V$ as
ϕ_* where

$$\lim_{u \to 0_{E_u}} \frac{\left|\left|\phi(x_{o_u} + u) - \phi(x_{o_u}) - \phi_*(x_{o_u})\right|\right|_F}{||u||_E} \leq \frac{E_E}{E_E}$$

It is clear that ϕ_* is only defined locally, in the sense that if ϕ_* is minimal at a pip x_{o_u}, then ϕ may not be constant at $x_o \in E$, although it appears "constant" at $x_{o_u} \in E_u$; therefore, a more stringent condition is needed to specify global constancy of ϕ over E_u, and we may take it as

$$\max_{u \in E_U} \frac{\left|\left|\phi(x_{o_u} + u) - \phi(x_{o_u}) - \phi_*(x_{o_u})\right|\right|_F}{||u||_E} \leq C(x_o) \frac{E}{E}$$

where $C(x_o)$ is the maximum number of V-pips along any geodesic loop based on $\phi(x_{o_u})$. This has immediately involved us in global considerations. It appears likely that useful results will be obtained only by use of cohomology ring structures, but detailed results are not yet known.

7.   FILTRATIONS

     It is interesting to notice that one must view the definition of constancy of functions of a planted structure in terms of closed geodesic

loops. This immediately suggests a connection with
Morse theory via critical levels. If the Lebesgue
number of a covering is 2^ϵ, then the natural loga-
rithm of the minimum number of pips of the associated planted structure of the covered space may be
identified with the metric entropy H_ϵ of the space
concerned. This quantity has the necessary properties for defining an increasing filtration that
may be applied in spectral homology theory. One
may therefore ask how one might knit together Morse
theory with approximations to dynamical systems
(defined by a variational principle) that can be
classified by the metric entropy of the covering,
thus pointing to a general theory of dynamics on
planted structures that could list all possible
new dynamical phenomena to be revealed by improve-
ments in the accuracy of physical measuring devices.

It also appears that it may be possible to
make some study of problems in structural stability
of differential equations by using an approximation
technique that introduces some fuzziness into a
local region of the flow diagram, and then proceeding to a limit in which the fuzziness disappears.
One may also notice that some almost periodic

flows become periodic when viewed in terms of flows

on planted structures; perhaps it may be useful to

approximate extremely complicated almost periodic

flows to a less complicated system of periodic

flows on a planted structure, then examining the

transition back to the original system by refining

the covering of the planted structure, so producing

a filtered sequence of solutions tending towards

the one desired.

REFERENCES

1.   Cole, M., On Causal Dynamics without Metrization
(1, 2, 3), Int. J. Theor. Phys., 1 (1968).

TWIST MAPPINGS, LINKING, ANALYTICITY, AND PERIODIC SOLUTIONS WHICH PASS CLOSE TO AN UNSTABLE PERIODIC SOLUTION[1]

C. Conley

(University of Wisconsin)

1. INTRODUCTION

This study concerns the existence of periodic orbits of a flow on a three-dimensional manifold. The flow is described by an autonomous Hamiltonian system of differential equations upon restricting attention to a particular (three-dimensional) integral surface of the Hamiltonian function.

In this surface there is to be an unstable periodic solution and our aim is to show the existence of infinitely many periodic solutions which pass close to this unstable one.

The work is motivated by a study of the

---

[1]This work was supported by Nonr 1202 (28).

planar restricted three-body problem for values of

the Jacobi constant such that the zero mass can

just make it from one positive mass point to the

other.   In this case the integral surface is homeo-

morphic to the connected sum of two three-dimensional

projective spaces (thus, is homeomorphic to the

product of an interval with a two-sphere after all

pairs of antipodal points lying on the same bound-

ing sphere have been identified).   The projection

into physical space of this manifold is then the

dumbbell–shaped Hill's region which includes both

of the positive mass points (Fig. 1).

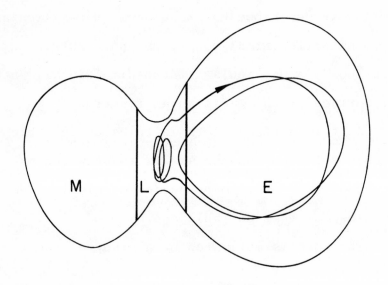

In Fig. 1 the two vertical segments divide the Hill's region into three parts, labeled M, L, and E, and in L the unstable periodic solution appears as an approximate ellipse. The application of the present work to the restricted problem enables one to prove:

THEOREM. If the mass in E is sufficiently large compared to the mass in M and the Jacobi constant is sufficiently close to (and above) that of the Lagrangian point between the mass points, then there exist infinitely many periodic solutions whose projections lie in L $\cup$ E and which pass close to the unstable periodic solution in L. (Figure 1 shows a "typical" such orbit.)

The proof begins with a detailed study of the flow in L which is carried out with the aid of a theorem of J. Moser [1] and requires the restriction of the Jacobi constant. This study leads to the construction of a mapping, defined by the flow in L, between two open annuli, which makes an infinite twist. Namely, radial segments in the first annulus are carried to infinite spirals in the second. This construction is described in

Section 2; the full details are given in [2] and
the picture for the restricted problem is obtained
in [3].

In Section 3 two criteria for the existence
of periodic solutions are given, the first resting
on the notion of nondegenerate homoclinic points
introduced by Poincaré and the second (which applies in the "totally degenerate" case) on the
Poincaré-Birkhoff fixed point theorem. The major
work is to show that one of these two criteria is
satisfied.

This work relies on the existence of a relative surface of section for the region E. Roughly,
this is a surface transverse to the flow which is
cut by orbit segments in E which either are "long
enough," or have their end points on the boundary
of E. In the case of the restricted problem the
relative surface of section is a disk bounded by
the retrograde circular orbits. Its existence can
be shown by a perturbation argument which, however,
requires the restriction on the mass ratio. The
details of the construction are omitted here.

This author doesn't know if such a relative
surface of section can be constructed in M, or

whether they exist for arbitrary mass ratios. The
retrograde periodic motions do exist in general
(for example, see [4] or [5]) but it is not even
clear that they span a disk transverse to the flow.
A positive answer to this question would lead to
many more results about the restricted problem.

The existence of the relative surface of
section implies that orbit segments in E, whose
end points lie on the boundary of E, link the
boundary of the section modulo the boundary of E,
and, further, that the linking number increases with
the length of the orbit segment. As a consequence
we see (in Section 4) that either seminondegenerate
homoclinic orbits exist, or that the Poincaré-Birkhoff
theorem can be applied to give our result.

Finally, in Section 5 we use the analyticity
of the equations of motion to see that the existence
of seminondegenerate homoclinic orbits implies that
of nondegenerate ones and our proof is completed
by applying the first criterion. (This portion of
the proof can be fitted to the general case of an
unstable periodic orbit of an analytic Hamiltonian
system with two degrees of freedom.)

For the case of the restricted problem, this

author does not know which criterion applies. It
seems most likely that nondegenerate homoclinic
orbits would exist. On the other hand, in the case
of Euler's problem of two fixed centers (to which
all our arguments also apply) there can be no nondegenerate homoclinic points as follows since the
equations admit a second (global) integral. Thus,
in this problem (where the existence of such periodic solutions is already known), we have an example
of the totally degenerate situation.

We can also remark in passing that our work
implies the existence of almost periodic solutions
which appear much as the periodic ones do. In the
nondegenerate case this follows from Birkhoff's
work on homoclinic points [6, 7, 8] and in the
degenerate case, from the theorem of J. Moser [10]
on invariant curves of annulus mappings.

2.

We now take as given a "Hamiltonian flow"
(see Section 1) on a three-dimensional manifold
and assume[2] that on a submanifold L, which is
homeomorphic to the product of a two-sphere and

an interval, the flow can be described by the equations which follow.

Let $K(\xi, \eta, \zeta, \bar{\zeta})$ be a (real analytic function of the two real variables ξ and η and the complex variable ζ. We suppose that K is of the form

$$K(\xi, \eta, \zeta, \bar{\zeta}) = \lambda\xi\eta + \frac{\mu}{2}|\zeta|^2$$
$$+ o_3(\xi, \eta, \zeta, \bar{\zeta})$$

(1)

where λ, $\mu > 0$, and, in fact, that K depends only on the products $\xi\eta$ and $\zeta\bar{\zeta}$.

For small positive h and c, the region L is that determined by

$$K = h \qquad |\xi - \eta| \leq c$$

(2)

L is easily seen to be homeomorphic to the product of an interval and a two-sphere provided h and c are small enough; namely, for each fixed value of $\xi - \eta$ between $-c$ and c, we see that the equation

---

[2]The following construction can always be carried out near critical points of Hamiltonian systems (with two degrees of freedom) provided the eigenvalues admit one real and one imaginary pair (for example, see [2]).

K = h determines the two-sphere

$$\frac{\lambda}{4}(\xi + \eta)^2 + \frac{\mu}{2}|\zeta|^2 + o_3(\,\cdot\,)$$
$$= h + \frac{\lambda}{4}(\xi - \eta)^2 \tag{3}$$

We will call the set of points on this two-sphere where $\xi + \eta = 0$ the equator, and the sets where $\xi + \eta > 0$ or $\xi + \eta < 0$ will be called the upper and lower hemisphere. It will be important to keep in mind that the coordinate ζ provides a homeomorphism of these hemispheres with the open disk in the complex plane determined by

$$|\zeta|^2 < k \approx h + \frac{\lambda}{4}(\xi - \eta)^2 \tag{4}$$

Now the flow on L is given by the following set of equations:

$$\dot{\xi} = \alpha\xi$$
$$\dot{\eta} = -\alpha\eta$$
$$\dot{\zeta} = \beta\zeta \tag{5}$$
$$\dot{\overline{\zeta}} = -\beta\overline{\zeta}$$

Here, α and β are, respectively, real and imaginary power series in the products $\xi\eta$ and $\zeta\overline{\zeta}$ which converge in L to values close to λ and $-i\mu$, respectively. It is easy to check that the products $\xi\eta$ and $\zeta\bar{\zeta}$ are (local) integrals for these equations so that K, which is the Hamiltonian function, is indeed an integral.

To analyze the flow in L one simply considers the projections on the ξ, η plane and ζ plane, respectively. In the first case we see the standard picture of an unstable critical point, and in the second, of a center.

With regard to the first projection we see (Fig. 2) that L itself projects to a set bounded

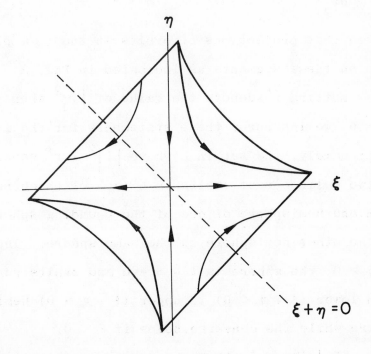

on two sides by the hyperbola $K(\xi, \eta, 0, 0) = h$
and on two sides by the line segments $\xi - \eta = \overset{+}{_-} c$,
which segments correspond to the bounding spheres
of L.

Now, except in the case $\xi\eta = 0$, each fixed
value of $\xi\eta$ determines two segments, one from each
branch of the corresponding hyperbola. If $\xi\eta < 0$,
the segments connect the bounding line $\xi - \eta = \pm c$
and if $\xi\eta > 0$, they have both end points on the
same segment. Computing from (5) that

$$\frac{d}{dt}(\xi - \eta) = \alpha(\xi + \eta) \qquad \alpha > 0 \qquad (6)$$

we see that projections of orbits in the ξ, η plane
move on these segments as indicated in Fig. 2.

Letting r^* denote the value of $\left| \varsigma \right|^2$ when
$\xi\eta = 0$, we interpret these statements for the flow
in L; namely, the set in L where $\left| \varsigma \right|^2 > r^*$ consists
of two cylinders of orbits in L each of which runs
from one hemisphere of one of the bounding spheres
to the other hemisphere on the same sphere. Thus
if $\xi > 0$, the sphere is $\xi - \eta = c$ and orbits run
from lower ($\xi + \eta < 0$) to upper ($\xi + \eta > 0$) hemisphere while the converse holds if $\xi < 0$.

If $\left| \varsigma \right|^2 < r^*$, then the corresponding set in

L consists of two cylinders (degenerate in the case $|\zeta| = 0$) which "cross" L from one bounding sphere to the other, meeting both in the same hemisphere — the upper one if they go from $\xi - \eta = -c$ to $\xi - \eta = c$, the lower one in the other case.

Finally the set where $|\zeta|^2 = r^*$ consists of an unstable periodic solution ($\xi = \eta = 0$) and four cylinders of orbits asymptotic to this periodic solution either as time increases ($\xi = 0$) or as time decreases ($\eta = 0$).

We now observe that on the two bounding spheres, each of the hemispheres is transverse to the flow, as is seen from (6). It follows that the flow in L defines four mappings — two between pairs of disks ($|\zeta|^2 < r^*$) and two between pairs of annuli $[r^* < |\zeta|^2 < k$; where k is as in (4) with $(\xi - \eta)^2 = c^2]$. Furthermore, all these mappings preserve the radial coordinate $|\zeta|^2$ since this is an integral in L.

Now computing that

$$\frac{d}{dt} \arg \zeta = i\beta \approx -\mu \qquad (7)$$

we see that the change in the argument of ζ for each of these mappings is approximately proportional

to the negative of the time required to go from
domain to range. Also, this time approaches in-
finity as $\left| \zeta \right|^2 \to r^*$; since for $\left| \zeta \right|^2 = r^*$ the orbits
are asymptotic to the unstable periodic solution.
In fact we can compute from (5) that the time T
required depends only on $\rho = \left| \zeta \right|^2$, and is of the
order of magnitude

$$T(\rho) \approx \ln(1\rho - r^*1) \tag{8}$$

for $\left| \zeta \right|^2$ close to r^*.

These facts imply that circles $\left| \zeta \right|^2 = \rho$ in
the domain of the mappings are rotated by an amount
that decreases to minus infinity as $\left| \zeta \right|^2 \to r^*$; it
is this "infinite twist" that provides us with
criteria for periodic solutions.

3.   TWO CRITERIA FOR THE EXISTENCE OF PERIODIC
     ORBITS

In order to discuss periodic solutions we
must now consider what happens to orbits when they
leave L. For our purposes it will be sufficient
to limit our attention to orbits crossing the
sphere $\xi - \eta = +c$, which we will call S. Also, it

is convenient to denote by H_+ and H_- the upper ($\xi + \eta > 0$) and lower ($\xi + \eta < 0$) hemispheres, respectively, and by R_+ and R_-, respectively, the annuli of "noncrossing" orbits in these hemispheres (that is, orbits where $r^* < |\zeta|^2 < k$). Finally, we will let A_+ and A_- denote the (inner) bounding circles ($|\zeta|^2 = r^*$) of R_+ and R_- – that is, the asymptotic orbits. (We will need no notation for the remaining disks of crossing orbits.)

As described in Section 2 the flow defines a mapping of R_- into R_+ as time increases; the orbit segments connecting the domain to the range lying in L. Our aim will be to combine this mapping with mappings defined outside L.

Before discussing what really happens we consider two possibilities:

3.1. NONDEGENERATE HOMOCLINIC ORBITS. First suppose we know that some orbit leaves L at $p \in A_+$ (hence is asymptotic to the unstable periodic solution as time decreases) and is carried eventually by the flow back to $q \in A_-$ – whence it winds asymptotically to the unstable periodic orbit as time increases also. (The orbit may or may not enter L between A_+ and A_-.)

Since the flow is transverse to H_+ and H_- we
can find neighborhoods U and V of p and q in H_+
and H_-, respectively, such that U is mapped homeomorphically to V by the flow. Indeed, U and V can
be so chosen that they meet A_+ and A_-, respectively,
in arcs γ and δ. We will denote by γ' the image
of γ by the flow mapping, and by δ' the preimage
of δ.

The orbit through p and q is called a homoclinic orbit (Poincaré). We classify such orbits
as:

(a)   Nondegenerate if γ' meets δ non-
      tangentially at q.

(b)   Seminondegenerate if q is an end
      point of $\gamma' \cap \delta \subset \gamma'$.

(9)

Now our first criterion for the existence of
periodic solutions is that a nondegenerate homoclinic orbit exists. If this is the case, we see
that the arcs γ and δ' divide U into four quadrants
while γ' and δ divide V into four quadrants and,
furthermore, that exactly one of the quadrants of
U in R_+ is carried to a quadrant of V in R_- (see

Fig. 3).

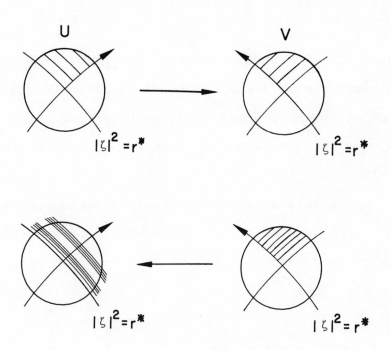

If we now follow the quadrant in V through L to its inverse in R_+, we see that in view of the infinite twist, the image spirals infinitely many times through the corresponding quadrant in U.

The analysis given by Birkhoff [6] (and more recently, by Smale and Sacker [7, 8]) now enables one to see that the composite mapping admits an

invariant Cantor set in which there are an infinite
number of periodic points corresponding to the
periodic orbits we seek.[3]

3.2. THE POINCARÉ-BIRKHOFF FIXED POINT THEOREM.

A situation in direct contrast to that above is
one where every point of A_+ is on a homoclinic orbit
- namely, where the flow (outside L) maps A_+ homeomorphically to A_-.

In this case we can choose a small subannulus
$(r^* < |\zeta| < r^* + \epsilon,\ \epsilon > 0$ and small) of R_-, which
is carried through L to the corresponding annulus
in R_+. This second annulus is then carried back
to R_- so that the outer boundary $(|\zeta| = r^* + \epsilon)$ is
carried to a star-like curve.

Now the composite mapping has a twist (indeed

---

[3]The condition on the Jacobian required in the
treatments of homoclinic points (but not needed if
one just wishes to conclude periodic orbits) is
actually easier to verify from the present viewpoint than in Birkhoff's original treatment. This
is because the Jacobian appears here as a product,
one factor of which can be computed explicitly
(that for the flow in L). The only relevant
feature of the other factor is that a certain co-
efficient is nonzero, which reduces precisely to
the condition of nontangential crossing.

an infinite one) and also preserves area (as a

result of the Hamiltonian character of the flow)

and so, by the theorem of Poincaré and Birkhoff

[9], admits infinitely many periodic points, which

again correspond to the periodic solutions we seek.

Now it is easy to imagine many situations

"between" the two discussed above; indeed there is

no a priori reason to suppose that any homoclinic

orbits exist.

In the next section we discuss a situation

in which we can prove that either seminondegenerate

homoclinic orbits exist, or that the second of the

above situations must hold. Finally, in Section 5

we show how to go from seminondegenerate to non-

degenerate homoclinic orbits in the case where the

equations are analytic, and thus show that one of

the two situations described above actually occurs.

4. LINKING

We now consider the flow outside of L and will

see that if we can find a "relative surface of

section" as described below, then either seminon-

degenerate homoclinic orbits exist, or every orbit

asymptotic at one end to the unstable periodic
orbit is also asymptotic at the other end.

First we suppose that on removing the interior
of L from our manifold we are left with two components (M and E of the introduction) and that the
one, say E, sharing the bounding sphere S ($\xi - \eta = c$)
with L is compact. (S is to be the only boundary
component of E.) Furthermore, we assume that every
two-sphere in E bounds a 3-cell (so that we can
apply the Stokes theorem to the 2-form preserved by
our flow and so compute areas of some sets in terms
of others).

We further suppose that in E there is a
periodic solution which bounds a disk D in E, which
disk is to be a relative surface of section for E
in the following sense:

(a)   The flow is transverse to D
      (except on the boundary of D).

(b)   Any orbit segment in E whose end
      points lie on the boundary of E   (10)
      meets D.

(c)   There exists T > 0 such that any
      orbit segment in E of (time)

length more than T meets D.

We use the relative surface of section as follows:

Suppose γ is an arc in H_+ (the hemisphere of S across which orbits leave L), and suppose the initial point p of γ is carried in time σ_0 to H_- without leaving E $\cup$ L. Then there is some maximal initial half-open subarc γ' of γ on which a continuous real-valued function σ can be defined in such a way that:

(a) $\sigma(p) = \sigma_0$.

(b)   If $q \in \gamma'$, then q is carried to
      H_- in time $\sigma(q)$.

Now let r be the first point of γ not in γ' and suppose r is not the last point of γ. Then in the presence of a relative surface of section, one of the following statements about r must be true:

(a)   r is carried to the equator
      $\xi + \eta = 0$ of S in time $\sigma(r)$
      $= \lim\limits_{q \to r} \sigma(q).$ (11)

(b)   r is carried to the set A_- of

points asymptotic to the unstable
periodic orbit.

To prove this, first suppose σ is bounded in
γ'. In this case the first alternative follows
from continuity in the initial conditions and
maximality of γ'.

Now suppose σ is not bounded on γ'. Let
$N(q)$ denote the number of times the orbit segment
δ_q, initiating at q and of length $\sigma(q)$, meets D.
Since D is transverse to the flow and is bounded
by an orbit, the function $N(q)$ must be constant on
γ'. Also, by (10b), there are at most $N(q)$ subarcs
of δ_q lying in E with end points on S, and by (10c),
none of these can be longer than $T \cdot N(q)$. It follows
that if q is close enough to r, the arc δ_q must
contain a long subarc in L. Because of our knowledge
of the flow in L, we know that long arcs in L must
lie close to the cylinders of asymptotic orbits
and an elementary argument shows that r must be
carried to A_-.

As a consequence of (11) we can now prove
that homoclinic orbits exist: namely, since E is
compact and our flow preserves a nondegenerate area

element we can conclude that some orbit which
crosses L (from $\xi - \eta = -c$ to $\xi - \eta = +c$) and so
enters E must also leave E and recross L the other
way.   Reworded, a point $p \in H_+$ with $\left| \zeta \right|^2 < r^*$ must
be carried to a point $q \in H_-$ with $\left| \zeta \right|^2 < r^*$.

Now let γ be an arc connecting p to A_+.
Excepting the case that the point $\gamma \cap A_+$ is on a
homoclinic orbit, we find, via (11), that either:
(1) all of γ is carried to the disk $\left| \zeta \right|^2 < r^*$; or
(2) the image of γ' in H_- crosses A_-; or (3) the
image of γ' lies inside the disk $\left| \zeta \right|^2 < r^*$ and the
point r is carried to A_-.

In any case, we conclude that there is an
orbit segment connecting the set $\left| \zeta \right|^2 < r^*$ in one
hemisphere to the set of asymptotic orbits in the
other.

For definiteness, suppose some point of A_+
is carried to the disk $\left| \zeta \right| < r^*$ in H_-.   We now
choose for γ the whole set A_+, and conclude that
either homoclinic points exist, or all of A_+ is
carried inside the disk $\left| \zeta \right| < r^*$.

Our proof of existence of homoclinic orbits
is completed by ruling out this final possibility
on the grounds that A_+ encloses a disk in H_+ with

area equal to that of the disk enclosed by A_- in

H_- . Also, the image of A_+ in H_- has to enclose

the same area (by Stokes' theorem applied to the

2-form preserved by our flow) and this leads to a

contradiction if the second possibility is assumed.

The obvious extension of this argument implies

that either seminondegenerate homoclinic points

exist or A_+ is carried to A_- .

It remains to see that the existence of semi-

nondegenerate homoclinic points implies that of

nondegenerate homoclinic points if the equations

are analytic.

5. ANALYTICITY

We suppose now that we have a real analytic

structure on our manifold, that ξ, η, ζ are analytic

coordinates, and that our equations are analytic.

Observing that S is an analytic surface we

see that the image in H_- of analytic curves in H_+

is analytic, and conversely. Also noting that A_+

and A_- are analytic curves we reason as follows:

Except in the case of total degeneracy there

is an analytic arc γ in $R_+ \cup A_+$ with one end point

in A_+, which is carried forward by the flow to A_-.
Similarly, there is an analytic arc δ in $R_- \cup A_-$
with an end point on A_-, which is carried backward
by the flow to A_+. Our aim will be accomplished
if we can see that δ is carried forward by the flow
so that it intersects γ nontangentially, for the
point of intersection must then lie on a nondegenerate homoclinic orbit.

Now we can assume that γ and δ meet the
relevant circle (A_+ or A_-) tangentially, for other-
wise we are done. Letting $\rho = \left| \zeta \right|^2$ and $\theta = \arg \zeta$
we see, in view of the analyticity of ζ, that ρ
and θ are real analytic in the same parameter.

In particular we can compute that for both
curves there is a positive ϵ such that

$$\frac{d\theta}{d\rho} < \frac{1}{(\rho - r^*)^{1-\epsilon}} \tag{12}$$

Now going back to (8) of Section 2, we find
for the image of δ in R_+ that

$$\left| \frac{d\theta}{d\rho} \right| \quad \text{is of the same order as}$$

$$\tag{13}$$

$$\frac{1}{\rho - r^*} \quad \text{as} \quad \rho \to r^*$$

Comparison of the orders of "growth" of the slope as $\rho \to r^*$ shows that the image arc of δ in R_+, and the arc γ cannot intersect tangentially everywhere, and our study is concluded.

REFERENCES

1. Moser, J., On a Generalization of a Theorem of Liapunov, C.P.A.M., XI (1958), pp. 257-271.

2. Conley, C., On the Ultimate Behavior of Orbits with Respect to an Unstable Critical Point, to be published in J. Diff. Eq.

3. Conley, C., Low Energy Transit Orbits in the Restricted Three-Body Problem (to be published).

4. Conley, C., The Retrograde Circular Solutions of the Restricted Three-Body Problem Via a Submanifold Convex to the Flow (to be published).

5. Birkhoff, G. D., The Restricted Problem of Three Bodies, Rend. Circ. Mat. Palermo, 39 (1915), pp. 265-334 (in particular, Part IV).

6. Birkhoff, G. D., Nouvelles recherches sur les systemes dynamiques, Pontifical Memoir, Collected Works, Vol. 2, Am. Math. Soc., New York, 1950.

7. Smale, S., Diffeomorphisms with Many Periodic

Points, Differential and Combinatorial Topology
(S. S. Cairns Ed.), Princeton University Press,
Princeton, New Jersey, 1965, pp. 63-80.

8.   Sacker, R., On Periodic Solutions Near Homoclinic Points -- A New Treatment of Smale's Work.
Notes on lectures presented in April, 1965, for
the Seminar on Ordinary Differential Equations
directed by Professor J. Moser at New York
University.

ON ψ-STABILITY AND DIFFERENTIAL INEQUALITIES

U. D'Ambrosio and V. Lakshmikantham

(University of Rhode Island)

The use of vector Liapunov functions, associated with the technique of differential inequalities, has been successfully employed to study conditional stability of solutions of a system of differential equations [1] and also for the study of conditional stability of general dynamical systems [2]. In this paper we further exploit these techniques to obtain sufficient conditions for conditional stability restricted to certain manifolds containing the origin, which can effectively be described by convenient choice of Liapunov functions. For obvious reasons, we call this kind of conditional stability ψ-stability. A similar situation is studied in Coddington and Levinson [3].

Consider the differential system

$$x' = f(t, x)$$
$$x(t_o) = x_o \quad t_o \geq 0 \qquad (*)$$

where x and f are n-dimensional vectors, $f(t, x)$
is defined and continuous in $I \times R^n$, where I stands
for the half-line $0 \leq t < +\infty$.

In what follows, if $v = (v_1, v_2, \ldots, v_N)$ and
$w = (w_1, \ldots, w_N)$, $v \leq w$ means $v_i \leq w_i$, $i = 1, \ldots, N$.

Let w be a vector of R^N and $w(t, r)$ be defined
on $I \times R^N$. For each $t \in I$ and each $i = 1, \ldots, N$,
assume $w_i(t, r)$ to be nondecreasing in $r_1, r_2, \ldots,$
$r_{i-1}, r_{i+1}, \ldots, r_N$. Then, it is well known (see [4])
that the system

$$r' = w(t, r)$$
$$r(t_o) = r_o \qquad (**)$$

admits a maximal solution $r(t; t_o, r_o)$ to the right
of t_o.

Now let V be a vector of R^N and the function
$V(t, x)$ be nonnegative and continuous on $I \times R^n$.
Suppose further that $V(t, x)$ satisfies a local
Lipschitzian condition in x and define

$$V^*(t, x) = \lim_{h \to 0^+} \sup \frac{1}{h}\{V(t + h, x + hf(t, x)) - V(t, x)\}$$

Then the following basic result is well known (see [4]):

LEMMA. Let the function $V^*(t, x)$ satisfy the inequality

$$V^*(t, x) \leq w(t, V(t, x)) \qquad\qquad (i)$$

where $w(t, r)$ is the function defined above, with the same monotonic property. Let $x(t)$ be any solution of (*) such that $V(t_o, x_o) \leq r_o$. Then

$$V(t, x(t)) \leq r(t; t_o, r_o)$$

where $r(t; t_o, r_o)$ is the maximal solution of (**).

Let $\phi(v)$ be a nonnegative real-valued function on R^N, nondecreasing in the sense that

$$0 \leq \phi(v_1) \leq \phi(v_2) \quad \text{if} \quad 0 \leq v_1 \leq v_2$$

and satisfying the following conditions:

(ii)   there exists a continuous non-
        decreasing real-valued function

b such that

b(t) > 0   if   t > 0   and

$$b(\|x\|) \leq \phi(V_1(t, x), \ldots, V_N(t, x))$$

(iii) $\phi(V_1(t, x), \ldots, V_N(t, x)) \to 0$

as $\|x\| \to 0$ for every $t \in I$

Now, let us introduce the concept of stability for which sufficient conditions will be established. We say that the zero solution of the system (*) is Ψ-stable if there exists an (n - k)-dimensional manifold Ψ in R^n, containing the origin and such that for each $\epsilon > 0$ and each $t_o \geq 0$, there exists a positive function d = $d(t_o, \epsilon)$, continuous in t_o for each ϵ, such that $\|x(t_o)\| \leq d$ and $x(t_o) \in Ψ$ imply

$$\|x(t)\| < \epsilon$$

Let the initial vector r_o of the system (**) have components r_{io}, i = 1, ..., N, and consider the following condition:

(iv) given any $\epsilon > 0$ and $t_o \geq 0$, there exists a positive function $\delta = \delta(t_o, \epsilon)$, continuous in t_o for each ϵ, and functions $\Phi_1, \Phi_2, \ldots, \Phi_k$ defined and continuous in R^N and null at the origin such that

$$\phi(r_{10}, r_{20}, \ldots, r_{N0}) \leq \delta \quad \text{and}$$
$$\Phi_i(r_{10}, \ldots, r_{N0}) = 0 \quad i = 1, \ldots, k$$

imply

$$\phi(r_1(t), r_2(t), \ldots, r_N(t)) < \epsilon \quad \text{for} \quad t \geq t_0$$

Then we can establish a sufficient condition for Ψ-stability, in the form of the following:

THEOREM. Let (i), (ii), and (iii) hold for the systems (*) and (**). Then condition (iv) implies that the zero solution of (*) is Ψ-stable.

Proof. For any $\epsilon > 0$, if $||x|| = \epsilon$ we have, from (ii),

$$b(\epsilon) \leq \phi(V_1(t, x), \ldots, V_N(t, x))$$

By condition (iv), given $b(\epsilon) > 0$, there exists a $\delta = \delta(t_0, \epsilon)$ continuous in t_0 for each $\epsilon > 0$, such that

$$\phi(r_{10}, r_{20}, \ldots, r_{N0}) \leq \delta \quad \text{and}$$
$$\Phi_i(r_{10}, r_{20}, \ldots, r_{N0}) = 0 \quad i = 1, \ldots, k$$

imply

$$\phi(r_1(t),\ r_2(t),\ldots,r_N(t)) < b(\epsilon) \qquad \text{for}$$
$$t \geq t_o \tag{v}$$

Now choose $r_o = (r_{10},\ r_{20},\ldots,r_{N0})$ satisfying

$$\phi(r_o) \leq \delta \quad \text{and} \quad \Phi_i(r_o) = 0 \quad i = 1,\ldots,k$$

Choosing $V(t_o,\ x_o) = r_o$, the conditions of the lemma are satisfied. We now define an $(n - k)$-dimensional manifold Ψ by putting, for each t,

$$\Psi_i(x_1,\ x_2,\ldots,x_n)$$
$$= \Phi_i(V_1(t,\ x(t)),\ldots,V_N(t,\ x(t)))$$
$$i = 1,\ldots,k$$

Then, clearly, $x(t_o) \in \Psi$, since, putting $x(t_o) = (x_{10},\ x_{20},\ldots,x_{n0})$, we have by the way the V's were choosen,

$$\Psi_i(x_{10},\ x_{20},\ldots,x_{no})$$
$$= \Phi_i(V_1(t_o,\ x(t_o)),\ldots,V_N(t_o,\ x(t_o)) = 0$$

for $i = 1,\ldots,k$. Now, by (ii), we have

$$b(\|x\|) \leq \phi(V_1(t,\ x),\ldots,V_N(t,\ x))$$

and so

$$b(\|x(t_o)\|) \leq \delta$$

because of the choice of r_o. Since b is a non-decreasing function, we have

$$\left|\left|x(t_o)\right|\right| \leq b^{-1}(\delta) = d_1$$

But (iii) means that, from δ, we can find a $d_2 = d_2(t_o, \delta)$ such that $\left|\left|x(t_o)\right|\right| \leq d_2$ implies

$$\phi(V_1(t_o, x(t_o)), \ldots, V_N(t_o, x(t_o))) \leq \delta$$

Let $d_3 = \min\{d_1, d_2\}$. Then, if $x(t_o) \in \Psi$ and $\left|\left|x(t_o)\right|\right| \leq d_3$, we have $\left|\left|x(t)\right|\right| < \epsilon$. In fact, if this is not true, we can find a solution of (*) satisfying

$$x(t_o) \in \Psi \quad \text{and} \quad \left|\left|x(t_o)\right|\right| \leq d_3$$

and such that, for a certain $t_1 > t_o$, we have $\left|\left|x(t_1)\right|\right| = \epsilon$. But then by (ii) we have

$$b(\left|\left|x(t_1)\right|\right|) \leq (V_1(t_1, x(t_1)), \ldots, V_N(t_1, x(t_1)))$$

and so, by the lemma and monotonicity of ,

$$b(\epsilon) \leq \phi(r_1(t_1; t_2, r_o), \ldots, r_N(t_1; t_o, r_o))$$

which is contradictory with (v). This finishes the proof.

The result established in this paper includes, as a special case, conditional stability studied in [1]. It is also expected that converse theorems for Ψ-stability can be obtained, as well as properties of regularity for the manifolds of stability of systems (*); these manifolds should bear properties of stability and their distribution in R^n could be studied. These questions will be treated in subsequent papers.

REFERENCES

1. Lakshmikantham, V., Vector Liapunov Functions and Conditional Stability, J. Math. Anal. Appl., 10 (1965), pp. 368-377.

2. Kayande, A. A., and Lakshmikantham, V., General Dynamical Systems and Conditional Stability, Proc. Cambridge Phil. Soc., 63 (1967), pp. 199-207.

3. Coddington, E. A., and Levinson, N., Theory of Ordinary Differential Equations, McGraw-Hill, New York, 1955.

4. Wazewski, T., Systemes des Equations et des Inegalites Differentielles Ordinaires aux Deuxiemes Membres Monotones et leurs Applications,

Ann. Soc. Pol. Math., 23 (1950), pp. 112-166.

THE BEGINNINGS OF AN ALGEBRAIC
THEORY OF MINIMAL SETS[1]

Robert Ellis

(University of Minnesota)

1. INTRODUCTION

The "algebraic theory" of the title consists
of attaching a group to each minimal set. In this
paper I shall describe how these groups may be
used to obtain a structure theorem for a wide
class of minimal sets generalizing the one of
Furstenberg [8]. I shall also discuss how these
groups may be used to study various recursive
properties of minimal sets.

Most of the results contained herein have
appeared or will soon appear elsewhere so that for

---

[1]This work was partially supported by the National
Science Foundation under Contract No. GP-6325.

the most part I shall quote references rather than give proofs.

Before proceeding I should like to recall some notions in order to make the exposition as self-contained as possible.

2. STANDING ASSUMPTIONS

Throughout this paper I assume that the phase group of the transformation groups involved is a fixed discrete group T and that the phase space is compact Hausdorff.

(In general one usually assumes that T is provided with a topology not necessarily discrete, making it a topological group. However, with regard to most of the problems discussed, for example, in [9], the topology on T plays no role when the phase space is compact Hausdorff. Thus it simplifies matters to assume that T is discrete.)

3. THE β-COMPACTIFICATION OF T

Let βT denote the Stone-Cech or β-compactification of T. Then βT is a compact Hausdorff space and T may be viewed as an everywhere dense open

subset of it. Moreover, βT may be provided with
a semigroup structure such that:

    (i) the maps $x \to yx$ $(x \in \beta T)$ of βT into
    βT are continuous for all $y \in \beta T$;

    (ii) the maps $x \to xy$ $(x \in \beta T)$ of βT into
    βT are continuous for all $y \in T$;

    (iii) the semigroup structure on βT induces
    the group structure on T

(for details see [2, 3]).

Thus the semigroup structure on βT defines
an action of T on βT. Since $\overline{T} = \beta T$, the orbit of
the identity e is dense. Hence $(\beta T, T)$ is point
transitive. Indeed, $(\beta T, T)$ is universal with
respect to this property; that is, if (X, T) is a
point transitive transformation group, then there
exists a continuous homomorphism Π of $(\beta T, T)$ onto
(X, T) [2, Lemma 1].

This means that we could study the class of
point transitive transformation groups by studying
the closed invariant equivalence relations on βT.
Rather than doing this, however, I shall consider
the situation from the point of view of the
function algebras involved.

4. THE ALGEBRA C

Henceforth C will denote the Banach algebra
of real-valued continuous functions on βT provided
with the supremum norm. Then the aforementioned
homomorphism Π induces an injective algebra homomorphism Π^* of $C(X)$ into C. The image of Π^* is a
closed T-invariant subalgebra of C. Thus we may
study the class of point transitive transformation
groups by studying the closed invariant subalgebras
of C (T-subalgebras for short). It is more convenient to do this than to study the closed invariant equivalence relations on βT.

Let me introduce some notation. Let $f \in C$,
$x \in \beta T$. Then $<f, x>$ will denote the image of x
under f, xf that map of βT into R such that $<xf, y>$
$= <f, yx>$ $(y \in \beta T)$, and fx the map of βT into R
such that $<fx, y> = <f, xy>$ $(y \in \beta T)$. Notice that
$fx \in C$ $(f \in C, x \in \beta T)$, but that in general $xf \in C$
only when $x \in T$.

Then A is a T-subalgebra of C if A is a
closed subalgebra of C and $tf \in A$ $(t \in T, f \in A)$.

There are several ways of recovering the
original transformation group (X, T) from the

image A in C of $C(X)$. The one I prefer is by means
of the set $\left|A\right|$ of T-homomorphisms of A into C.
[A T-homomorphism φ of A into C is an algebra homo-
morphism such that $\varphi(tf) = t\varphi(f)$ $(f \in A, t \in T)$.]
For details, see [4].

The advantages of this approach is that $\left|A\right|$
can be described by means of βT. If $p \in \beta T$ the
map $f \to fp$ $(f \in C)$ of C into C is in $\left|C\right|$. Denote
the above map by $\overline{p}$. Then the map $p \to \overline{p}$ of βT into
$\left|C\right|$ is an isomorphism onto. Moreover, given any
$\varphi \in \left|A\right|$, there exists $p \in \beta T$ such that $\varphi(f) = fp$
$(f \in A)$ [4]. Of course, p is in general not unique.

5.   MINIMAL SETS

In this paper I am primarily concerned with
those T-subalgebras A such that $\left|A\right|$ is minimal.

To characterize these, let M be an arbitrary
minimal right ideal of βT and J the set of idempotents in M.

Then $\left|A\right|$ is minimal if and only if there
exists $v \in J$ such that $A \subset \underline{A}(v) = [f\,|\,fv = f]$ [5,
Corollary 4].

Now let $u \in J$. Then $\overline{u} \mid \underline{A}$ (v) is an isomorphism of $\underline{A}(v)$ onto $\underline{A}(v)u = \underline{A}(u)$, and if A is a T-subalgebra of $\underline{A}(v)$, Au is a T-subalgebra of $\underline{A}(u)$ which is isomorphic to A.

Thus we can study the class of minimal sets by means of the T-subalgebras of $\underline{A}(u)$.

For the remainder of this paper M will denote a fixed minimal right ideal in βT, J the set of idempotents of M, and u a fixed element of J.

Although several seemingly arbitrary choices have been made, the results obtained are independent of these choices (see [3, 11]).

6. THE GROUP ASSOCIATED WITH A MINIMAL SET

I am now in a position to define the groups mentioned at the beginning of this paper.

The semigroup structure on βT induces the structure of a group on the subset G = Mu of M [6].

Now let A be a T-subalgebra of $\underline{A}(u)$. Then the group associated with A is the subgroup $G(A) = [\alpha | \alpha \in G$ and $f\alpha = f, f \in A]$ of G [5].

It would be desirable to be able to distinguish T-subalgebras by means of their groups and also to recover the T-subalgebra from its group. However, neither of these desirata can be realized in general.

There exist T-subalgebras A, B of $\underline{A}(u)$ with $A \subsetneq B$ and $G(A) = G(B)$. Thus, in general, even if we know that $A \subset B$ and $G(A) = G(B)$, we cannot conclude that $A = B$.

Again if A is a T-subalgebra of $\underline{A}(u)$ and $A = G(A)$ the "natural" way of retrieving A from A would be to consider $\underline{A}(A) = \left[f \mid f \in \underline{A}(u) \text{ and } f\alpha = f, \alpha \in A \right]$. Then $\underline{A}(A)$ is indeed a T-subalgebra of $\underline{A}(u)$, and $A \subset \underline{A}(A)$. However, A need not be equal to $\underline{A}(A)$.

The obvious remedy is to restrict, in some manner, the algebras considered. This brings us to the notion of a group-like extension.

7. GROUP-LIKE EXTENSIONS

Let A, B be T-subalgebras of $\underline{A}(u)$. Then B is a group-like extension of A (written $A \leq B$) if $A \subset B$ and if $Ap \subset \underline{A}(w)$ implies that $Bp \subset \underline{A}(w)$ for all $p \subset \beta T$ and $w \in J$.

In general, if $A \leq B$, then $A = B$ if and only if $G(B) = G(A)$ [5]. Thus the first of the two desirata is achieved.

With regard to the second it is also true that if $A \leq B$ then $A = \underline{A}(A) \cap B$ where $A = G(A)$ [11].

This leads one to suspect that when $A \leq B$ there is a Galois connection between subgroups H of G with $G(B) \subset H \subset G(A)$ and T-subalgebras F with $A \subset F \subset B$. This is indeed the case and the connection is given by $F \to G(F)$ and $H \to \underline{A}(H) \cap B$ [11]. However, one must insist that H be a closed subgroup of G when G is provided with the so-called τ-topology [3, 5].

Let me now describe the topological significance of the relation $A \leq B$ (see [5] for proofs). Since $A \subset B$, $G(B)$ is a subgroup of $G(A)$. Consider first the case when $G(B)$ is a normal subgroup of $G(A)$. Then there exists an action of $H = G(A)/G(B)$ on $|B|$ such that the elements of H commute with those of T and $(|B|/H, T) \cong (|A|, T)$. The above isomorphism is induced by the restriction map $x \to x|A$ $(x \in |B|)$ of $|B|$ onto $|A|$.

No mention was made above of a topology on H. It sometimes happens that the topology of pointwise convergence on H is compact. When this is the case the extension B of A is called

principal. It is easy to see [3, Proposition 4.7]
that if $|B|$ is a metrizable principal extension of
$|A|$, then it is an isometric extension in the
sense of Furstenberg [8].

Now suppose $A \leq B$ but $G(B)$ is not a normal
subgroup of $G(A)$. Then one forms the T-invariant
algebra S generated by $\cup[B\alpha \mid \alpha \in G(A)]$. Then
$A \leq B \leq S$, $A \leq S$, and $G(S)$ is a normal subgroup of
$G(A)$. Let $K = G(A)/G(S)$. Then, as before, K acts
on $|S|$ and $(|A|, T) \cong (|S|/K, T)$.

With regard to $|B|$ there exist a compact
Hausdorff space F and an action of H on F such
that $(|B|, T) \cong (|S| \underset{H}{\times} F, T)$ where T acts trivially
on F (see [3, 5] for details). The above statement
is not quite precise in the general case because
of topological considerations. However, when S is
a principal extension of A it is exact. In this
case then $|S|$ is a principal fiber space over $|A|$
with structure group K, and $|B|$ is the associated
fiber space with fiber F.

8. THE STRUCTURE OF GROUP-LIKE EXTENSIONS

In [3] a structure theorem for group-like

extensions is proved, a theorem quite similar to
the Furstenberg structure theorem for minimal
distal flows [8]. This is not surprising since
$|A|$ is distal if and only if $A \geq R$ [5].

Let $A \leq B$, and for simplicity's sake assume
that $G(B)$ is a normal subgroup of $G(A)$. Then there
exists an ordinal ν and a family of T-subalgebras
$(A\hat{\alpha} \mid \alpha \leq \nu)$ such that: (i) $A_{\hat{1}} = A$, $A_\nu = B$;
(ii) $A_\alpha \leq A_\beta$ $(\alpha \leq \beta)$; (iii) $A_{\alpha+1}$ is a nontrivial
principal extension of A_α if $\alpha + 1 \leq \nu$; (iv) A_α
is the T-algebra generated by $\underset{\beta > \alpha}{\cup} A_\beta$ if α is a
limit ordinal $\leq \nu$.

As in Furstenberg's work some sort of
countability assumption is needed.

[When $A \leq B$ and $G(B)$ is not normal in $G(A)$,
we obtain a similar theorem by means of the algebra
S introduced above.]

Because of the Galois connection the algebras
(A_α) may be described by means of certain subgroups
of G.

Thus suppose A_α has been defined and that
$A_\alpha \subsetneq B$. Then $G(B)$ is a normal subgroup of
$A_\alpha = G(A_\alpha)$. This implies that $B A_\alpha \subset B$. In this
situation, the algebra B may be used to define a

topology $\tau(B)$ on A_α [5] such that A_α is compact T_1 and the group operation is unilaterally continuous.

Then $Q = \cap \, [\bar{v} \,|\, v \in N_e]$ is a closed invariant subgroup of A_α such that A_α/Q is a compact Hausdorff topological group.

Now set $A_{\alpha+1} = \underline{A}(Q) \cap B$. Then $A_{\alpha+1}$ is a principal extension of A_α with group A_α/Q. It will be a nontrivial extension if and only if $Q \neq A_\alpha$. (It is here that some sort of countability assumption is required.)

9. THE GENERAL CLASSIFICATION PROBLEM

Let A be a T-subalgebra of $\underline{A}(u)$. Then how can we describe the structure of an arbitrary extension B of A? We have seen how to do this when $A \leq B$.

Horelick [11] has observed that there exists a maximum group-like extension of A, namely a T-subalgebra $A*$ of $\underline{A}(u)$, such that $A \leq A*$ and $A \leq F$ if and only if $F \subset A*$.

Moreover, if $A \subset B$ and $G(A*) \subset G(B)$ then there exists a unique T-subalgebra F of $\underline{A}(u)$ such

that $A \leq F$ and $G(F) = G(B)$. Indeed, $F = \underline{A}(G(B)) \cap A$
and F is the smallest T-subalgebra containing A
with group equal to $G(B)$.

Thus if $A \subset B$ and $G(A*) \subset G(B)$, the extension
B of A splits naturally into two parts, a group-like
extension F of A and what might be termes a "singular" extension B of F.

This latter type of extension leads naturally
to the structure of the set $A(B) = [F | A \subset F, G(F) = 1$
Horelick [11] has discovered some interesting
relations among the sets $[A(B) | G(A*) \subset B]$.

10. THE GROUP $G(A)$ AND THE RECURSIVE PROPERTIES OF $|A|$

In this section I would like to discuss how
some of the dynamical properties of $|A|$ are re-
flected by $G(A)$.

Let me first introduce some constants. From
now on E will denote the T-algebra of all almost
periodic functions on T, E its group $G(E)$, and D
will denote the T-algebra of all distal functions
on T, D its group $G(D)$.

Then $E = D \cap \underline{A}(E)$, E is a closed invariant

subgroup of G, and G/E is the Bohr compactification of the discrete group T [3].

Now let A be a T-subalgebra of $\underline{A}(u)$, $A = G(A)$. Then proximal is a closed equivalence relation on A if and only if $D \subset A$; $|A|$ is proximally equi-continuous if and only if $E \subset A$; $D \subset A$ if and only if $A \subset D$; $E \subset A$ if and only if $A \subset E$. (These results are due to Horelick [11].)

Recently Auslander [1] introduced the notion of regularity; (X, T) is regular if and only if it is isomorphic to a minimal ideal in its enveloping semigroup.

It turns out [11] that $|A|$ is regular if and only if $AG \subset A$. In this case A is normal in G and G/A is isomorphic with the group of automorphisms of $(|A|, T)$.

Some time ago Gottschalk and I introduced the notion of the structure group $\Gamma(X, T)$ associated with a transformation group (X, T) [7].

I shall now describe the relation between $\Gamma(|A|)$ and $A = G(A)$.

DEFINITION. Let B be a T-subalgebra of $\underline{A}(u)$ and $B = G(B)$. Then the <u>regularizer of</u> B, $r(B)$, is the

T-subalgebra of $\underline{A}(u)$ generated by the set
$[B\alpha \,|\, \alpha \in G]$.

I shall set $r(B) = \cap[\alpha B \alpha^{-1} \,|\, \alpha \in G]$. Then it
is known [11] that $r(B)$ is regular; B is regular
if and only if $B = r(B)$; and $G(r(B)) = r(G(B))$.

From the definition of $\Gamma(|A|)$ it follows
that $\Gamma(A)$ [the T-subalgebra associated with $\Gamma(|A|)$]
is just $r(A \cap E)$.

Moreover, $\Gamma(|A|)$ is regular and a topological
group. Hence it is isomorphic with its automorphism
group $G/G(\Gamma(A))$.

The problem now is to compute $G(\Gamma(A))$
$= G(r(A \cap E)) = r(G(A \cap E))$. Set $K = G(A \cap E)$.
Since $A \cap E$ is contained in both A and E, $A \cup E \subset K$.
Hence $K \supset \{A \cup E\}$, the closed subgroup of G gener-
ated by $A \cup E$.

PROPOSITION. Let B, F, and H be T-subalgebras of
$\underline{A}(u)$ such that $F \subset B$ and $F \leq H$. Then $G(B \cap H)$
$= \{G(B) \cup G(H)\}$.

Proof. Set $L = G(B \cap H)$, $B = G(B)$, and $H = G(H)$.

Since $B \cap H$ is contained in both B and H,
$B \cup H \subset L$, whence $\{B \cup H\} \subset L$.

Now $F \leq H$ implies that $H \subset F*$. Hence $G(F^*) \subset H \subset \{B \cup H\}$. Moreover, $F \subset B \cap H$ implies $\{B \cup H\} \subset F$. Hence by [11] there exists a T-sub-algebra N of $\underline{A}(u)$ such that $F \leq N$ and $N = G(N) = \{B \cup H\}$.

Since $F \leq N$, it follows from the definition that $\{F \cup B\} \leq \{N \cup B\}$, that is, $B \leq \{N \cup B\}$. But $G\{N \cup B\} = N \cap B = B$. Hence $B = \{N \cup B\}$ or, in other words, $N \subset B$.

Similarly, replacing B by H in the above discussion we conclude that $N \subset H$.

Thus $N \subset B \cap H$, whence $L \subset N$; that is, $G(B \cap H) \subset \{B \cup H\}$. The proof is completed.

Since $R \leq E$ and $R \subset A$, we may apply the above proposition to conclude that $G(A \cap E) = \{A \cup E\}$.

Now let $\pi : G \to G/E$ be the canonical map. Then, as was remarked previously, G/E is a compact T_2 topological group, and A is a closed subgroup of the compact group G. Hence $\pi(A)$ is a compact subgroup of G/E. This means that it is also closed. Hence $AE = EA = \pi^{-1}\pi(A)$ is a closed sub-group of G. Thus $\{A \cup E\} = AE$.

To sum up we have proved the following:

PROPOSITION.   Let A be a T-subalgebra of $\underline{A}(u)$.
Then the structure group of $|A|$ is $G/r(AE)$.

It is easy to see that if, in addition, A is
regular, then $\Gamma(|A|) = G/AE$.

11.   PROBLEMS AND DIRECTIONS FOR RESEARCH

In this final section I would like to discuss
problems and directions for research suggested by
the preceding material. There is no dearth of
questions that one can raise, the problem is rather
to suggest fruitful ones. The following then is a
list of some of the problems in this area which
seem interesting to me.

(A)   Using the groups introduced above it
should be possible to pick out classes of T-subalgebras of $\underline{A}(u)$ which would be amenable to further
classification.

Thus, for example, those T-subalgebras of
the form $\underline{A}(H)$, where H is a closed subgroup of G,
have some special properties, for example, $\underline{A}(H)$ is
regular if and only if H is normal, if $H \supset E$ then
$\underline{A}(H)$ is coalescent [11], if $f \in \mathcal{g}(H)$ and φ is a
continuous function on the range of f then

$\varphi \cdot f \in \underline{A}(H)$ (Knapp).

In particular, what can be said about $\underline{A}(G)$? When T is Abelian $\underline{A}(G) = R$, but in general $\underline{A}(G) \neq R$ [11].

Can one show directly that if a weakly almost periodic function is in $\underline{A}(G)$ then it must be a constant? An affirmative answer would enable one to prove by the above method that the weakly almost periodic functions on T were amenable.

(B)   It would be of interest to know more about the group $D = G(\mathcal{V})$ and $E = G(E)$.

Let P be the closed subgroup of G generated by elements of the form $p\eta(pu)^{-1}$ where $p \in M$ and η is an idempotent of βT with $\eta u = \eta$ and $u\eta = \eta$. Then it is known [11] that proximal is an equivalence relation on A if and only if $P \subset A$. Hence $P \subset D$. It is conjectured that $P = D$. This amounts to saying that if proximal is an equivalence relation, then it is closed.

(C)   The general theory developed above should simplify considerably under the additional assumption that the phase spaces involved be zero-dimensional.

Thus if T is the integers and β is a principal

extension of A where $|A|$ and $|B|$ are zero-dimension-
al and $(|A|$, T) is equicontinuous, then one may
conclude that $(|B|$, T) is also equicontinuous. This
result is, of course, false when the assumption of
zero-dimensionality is dropped.

However, one way of proving the above result
is by reducing it to the case where $G(B)$ is of
finite index in $G(A)$.

This leads to the following question: suppose
that $A \subset E$ [that is, $(|A|$, T) is equicontinuous
and that $A \leq B$ with $G(B)$ of finite index in $G(A)$,
then is $B \subset E$?

The above is true when T is finitely generated,
but nothing is known about the case of arbitrary T.

(D) Furstenberg's structure theorem is being
applied in a variety of situations. Thus it would
be convenient to be able to dispense with the
countability assumptions so far needed for its
proof [3, 8].

(E) Knapp's recent work on the analysis of
distal functions on a group [12] should generalize
to the case of group-like extensions.

(F) One should be able to discuss minimal
discrete flows $|A|$ with quasidiscrete spectrum

(see [10] from the point of view of $G(A)$. In fact it should be possible to relate the groups defined in [10] to $G(A)$ and to generalize the results of [10] to a wider class of groups.

(G) Finally I think it would be of value to investigate how the structure introduced above transforms when the group T is mapped into the group S by means of a homomorphism φ. In particular, what happens when φ is an automorphism of T?

REFERENCES

1. Auslander, J., Regular Minimal Sets I, Trans. Am. Math. Soc., 123 (1966), pp. 469-479.

2. Ellis, R., Universal Minimal Sets, Proc. Am. Math. Soc., 11 (1960), pp. 540-543.

3. Ellis, R., The Structure of Group-Like Extensions of Minimal Sets (to be published).

4. Ellis, R., Point Transitive Transformation Groups, Trans. Am. Math. Soc., 101 (1961), pp. 384-395.

5. Ellis, R., Group-Like Extensions of Minimal Sets, Trans. Am. Math. Soc., 127 (1967), pp. 125-135.

6. Ellis, R., A Semigroup Associated with a
Transformation Group, Trans. Am. Math. Soc., 94
(1960), pp. 272-281.

7. Ellis, R., and Gottschalk, W. H., Homomorphisms
of Transformation Groups, Trans. Am. Math. Soc.,
94 (1960), pp. 258-271.

8. Furstenberg, H., The Structure of Distal Flows,
Am. J. Math., 85 (1963), pp. 477-515.

9. Gottschalk, W. H., and Hedlund, G. A., Topological Dynamics, Am. Math. Soc. Coll. Publ., 36,
Am. Math. Soc., Providence, 1955.

10. Hahn, F., and Parry, W., Minimal Dynamical
Systems with Quasi-Discrete Spectrum, J., London
Math. Soc., 40 (1965), pp. 309-323.

11. Horelick, B., An Algebraic Approach to the
Study of Minimal Sets in Topological Dynamics,
thesis, Wesleyan University, 1967.

12. Knapp, A. W., Distal Functions on Groups,
Trans. Am. Math. Soc., 128 (1967), pp. 1-40.

P-RECURRENCE AND QUASIMINIMAL SETS

J. W. England and J. F. Kent, III

(University of Virginia)

1. INTRODUCTION

Hilmy has given a characterization of quasi-minimal sets for real flows on a compact metric space [5]. The object of this paper is to generalize this result, so far as it is possible, to a transformation group with a noncompact generative phase group. The principal results are: (1) the orbit closure of a point which is P-recurrent for some proper replete semigroup and whose isotropy subgroup is contained in the compact subgroup of T is a quasiminimal set; (2) if E is a quasiminimal set then there exists a point of E whose orbit closure is E and has the properties that it is P-recurrent and has a nonsyndetic isotropy subgroup.

Examples are then given to show that these theorems provide the strongest form of Hilmy's theorem for the more general phase group.

Throughout this paper (X, T, π) will denote a transformation group for which X is a first countable Hausdorff space. The phase group T will be assumed to be a noncompact generative group. That is, T is isomorphic to $C \times R^n \times Z^m$, $n \geq 0$, $m \geq 0$, C is a compact Abelian group, R is the real numbers, and Z is the integers [7].

2. P-LIMIT SETS AND P-RECURRENCE

DEFINITION 2.1. Let u be a unit vector in R^n and let $0 < \beta < 1$, then $C_u = \{p \in R^n : p \cdot u \geq \beta \|p\|\}$ is called a <u>solid</u> <u>cone</u> with vertex at the origin and axis u.

LEMMA 2.2. Let C_u be as above and let p, q $\in C_u$ such that $q \cdot u / \|q\| > \beta$. Then there exists a non-negative number M such that $Mq \in p + C_u$, and if $N < M$ then $Nq \notin p + C_u$.

<u>Proof</u>. It is sufficient to show that for some

positive number J, $Jq \in p + C_u$. Then M may be
taken as the infimum of the set $\{J \geq 0 : Jq \in p + C_u\}$.
Since C_u is closed, $p + C_u$ is closed, which implies
$Mq \in p + C_u$.

Let K be a positive number with the property
that $K(1 - \beta^2)^{1/2} \geq ||p||$ and $Ku - p \neq 0$. We first
show that $Ku - p \in C_u$. Let $z = Ku - p$, then
$||Ku - z||^2 = ||p||^2 \leq K^2(1 - \beta^2)$. However, $||Ku - z||^2$
$= K^2 - 2K(z \cdot u) + ||z||^2 \leq K^2(1 - \beta^2)$. This implies
that $K^2\beta^2 + ||z||^2 \leq 2K(z \cdot u)$. Rearranging this in-
equality gives

$$\frac{z \cdot u}{||z||} \geq \frac{1}{2}[(\frac{K\beta^2}{||z||}) + (\frac{||z||}{K})]$$

The right-hand side of this inequality is seen to
be greater than β by considering the inequality

$$0 \leq [(\frac{K\beta}{||z||}) - 1]^2 = (\frac{K^2\beta^2}{||z||^2}) - (\frac{2K\beta}{||z||}) + 1$$

This implies that

$$\frac{2K\beta}{||z||} \leq (\frac{K^2\beta^2}{||z||^2}) + 1$$

or

$$\beta \le \frac{1}{2} \left[\left(\frac{K\beta^2}{||z||} \right) + \left(\frac{||z||}{K} \right) \right.$$

Thus $z \cdot u \ge \beta ||z||$ and $z = Ku - p \in C_u$. Since C_u is a semigroup we have $Ku + C_u \subset p + C_u$.

The point q was assumed to be an interior point of C_u. Thus there exists an $R > 0$ such that the closed sphere with center q and radius R is contained in C_u. This implies that $q - R_u \in C_u$. Let $J = K/R$, then $Jq \in Ku + JC_u \subset Ku + C_u \subset p + C_u$, which completes the proof.

LEMMA 2.3. Let C_u be as above and let $p, q \in C_u$ such that $||p|| = ||q|| \ne 0$, $p \cdot u/||p|| > q \cdot u/||q|| > \beta$, and let K and L be positive numbers such that $Lq \in Ku + C_u$. Then there exists a positive number N with $N \le L$ such that $Np \in Ku + C_u$.

Proof. Since L satisfies the condition $Lq \in Ku + C_u$ we may assume that L is the smallest such number. That is, $Lq \in \partial(Ku + C_u)$, the boundary of $Ku + C_u$.

We now show that $Lp \in (Ku - C_u) - \partial(Ku + C_u)$. Since $Lq - Ku \in \partial(C_u)$, we have $(Lq - Ku) \cdot u = \beta ||Lq - Ku||$. The hypothesis implies that $p \cdot u > q \cdot u$. Thus

$$\beta = \frac{(Lq - Ku) \cdot u}{||Lq - Ku||}$$

$$= \frac{L(q \cdot u) - K||u||^2}{L^2||q||^2 - 2KL(q \cdot u) + K^2||u||^2 \quad 1/2}$$

$$< \frac{L(p \cdot u) - K||u||^2}{L^2||p||^2 - 2KL(p \cdot u) + K^2||u||^2 \quad 1/2}$$

$$= \frac{(Lp - Ku) \cdot u}{||Lp - Ku||}$$

This implies that $Lp - Ku \in C_u - \partial(C_u)$ or $Lp \in (Ku + C_u) - \partial(Ku + C_u)$. By the previous lemma, there exists a nonnegative number N such that $Np \in Ku + C_u$ and if $M < N$, then $Mp \notin Ku + C_u$. Thus $N \leq L$ and the lemma is proved.

DEFINITION 2.4 [3, 3.37]. Let P be a proper semi-group of T. P is said to be replete in T provided that if K is a compact subset of T then there exists a $t \in T$ such that $Kt \subset P$.

DEFINITION 2.5 [3, 6.33]. Let P be a proper replete semigroup of T and let $x \in X$. The P-limit set of $\underline{x}$, P_x, is defined by $P_x = \bigcap_{t \in T} cl(xtP)$.

The preceding lemmas will be used to establish certain properties of replete semigroups in R^n x Z^m. In order to shorten the proofs, they were given for R^n. Minor modifications will adapt them to the cases R^n x Z^m and Z^m. For the rest of this section we will identify T with C x R^n x Z^m so that for t $\in$ T, t = (a, b, c) where a $\in$ C, b $\in R^n$, and c $\in Z^m$.

LEMMA 2.6. For x $\in$ X, let z $\in$ cl(xT). If there exists a sequence of points $\{xt_n\}$ converging to z with the property that $\lim_{n\to\infty} ||(b_n, c_n)|| =$ where $t_n = (a_n, b_n, c_n)$ then there exists a proper replete semigroup P such that z $\in P_x$.

Proof. Let A = $\{(b_n, c_n)/||(b_n, c_n)|| : n = 1, 2, 3, ..$ A is a collection of unit vectors in R^{n+m}. Two cases must be considered: (1) A is infinite; (2) A is finite.

In the first case, A is an infinite subset of a compact subset of R^{n+m}. Thus there exists a point u = (b, c) $\in R^{n+m}$ with $||u|| = 1$ such that u is a cluster point of A. There exists a sub-sequence $\{(b_n', c_n')/||(b_n, c_n)||\}$ of A which converges to u. Since $\lim_{n\to\infty} ||(b_n, c_n)|| = \infty$ we may assume

that $||(b_n', c_n')||$ converges monotonically to infinity.
To simplify notation we denote this subsequence by
$\{(b_n, c_n)\}$. Let $0 < \beta < 1$ and let C_u denote the
cone used in the previous lemmas. Let P'
$= C_u \cap (R^n \times Z^m)$ and $P = C \times P' \subset T$. Then P is a
proper replete semigroup of T [4]. We now show
that $z \in P_x$.

Let U be an open subset of X which contains
z. There exists a positive integer N such that if
$n \geq N$ then $x t_n = x(a_n, b_n, c_n) \in U$. Let $p = (a, p')$
$\in P$. Then $pP = C \times (p' + P')$ and $p' + P'$
$= (p' + C_u) \cap (R^n \times Z^m)$. By Lemma 2.2 there exists
a positive number K such that $Ku \in p' + C_u$. For
each $n = 0, 1, 2, \ldots$, let $\beta_n = (b_n, c_n) \cdot u / ||(b_n, c_n)||$.
Since $\{(b_n, c_n)/||(b_n, c_n)||\}$ converges to u,
$\lim_{n \to \infty} \beta_n = 1 = u \cdot u / ||u||$. Thus there exists an N'
such that for $n > N'$ we have $\beta_n \geq \beta_N' \geq \beta$. Lemmas
2.2 and 2.3 imply the existence of a number L_N'
such that

$$L_N'\left[\frac{(b_n, c_n}{||(b_n, c_n)||}\right] \in Ku + C_u \subset p' + C_u$$

$$\text{for all} \quad n \geq N'$$

Since $\lim_{n \to \infty} ||(b_n', c_n)|| = \infty$ there exists an N'' such

that for $n > N''$, $L_N' \leq ||(b_n, c_n)||$. For
$n > \max(N, N', N'')$ we have $xt_n \in U$ and t_n
$= (a_n, b_n, c_n) \in C \times (p' + P') = pP$. Thus
$U \cap xpP \neq 0$ for all open subsets of X which
contain z. This implies $z \in cl(xpP)$. Since p
was an arbitrary element of P we have
$$z \in \bigcap_{p \in P} cl(xpP) = P_X \; [1].$$
The proof of case (2) is similar to the
above and is not given.

This lemma gives a characterization of the
orbit closure of a point. In the case of a real
flow the well-known result is that the orbit
closure of a point is equal to the union of the
orbit and the α and ω limit sets.

THEOREM 2.7. Let $x \in X$ and let T be a noncompact
generative topological group. If A is the collection of all closed proper replete semigroups
of T then $cl(xT) = xT \cup \left(\bigcap_{P \in A} P_X \right)$.

Proof. Since $P_X \subset cl(xT)$ for all $P \in A$ we have
$xT \cup \left(\bigcup_{P \in A} P_X \right) \subset cl(xT)$.
Let $y \in cl(xT) - xT$. Since X is a first
countable Hausdorff space there exists a sequence

$\{xt_n\} \subset xT$ such that $\lim\limits_{n \to \infty} xt_n = y$. Let t_n
$= (a_n, b_n, c_n)$ for $n = 1, 2, 3, \ldots$. Since C is
compact, there exists an element $a \in C$ and subse-
quence $\{a_n'\}$ of $\{a_n\}$ such that $\lim\limits_{n \to \infty} a_n = a$. If
$||(b_n', c_n')||$ is bounded then there exists an element
$(b, c) \in R^n \times Z^m$ and a subsequence $\{(b_n'', c_n'')\}$ of
$\{(b_n', c_n')\}$ such that $\lim\limits_{n \to \infty} (b_n'', c_n'') = (b, c)$. In
this case if we let $t = (a, b, c)$ we have $\lim\limits_{n \to \infty} xt_n''$
$= xt = y$. This implies that $y \in xT$ which is a
contradiction. If $||(b_n', c_n')||$ is not bounded, then
Lemma 2.6 implies that there exists a $P \in \Lambda$ such that
$y \in P_x$ and the theorem is proved.

DEFINITION 2.8 [3, 6.35]. Let P be a proper
replete semigroup in T. A set $E \subset T$ is said to be
P-extensive provided $E \cap pP \neq \phi$ for all $p \in P$.

DEFINITION 2.9 [3, 6.36]. Let $x \in X$ and let P be
a proper replete semigroup in T. The point x is
said to be P-recurrent provided that for every open
subset U of X which contains x there is a P-extensive set $E \subset T$ such that $xE \subset U$.

LEMMA 2.10. Let L be a compact neighborhood of the

identity of T with the property that $T = \bigcup_{n=1}^{\infty} L^n$
and let $x \in X$. If for every open set U containing
x, $U \cap x(T - L^n) \neq \phi$ for all positive integers n,
then there ecists a proper replete semigroup P of
T such that x is P-recurrent.

Proof. Let $\{U_n\}$ be a decreasing sequence of open
subsets of X such that $\bigcap_{n=1}^{\infty} U_n = x$. For each positive integer n there exists an element $t_n \in T$ such
that $t_n \in (T - L^n)$ and $xt_n \in U_n$. Thus $\lim_{n \to \infty} xt_n = x$.
Since $t_n = (a_n, b_n, c_n) \in (T - L^n)$, then $\{||(b_n, c_n)||\}$
is an unbounded set. Thus, by Lemma 2.6, there
exists a proper replete semigroup P contained in T
such that $x \in P_x$. This implies that x is P-recurrent
[1, p. 1147].

LEMMA 2.11. Let E be a P-extensive set for some
proper replete semigroup P and let L be a compact
neighborhood of the identity of T with the property
that $T = \bigcup_{n=1}^{\infty} L^n$. Then $E \cap (T - L^n) \neq \phi$ for all
positive integers n.

Proof. Suppose there exists an integer $M \geq 1$ such
that $E \cap (T - L^M) = \phi$. Since E is P-extensive,
$E \cap pP \subset L^M \cap pP \neq \phi$ for all $p \in P$. This implies

that $P \subset L^M P^{-1}$. Since P is a replete semigroup we
have $T = PP^{-1}$ [3, 6.04]. Thus $T = PP^{-1} \subset L^M P^{-1} P^{-1}$
$\subset L^M P^{-1}$. This gives $T = P(L^M)^{-1}$. Since $(L^M)^{-1}$ is
compact there exists a $t \in T$ such that $(L^M)^{-1} t \subset P$.
Hence $T = Tt = P(L^M)^{-1} t \subset PP \subset P$. Thus $T = P$,
which is a contradiction. Therefore $E \cap (T - L^n)$
$\neq \phi$ for all positive integers n.

COROLLARY 2.12. Let A be the collection of all
closed proper replete semigroups of T. If
$x \notin \underset{P \in A}{\cup} P_x$, then there exists an open subset U of X
which contains x and has the property that
$(\underset{P \in A}{\cup} P_x) \cap U = \phi$.

Proof. Let U be an open subset of X which contains
x and assume $(\underset{P \in A}{\cup} P_x) \cap U \neq \phi$. Then there exists
a $y \in U$ and a $P \in A$ such that $y \in P_x$. Thus
$U \cap xpP \neq \phi$ for all $p \in P$. This implies that there
exists a P-extensive set $E \subset T$ such that $xE \subset U$.
Let L be a compact neighborhood of the identity in
T such that $T = \underset{n=1}{\overset{\infty}{\cup}} L^n$. Lemma 2.11 implies that
$E \cap (T - L^n) \neq \phi$ for all positive integers n. Thus
for all n, $U \cap x(T - L^n) \neq \phi$. Therefore if all open
subsets of X which contain x have the property that

($\bigcup_{P \in A} P_x$) $\cap$ U $\neq$ ϕ, Lemma 2.10 implies that there
exists a P $\in$ A such that x $\in$ P_x. This contra-
diction implies that there exists an open subset
U of X containing x such that ($\bigcup_{P \in A} P_x$) $\cap$ U = ϕ,
and the corollary is proved.

From this corollary it follows that if x is
not P-recurrent for any P $\in$ A, then the orbit of
x is open in its orbit closure.

3.   QUASIMINIMAL SETS

Throughout this section we will assume that
X is a metric space. While this assumption is not
always necessary it will shorten many proofs.

DEFINITION 3.1 [6, p. 61]. A subset M of X is said
to be dynamically indecomposable provided it cannot
be represented as the union of two closed invariant
sets neither of which equals M.

DEFINITION 3.2 [6, p. 61]. Let M be a closed
invariant set and let x $\in$ M. The orbit of x is
isolated in M provided xT is open relative to M.

DEFINITION 3.3 [6, p. 61]. A compact invariant set is a _quasiminimal_ _set_ if and only if it is dynamically indecomposable and contains no isolated orbits.

The following lemma is proved by Nemyckiǐ [6, p. 62] for a real flow. His proof applies to the case of a generative phase group and is not given here.

LEMMA 3.4. If $M \subset X$ is a compact invariant set and M is dynamically indecomposable then there exists a point $x \in M$ such that $M = cl(xT)$.

We say that the isotropy subgroup of x, $T_x = \{t \in T : xt = x\}$, is contained in the compact group of $T = C \times R^n \times Z^m$ provided that for $t \in T_x$, $t = (a, 0, 0)$, where $a \in C$.

A minor modification of the proof of Theorem 1 in [2] gives the following result.

LEMMA 3.5. Let $x \in X$. If $g : T/T_x \to xT$ is a homeomorphism and if T_x is contained in the compact group of T then x is not P-recurrent for any proper replete semigroup.

THEOREM 3.6. Let M be a compact invariant subset
of X. If M is a quasiminimal set then M is the
closure of the orbit of a point which is P-recurrent for some proper replete semigroup and
which has a nonsyndetic isotropy subgroup.

Proof. Since M is dynamically indecomposable,
Lemma 3.4 implies that there exists a point $x \in M$
such that $cl(xT) = M$. If x is not P-recurrent for
any proper replete semigroup, then by [1, p. 1147],
$x \notin \bigcup_{P \in A} P_x$. Corollary 2.12 implies that there
exists an open set U containing x such that
$U \cap (\bigcup_{P \in A} P_x) = \phi$. Theorem 2.7 gives $M = cl(xT)$
$= xT \cup (\bigcup_{P \in A} P_x)$. Therefore $(U \cap M) \subset xT$. This
implies that xT is open in M or that xT is iso-
lated, which is a contradiction. Therefore x is
P-recurrent for some proper replete semigroup $P \subset T$.

        Suppose now that T_x is a syndetic subgroup of
T. Then xT is compact [3, 3.07]. Thus $M = cl(xT)$
$= xT$ and xT is clearly isolated in M. Since M
contains no isolated orbits, this is a contradiction. Therefore T_x is not syndetic.

THEOREM 3.7. Let M be a compact invariant subset

of X. If M is the closure of the orbit of a point
which is P-recurrent for some proper replete semigroup and has its isotropy subgroup contained in
the compact subgroup of T, then E is a quasiminimal
set.

Proof. Let x $\in$ M satisfy the hypothesis of the
theorem. Since cl(xT) = M, it follows directly that
M is dynamically indecomposable.

Suppose M contains an isolated orbit yT.
Since yT is open in M and cl(xT) = M it follows
that xT $\cap$ yT $\neq$ ϕ. This implies xT = yT. Thus xT
being open in M, it is a second category in it-
self. From [3, 3.08] we have that T/T$_x$ $\rightarrow$ xT is
a homeomorphism. However Lemma 3.5 implies x is
not P-recurrent for any proper replete semigroup,
which is a contradiction. Therefore M contains
no isolated orbits.

Theorems 3.6 and 3.7 give a generalization
of Hilmy's result on quasiminimal sets. In the
next corollary this result is stated in our
terminology in order to indicate the obstructions
to a straightforward generalization.

COROLLARY 3.8 [5]. Let X be a compact metric
space, let T be the real numbers, and let M be a
closed invariant subset of X. M is the closure of
the orbit of a point which is P-recurrent for some
proper replete semigroup and has its isotropy
subgroup nonsyndetic in T if and only if M is a
quasiminimal set.

The problem in generalizing this result lies
in the fact that for the reals a nontrivial subgroup is necessarily syndetic. For the more
general class of phase groups this is not the case.
The following examples show that it is not possible
to relax the conditions of the isotropy subgroup
of a point to obtain a necessary and sufficient
condition for its orbit closure to be a quasiminimal set.

EXAMPLE 3.9. First consider the transformation
group (X_1, T_1, π_1) where $X_1 = \{(r, \theta) \in E^2 : r = 1\}$,
$T = R$, and $\pi_1((r, \theta), t) = (r, \theta + t)$. For each
$(r, \theta) \in X_1$, $T_{1(r, \theta)} = \{2n\pi : n = 0, \pm 1, \ldots\}$.
Now we define the transformation group (X_2, T_2, π_2)
where $X_2 = [0, 1]$, $T_2 = R$, and $\pi_2(x, t)$
$= x/[x - e^t(x - 1)]$. The points 0 and 1 are the

only fixed points, and for $0 < x < 1$, $\lim_{t \to +\infty} \pi_2(x, t)$
$= 0$ and $\lim_{t \to -\infty} \pi_2(x, t) = 1$.

The desired transformation group is the product
of these two transformation groups. That is,
(X, T, π) where $X = X_1 \times X_2$, $T = T_1 \times T_2$, and
$\pi = \pi_1 \times \pi_2$. Let $A = \{((r, \theta), x) : x = 0\}$ and
$B = \{((r, \theta), x) : x = 1\}$. For $z \in X - (A \cup B)$ we
see that $T_z = \{(2n\pi, 0) : n = 0, \pm 1, \pm 2, \dots\}$,
which is nonsyndetic in $T = R^2$. Also for
$z \in X - (A \cup B)$, $zT = X - (A \cup B)$ and $cl(zT) = X$.
If $P = \{(t_1, t_2) \in T : t_1 > |t_2|\}$ then z is P-re-
current for all $z \in X - (A \cup B)$. Therefore X is
the closure of the orbit of a P-recurrent point;
however $cl(xT)$ is not a quasiminimal set.

This example shows that it is not possible
to relax the conditions in Theorem 3.7 so that the
isotropy subgroup be contained in the compact group
and still have the orbit closure be a quasiminimal
set.

EXAMPLE 3.10. Let (X_3, T_3, π_3) be the transformation
group with $X_3 = X_1$ (from the previous example),
$T_3 = Z$, and $\pi_3((r, \theta), n) = (r, \theta + n\alpha)$, where
α is a real number which is irrationally related

to π.

In this case we consider the transformation group (X, T, π), where $X = X_1 \times X_3$, $T = T_1 \times T_3$ $= R \times Z$, and $\pi = \pi_1 \times \pi_3$. As before we list the properties that are of interest. For each $x \in X$, $T_x = \{(2n\pi, 0) : n = 0, \pm 1, \pm 2, \ldots\}$, which is non-syndetic and yet nontrivial in T. For each $x \in X$, xT is not isolated in X and $cl(xT) = X$. Thus X is a quasiminimal set.

This example shows that assuming $cl(xT)$ is a quasiminimal set will not imply that T_x is contained in the compact group of T.

REFERENCES

1. Baum, J. D., P-Recurrence in Topological Dynamics, Proc. Am. Math. Soc. 7 (1956), pp. 1146-1154.

2. England, J. W., A Characterization of Orbits, Proc. Am. Math. Soc. 17 (1966), pp. 207-209.

3. Gottschalk, W. H., and Hedlund, G. A., Topological Dynamics, Am. Math. Soc. Colloq. Publ. 36 (1955).

4. Hahn, F. J., Some Embeddings, Recurrence

Properties, and the Birkhoff-Markov Theorem for Transformation Groups, Duke Math. J., 27 (1960), pp. 513-525.

5. Hilmy, H., Sur les ensembles quasi-minimaux dans les systemès dynamiques, Ann. Math., 37 (1936), pp. 899-907.

6. Nemyckiĭ, V. V., Topological Problems of the Theory of Dynamical Systems, Am. Math. Soc. Transl., No. 103 (1954).

7. Weil, A., L'intègration dans les groupes topologiques et ses applications, Actualités Sci. Ind., No. 869 (1940).

BOUNDS FOR THE PERIODS OF PERIODIC ORBITS

F. Brock Fuller

(California Institute of Technology)

In their paper Topologie et Equations
Fonctionelles, Leray and Schauder showed how the
existence of solutions of certain functional
equations could be deduced from the existence of
bounds for the norms of solutions [6]. We shall
indicate here how the existence of periodic orbits
of an autonomous differential equation can in a
similar way be deduced from the existence of a
bound for the periods of the periodic orbits.
Finally, as an example, we shall derive such a
bound from a local condition on the differential
equation.

We consider a compact C^∞ manifold M bearing
a C^∞ velocity field F. M may have a regular
boundary if we suppose that the field F is

directed into M at its boundary. We assume further
that the field F has no zeros, so that it defines
a field of oriented directions without singular
points. The question which concerns us is this:
How do the periodic orbits of the autonomous
differential equation $\dot{x} = F(x)$ vary as F is
continuously deformed through other fields which
satisfy the above conditions? A rough answer to
the analogous question for the solutions of an
equation $T(x) = x$ is provided by the fixed point
index. We seek to treat the periodic orbits in a
similar way by constructing an index for periodic
orbits.

To fix our objective we review certain
properties of the fixed point index [7]. Let
$T:V \to V$ be a continuous mapping of a manifold V,
not necessarily compact, into itself. Let Ω be an
open relatively compact set in V such that T has
no fixed points on the boundary of Ω. Then the
index $i(\Omega, T)$ is an integer equal to the algebraic
number of fixed points of T inside Ω. The index
has the following two essential properties: first,
$i(\Omega, T) = 0$ implies that Ω contains at least one
fixed point of T; second, $i(\Omega, T)$ does not change

if Ω and T are continuously deformed in such a way
that no fixed points cross the boundary of Ω.
Roughly stated, a set of fixed points with nonzero
index may move away as T is deformed, but it cannot
just disappear.

Now let us return to the manifold M and its
velocity field F. Let us imagine that an "index"
i (Ω, F) can be constructed for sets of periodic
orbits of F with the essential properties of the
fixed point index. Since M is compact we may take
Ω = M and conclude that the index of the totality
of periodic orbits of M should remain invariant as
F is deformed. But consider the following examples.
Let M be a solid torus, the product of an n-ball
and a circle, and let F_o be the obvious field for
for which all the positive trajectories converge
to a single periodic orbit going once around inside
the torus. Only a very disappointing index theory
would assign a zero index to this orbit. Yet, for
n > 2, F_o can be deformed through Fields F_α without
singularities, whose positive trajectories lie in
the solid torus, to a field F_1, which has no
periodic orbits [2]. Thus it does not appear
possible to construct a useful index theory for

periodic orbits in M.

Close observation of the above example shows
that the periodic orbit does not die gracefully as
the fields F_α approach F_1, but coils up in such a
way that its length and period diverge. Thus if
the periodic orbits of M were relocated in the
product manifold M x $(0, \infty)$, assigning the period
of each orbit to the second component, then the
loss of the periodic orbit in the solid torus
could be readily explained: the orbit moves out
of any relatively compact open Ω in M x $(0, \infty)$ as
α approaches 1. By taking the periods into account
in this way an index theory for orbits can in fact
be constructed [4, 5] with the following features.
The periodic orbits of M are relocated in M x $(0, \infty)$
as indicated, together with all multiples of the
orbits with least period. The index $i(\Omega, F)$ is a
rational number defined for each relatively compact set Ω in M x $(0, \infty)$ whose boundary does not
meet any periodic orbits. The index $i(\Omega, F)$ then
has the same basic properties as the fixed point
index.

Let us review now the method of Leray and
Schauder for obtaining existence theorems from

bounds. Suppose one wishes to demonstrate the

existence of a solution to the equation $T_1(x) = x$,

where T_1 is a possibly nonlinear compact operator

acting on a Banach space. Suppose that T_1 can be

continuously deformed through compact operators

T_α to an operator T_o, perhaps linear, which has a

single fixed point of index not equal to zero.

Suppose finally that any fixed point of any of the

operators T_α must have its norm bounded by B, so

that all these fixed points lie in the ball Ω

defined by $||x|| < B$. Then by considering the index

$i(\Omega, T)$ (defined, for compact operators, for bounded

open sets Ω), one deduces that T_1 must have a fixed

point.

We can now attempt to use the index $i(\Omega, F)$

for periodic orbits in exactly the same way.

Suppose that the fields F_α are a homotopic family

of velocity fields in M depending on the parameter

α in $[0, 1]$. Suppose that all the periods of the

periodic orbits of any F_α are bounded below by a

positive b and above by B. Then if we define Ω

in M x $(0, \infty)$ by the condition $b < t < B$ and can

show that $i(\Omega, F_0) \neq 0$, then the existence of

periodic orbits of F_1 follows from the properties

of the index. As described, this program encounters a fatal difficulty: since the multiples of any periodic orbit are included in M x (0, ∞) the upper bound B will never exist unless there are no periodic orbits.

Fortunately the index for periodic orbits has a refinement analogous to the splitting of fixed points into Nielsen classes which will resolve the difficulty just encountered. The periodic orbits may be partitioned into their homology classes in M and an index $i(\Omega, F, h)$ defined for each homology class h. The properties of $i(\Omega, F, h)$ are like those of $i(\Omega, F)$, except that the periodic orbits which do not belong to the class h may be ignored. If, in the preceding paragraph, we substitute $i(\Omega, F, h)$ for $i(\Omega, F)$ and "periodic orbits of class h" for "periodic orbits," then the difficulty caused by the multiples disappears (unless h is a torsion cycle).

The discussion to this point serves to motivate our interest in the following question: for a homotopic family of velocity fields F on M, is it possible to obtain a bound for the periods of the periodic orbits belonging to a given homology

class? We now describe a differential inequality
for F which will ensure the existence of such a
bound. The differential inequality will, in fact,
do more. In the spirit of Schwartzman's asymptotic
cycles [8] one may consider the approximate homology
classes of all the trajectories, including those
which are not periodic, and show that the homology
classes diverge uniformly (independently of the
parameter a and the starting point of each tra-
jectory) as $t \to \infty$. Specifically, let ϕ_1, ϕ_2, ..., ϕ_p
be a cohomology basis for the closed differential
1-forms in M and define $H(T_t)$ for any trajectory
T_t to be the p-dimensional vector whose ith component is the integral of ϕ_i over T. The Euclidean
norm $|H(T_t)|$ then measures the homological com-
plexity of each trajectory T_t.

     To describe our condition on F we need the
following preliminary lemma, which we shall not
stop to prove.

LEMMA. Let M be a compact C^∞ Riemannian manifold.
Then there exists a positive number λ such that
any piecewise C^∞ bounding 1-cycle, of length at
most L, bounds a 2-chain of area at most λL.

PROPOSITION. Let M and λ be as in the above lemma.
Let M bear a homotopic family of nowhere zero
velocity fields and suppose that for some $c > \lambda$
each field F in the family satisfies the following
differential inequality:

$$\left| \text{curl } F \right| < c^{-1} \min \left| F \right|$$

Then $\left| H(T_t) \right|$ diverges uniformly as $t \to \infty$.

__Proof__. For any piecewise C^∞ 1-chain C let $\left| C \right|$
denote its length. A straightforward construction
shows that any trajectory T_t can be completed to a
bounding 1-cycle $T_t + \Delta_t$ by adding a C^∞ 1-chain
Δ_t whose length $\left| \Delta_t \right|$ is no greater than $a + b \left| H(T_t) \right|$
where the constants a and b depend only on M and
its metric.

Let I denote the integral of F over $T_t + \Delta_t$

$$I = \int_{T_t + \Delta_t} F \cdot ds$$

By Stokes's theorem I can be written as a
surface integral over a 2-chain S. The area of S,
by the definition of λ, may be chosen not to
exceed $\lambda(\left| T_t \right| + \left| \Delta_t \right|)$, so that I may be estimated
above as follows:

$$I = \iint_S \text{curl } F \cdot dA \leq \lambda(\left|T_t\right| + \left|\Delta_t\right|) \sup\left|\text{curl } F\right|$$

In the other direction, since F is always tangent to the trajectory T_t, I can be estimated below as follows:

$$I = \int_{T_t} F \cdot ds + 0(\left|\Delta_t\right|) \geq \left|T_t\right|\min\left|F\right| + 0(\left|\Delta_t\right|)$$

By combining these inequalities one obtains the inequality

$$\frac{\left|T_t\right| + 0(\left|\Delta_t\right|)}{\left|T_t\right| + \left|\Delta_t\right|} \leq \frac{\lambda}{c} < 1$$

Since $\left|T_t\right|$ diverges uniformly as $t \to \infty$ this inequality can hold only if $\left|\Delta_t\right|$ diverges uniformly. But the estimate for $\left|\Delta_t\right|$ shows that $\left|H(T_t)\right|$ also diverges uniformly, as was to be shown.

The above condition is disappointing in that it has the further very strong implication that each field F in the homotopic family has a global surface of section in the sense of Birkhoff [1, 3]. By applying the above inequalities to positive linear combinations of trajectories one shows that the convex hull of the values assumed by $H(T_t)$ is,

for sufficiently large t, disjoint from a neighborhood of the origin in p-space. Hence a closed
1-form Ψ can be found such that, for sufficiently
large t, the integral of Ψ over every trajectory
is positive and, by approximation, Ψ may be taken
to assume rational values when integrated over the
integral 1-cycles of M. The integral of a multiple
of Ψ then defines an angular variable on M whose
net change of value is positive somewhere on each
trajectory, a situation which implies the existence
of a global surface of section [3].

The following question may be of interest.
Is it possible to find a weaker condition, especially one occurring naturally in Hamiltonian
systems, which is still sufficient to bound the
periods of the periodic orbits?

REFERENCES

1. Birkhoff, G. D., Dynamical Systems, New York,
1927.

2. Fuller, F. B., Note on Trajectories in a Solid
Torus, Ann. Math., 56 (1952).

3.   Fuller, F. B., On the Surface of Section and
Periodic Trajectories, Am. J. Math., 87 (1965).

4.   Fuller, F. B., The Treatment of Periodic Orbits
by the Methods of Fixed Point Theory, Bull. Am. Math.
Soc., 72 (1966).

5.   Fuller, F. B., An Index of Fixed Point Type for
Periodic Orbits, Am. J. Math., 89 (1967).

6.   Leray, J., and Schauder, J., Topologie et
Équations Fonctionelles, Ann. Ecole Norm. Super.,
51 (1934).

7.   Leray, J., La Théorie des Points Fixes et ses
Applications en Analyse, Proc. Int. Congr. Math.,
II (1950).

8.   Schwartzman, S., Asymptotic Cycles, Ann. Math.,
66 (1957).

DYNAMICAL ASPECTS OF ORBIT-CLOSURES[1]

Walter Gottschalk

(Wesleyan University)

The most abstract part of topological dynamics is concerned mainly with transformation groups. There are at least six broad reasons for studying the dynamical properties of transformation groups:

1. The theory of transformation groups subsumes both the theory of discrete flows and the theory of continuous flows. The famous dictum of E. H. Moore is brought to mind.

2. The study of discrete flows and continuous flows inevitably leads to groups of transformations and topological groups. In some instances, such

---

[1]The research represented in this paper was performed while the author received support from the National Science Foundation under Grant No. GP-6325.

217

as Lie groups, the study of topological groups
leads to flows.

3.   The theory of almost periodic functions
has been extended to functions on groups. There
is some evidence that future developments in the
theory of transformation groups will encompass
more and more of the basic part of the theory of
almost periodic functions.

4.   The notation for transformation groups
in many respects and in many instances is more
concise than the notation for flows. In particular,
this permits more complicated notions to suggest
themselves more easily.

5.   Transformation groups with compact acting
groups have been intensively studied. What can be
said about transformation groups whose acting groups
are not compact? Although compactness properties
in the phase space X and in the acting group T
have major roles in most aspects of topological
dynamics, it is generally the case that the properties of transformation groups studied in topological
dynamics are significant only when the original
acting group T is not compact.

6.   In the quest for more generality the

additive groups of integers and real numbers are
replaced by more inclusive structures not using the
notion of number ab initio.

The work of Poincaré on ordinary differential
equations is regarded as pioneering in the qualitative theory of ordinary differential equations.
He was concerned with the interaction of both
components: analysis and topology. Apparently, it
was G. D. Birkhoff in his 1912 paper who first
recognized the possibility of defining and exploring
dynamical properties from an exclusively topological
point of view. His 1912 paper contains the notion
of minimal set and a variant of almost periodicity.
Remarkably, the paper was written before the axioms
for a topological space were crystallized, but its
general intent is clear. In his 1912 paper his
phase spaces were subsets of Euclidean spaces. In
later papers his phase spaces were metric spaces.
Birkhoff always adhered to time as a real number
parameter; that is, he studied continuous flows.
General transformation groups with their general
topological spaces and general topological groups
appeared in the study of dynamical properties in
the mid 1940's.

I wish to introduce and begin to develop a
general dynamical notion involving transformation
groups which appears to have considerable growth
potential.

Let (X, T) be a transformation group. Choose
a point x of X. Then xT is the orbit of x and $\overline{xT}$
is the orbit-closure of x. We may call the ordered
pair $(\overline{xT}, x)$ the pointed orbit-closure of x. Since
$\overline{xT}$ is invariant, we may then consider the pointed
orbit-closure transformation group of x, in
symbols, $(\overline{xT}, x; T)$. Since the last phrase is
long, it is desirable to introduce a short word in
its place.

A pointed transformation group is defined to
be an ordered triple $(X, x_o; T)$ such that (X, T)
is a transformation group and $x_o \in X$; here x_o may
be called the base point. An ambit is defined to
be a pointed transformation group $(X, x_o; T)$ such
that $\overline{x_o T} = X$. The word "ambit" is a standard
English word with meanings such as "a moving
around," "space surrounding," "range of action,"
which seem appropriate to the situation.

If T is a topological group, then an ambit
under T is defined to be an ambit whose acting

group is T. If (X, T) is a transformation group
and if x ∈ X, then the _ambit_ _of_ x _under_ (X, T) is
defined to be the ambit $(\overline{xT}, x; T)$. If (X, T) is
a transformation group, then an _ambit_ _in_ (X, T) is
defined to be the ambit of some point of X under
(X, T).

An exposition of the initial aspects of
ambits is contained in the M. A. thesis of Richard
Eells, written at Wesleyan University (1967) under
my supervision.

Let us restrict attention to transformation
groups whose phase spaces are compact Hausdorff.
We write X for the transformation group (X, T) and
we write Xx_o for the pointed transformation group
$(X, x_o; T)$. We say that $\varphi : Xx_o \to Yy_o$ is _homo-_
morphic in case $\varphi : X \to Y$ is continuous equivariant
and $x_o\varphi = y_o$.

Let Xx_o, Yy_o be ambits. Then there exists
at most one homomorphism of Xx_o into Yy_o, and this
homomorphism, if it exists, is onto. We define
$Xx_o \geq Yy_o$ to mean Xx_o is homomorphic to Yy_o. We
may read $\geq$ as "homomorphic to," or "dominates," or
"greater than," and so on. We note that $Xx_o \geq Yy_o$
and $Yy_o \geq Xx_o$ if and only if Xx_o is isomorphic to

Yy_o.

Letting A stand for the class of all ambits
under a given topological group T, the relation
$\geq$ in A is reflexive, transitive, and "antisymmetric"
in the above sense. Define L to be the <u>set</u> of all
ambit-types under T. Here "ambit-type" may mean
ambiguously either the class of all ambits isomorphic to a given ambit or a distinguished member
of this class. Clearly L has a natural relation
$\geq$ which is a partial ordering in the customary
sense. Indeed, L is a complete lattice.

If Xx_o and Yy_o are ambits, then the (<u>con-
structive</u>) <u>join</u> $Xx_o \vee Yy_o$ <u>of</u> Xx_o <u>and</u> Yy_o is defined
to be the ambit $\overline{x_oy_oT}x_oy_o$ in the product transformation group (X x Y, T) with standard action
$(x, y)t = (xt, yt)$. If $F = (X_ia_i | i \in I)$ is a
family of ambits, then the (<u>constructive</u>) <u>join</u> $\vee F$
<u>of</u> F is defined to be the ambit $\overline{aT}a$ in the product
transformation group $(X_{i \in I} X_i, T)$ with standard
action $(x_i | i \in I)t = (x_it | i \in I)$ where $a = (a_i | i \in I)$
We note that the join is the least of all the ambits
dominating the given ambits. The least ambit-type
is the singleton ambit. The greatest ambit-type is
the join of the family of all ambit-types.

An orbit may be named by a property which the
base point enjoys. For example, the ambit Xx_0 is
almost periodic in case x_0 is an almost periodic
point; the orbit Xx_0 is distal in case x_0 is a
distal point. If (X, T) is a transformation group
and if $x \in X$, then x is said to be <u>distal</u> <u>under</u>
(X, T) in case x is distal from every point of
$X - \{x\}$. If (X, T) is a transformation group and
if x, y $\in$ X, then x is distal from y in case there
exists an index a of X such that $(xt, yt) \notin a$ for
all t $\in$ T. The meanings of "pointwise almost
periodic" and "pointwise distal" seem clear.

Let M denote the set of all almost periodic
ambit-types, and let N denote the set of all
distal ambit-types. Then $L \supset M \supset N$; M need not be
a lattice; N is a complete sublattice of L. Every
chain in M has a join and the join belongs to M.
Every element of M is dominated by a maximal
element of M; that is, every almost periodic ambit-
type is dominated by a maximal almost periodic
ambit-type. It follows that if Xx_0 is a maximal
almost periodic ambit, then X is coalescent. The
isomorphic uniqueness of a universal minimal set
follows. Indeed, if X is the universal minimal

set, then $\{Xx_o | x_o \in X\}$ is the class of all almost periodic ambits.

An ambit Xx_o is said to be mobile provided that if $x \in X$, then there exists an endomorphism φ of X such that $x_o\varphi = x$.

The ambience of a given transformation group X is defined to be the join of the family of orbits in X, that is, $\vee_{x \in X} \overline{xT} x$ or $\overline{dTd}$, where $d = (x | x \in X) = id_X \in X^X$. Of course, X^X is a transformation group with action $(a_x | x \in X)t = (a_x t | x \in X)$. It is readily proved that the ambience is always mobile. If X is a transformation group and if Ad is the ambience of X, then as a set and a topological space, A is equal to the enveloping semigroup of X, and as a semigroup, $EndA$ is anti-isomorphic to the enveloping semigroup of X.

The following theorem may be proved:

THEOREM. The meet of the class of all maximal almost periodic ambits is the greatest distal ambit.[2]

---

[2] A bibliography of topological dynamics is available upon request to: Secretary, Mathematics Department, Wesleyan University, Middletown, Connecticut 06457.

TRANSVERSALS TO A FLOW[1]

L. W. Green

(University of Minnesota)

Because I think it is an extremely important
paper, a large part of this talk will be a review
of the paper by Sinaĭ, "Classical Dynamical
Systems with Countable Lebesgue Spectrum II" [8].[2]
Later I shall describe some work of mine related
to his, and indicate directions of investigation
which deserve attention.

The objects we are concerned with are infinite cyclic or one parameter groups of measure
preserving transformations. In general, the group

[1]Research supported in part by the National Science
Foundation under Grant No. GP-5252.

[2]This paper is designated "S" in subsequent ci-
tations.

will act differentiably on a compact differentiable
manifold, although other examples will also be
cited.

In order to define transversals, we first
introduce the notion of measurable foliation. This
is the basic link between the differential and
measure theoretic structures of the manifold, and
is first defined locally. The manifold M is an
orientable, connected, C^∞ Riemannian manifold,[3]
so the invariant measure is given by a smooth
density, and the total measure is assumed to be
one. A neighborhood U supports a local measurable
foliation ξ if ξ is, simultaneously, a foliation
of U in the differential geometric sense into, say,
k-dimensional sheets, and is a measurable partition
of the measure space U in Rohlin's sense [7]. Hence
the sheets of ξ inherit two different measures,
that which comes from the Riemannian structure and
the measure "transverse" to the ξ-conditional
measure which is induced by the quotient measure

---

[3]Sinaĭ allows manifolds with boundary and merely
piecewise smooth foliations in order to include
his very important treatment of the Boltzmann
problem [9]. For simplicity I shall avoid this
refinement.

space structure. The basic assumption is that
these measures are equivalent on each sheet, and
that the derivative of one with respect to the
other is a measurable function in U. In order to
define a measurable foliation on the whole manifold,
these local structures are pasted together in such
a way that in their natural intersections both the
differential and measure structures match up.

To accomplish the latter in the proper way,
Sinai introduces the simple but useful idea of a u
local basis for a measure space. A collection
of subsets of M is called a local basis if it is a
basis (that is, generates the σ-algebra of all
measurable sets) and if it is impossible to de-
compose M into two disjoint subsets A and B, each
of positive measure, in such a way that
$\mu(U \cap A) \cdot \mu(U \cap B) = 0$ for every U in u. Hence a
local basis provides a measure theoretic analogue
of connectedness. The relevance of this idea to
ergodic theory is evident.

A global measurable foliation is then defined
relative to a fixed countable local basis u, each of
whose subsets supports a local measurable foliation,
and such that the respective local sheets coincide

in any nontrivial intersections. Consequently, a
global differential geometric foliation Z is obtained. However, the partition of M into maximal
connected sheets of Z is, in general, not a
measurable partition in Rohlin's sense; in fact,
the interesting case is when the associated
measurable partition is trivial; that is, when any
measurable function which is constant on maximal
sheets must be constant almost everywhere. (To
define, modulo null sets, constancy of such a
function on sheets, one of course returns to the
local measurable foliations and requires that the
function be measurable relative to the conditional
σ-algebra generated by ξ.)

Finally, a measurable foliation Z is said to
be a transversal field for the automorphism T
(flow $\{S_t\}$) if $T^{-1}\Gamma \in Z$ $(S_t\Gamma \in Z)^4$ for every sheet
Γ of the foliation.

What are some examples of transversal fields?
A trivial set of examples are global (smooth)

---

[4]For flows there is an additional technical condition needed to force compatibility of the local
measure structure on orbits with that of the
foliation.

cross sections to flows which have them. But the
prime motivation for Sinaï's definitions are the
C-systems (see, for example [3, Chapter 3]). Since
Avez has given a thorough discussion of C-systems
at this conference, I will not repeat the definitions. For our purposes today, however, it is
essential to keep in mind the "ur-examples":
namely, an ergodic automorphism of the 2-torus and
the geodesic flow in the unit tangent bundle of a
compact surface of constant negative curvature.

If one takes as model of the torus the
quotient space of the Euclidean plane modulo the
Gaussian lattice, an automorphism is induced by a
unimodular linear transformation T of the plane.
A T which induces an ergodic automorphism has
distinct real eigenvalues, and the collection of
lines in the plane parallel to one of the eigen-
vectors is clearly mapped into itself by T. The
projection onto the torus of this system of lines
is a measurable foliation transverse to the automorphism. Any function constant on sheets is
thereby invariant under the irrational flow induced
by the eigenvector, and is therefore constant.
This is an example, then, of the ergodic case

mentioned above.

The easiest model of the geodesic flow to
work with is that afforded by thinking of SL(2, **R**)
as (almost) the unit tangent bundle of the hyperbolic plane, and looking at the homogeneous spaces
of the form M = F\SL(2,**R**), where F is a discrete,
cocompact subgroup. The geodesic flow is the
action of exp(tX) on the right, if we take

$$X = \begin{pmatrix} 1 & 0 \\ 0 & -1 \end{pmatrix}$$

in the Lie algebra. If

$$H_1 = \begin{pmatrix} 0 & 1 \\ 0 & 0 \end{pmatrix}$$

it is easily seen that exp(tH$_1$) induces a flow on
M whose orbits form a field transverse to the
geodesic flow; it is called the horocycle flow.
Indeed, the relation

$$[X, \ H_1] = 2H_1$$

is the infinitesimal condition for this transversality. (Again in this case the transversal
field is ergodic, but the proof is not as easy as

for the torus.)

The generalizations of these examples are
clear. The problem of the existence of transversals
to automorphisms of compact Abelian groups can be
formulated in the character group (compare with S,
Section 7.3). Flows induced on homogeneous spaces
of Lie groups by one-parameter subgroups have been
extensively investigated by C. C. Moore in [6] and
L. Auslander, F. Hahn, and myself in [4] and [5].
The analogues of the geodesic flows all have
transversal fields, but they are in general not
C-systems.

Finally, the fact that these ideas transcend
the smooth manifold case is illustrated by Sinai's
construction of transversals to the shift on an
infinite product of circles. A simple discrete
analogue is obtainable in the Bernoulli shift on
an equiweighted finite set by considering as transversals the orbits of transformations induced by
permutations of the set.

After this catalog, one may well ask what
dynamical systems do not have transverse fields.
It can be shown that the horocycle flow cannot
have a smooth transversal field. But notice, this

flow is itself a transversal to another flow.

What good are transversal fields? In order
to state his theorems economically, we introduce
Sinaǐ's notation. If Z is a measurable foliation,
ν_Z is the partition of M into maximal connected
sheets of Z, and $G(Z)$ the σ-subalgebra of measurable
sets generated by this partition. When there is
no danger of misunderstanding, we abbreviate $G(Z)$,
$G(Z')$, and so on, by G, G', and so on. N is the
trivial σ-subalgebra, ϵ the partition into points.

The field Z, transverse to the automorphism
T, is said to be expanding if dT, restricted to
the tangent subspaces of the foliation, has norm
greater than one. (The norm is taken as a linear
operator, when the tangent spaces have the metrics
induced by the Riemannian structure.) Let $\Delta(x)$ be
the determinant of this restriction of dT. Contracting fields are defined analogously. C-systems
require uniform bounds on the differentials, but
Sinaǐ hypothesizes somewhat less in order to cover
the piecewise smooth case.

THEOREM (S, 4.1). If the automorphism T has an
expanding field Z' and a contracting field Z", and

G is the σ-algebra of T-invariant measurable sets, then

$$G \subseteq G' \wedge G''$$

The proof of this theorem is actually fairly easy, once one understands E. Hopf's use of asymptotic rays in the corresponding step for proving the ergodicity of geodesic flows. As an immediate consequence, if $G' \wedge G'' = N$, T is ergodic. Hence we need conditions, preferably local, on Z' and Z'' to guarantee that $G' \wedge G'' = N$. Sinaĭ gives us one such set of conditions in his notion of absolute continuity.

Take the intersection of a local sheet of Z' with one of the neighborhoods defining the local structure of Z", and saturate it in this neighborhood with respect to the local foliation of Z". Z' is called absolutely continuous with respect to Z" if almost all such local saturations have positive measure, and if the resulting collection of subsets is itself a local basis. Roughly speaking, we can imagine a particle whose motion is confined to the sheets of Z' and Z"; such a particle can reach almost every point. When one of these

foliations is absolutely continuous with respect
to the other, then $G' \wedge G'' = N$; so, under the
hypotheses of the preceding theorem, T is ergodic.
Note that the sum of the dimensions of absolutely
continuous foliations equals that of the space.
(For flows, similar results hold, modulo a modification of the foliations of which absolute continuity is required. Here the sum of the dimensions
is one less than that of the space, since the flow
is transversal to both foliations.)

THEOREM (S, 5.1). Let the ergodic automorphism T
have an expanding transversal field Z. Then there
exists a partition ζ, almost every element of which
is an open connected subset of a sheet of Z, such
that

    (a) $T\zeta > \zeta$

    (b) $\prod T^k \zeta = \epsilon$

    (c) $\cap T^k \zeta = \nu_Z$

    (d) $H(T\zeta \mid \zeta) = \int \log \Delta(x) \, d\mu$

    This theorem (together with its analogue for
flows) is perhaps the most important in the paper.
Not only does it assert the existence of a useful
partition, but it gives a formula in terms of the

local structure of T for its entropy relative to
this partition. An immediate corollary is that if
$G(Z) = N$, T is a K-automorphism. This implies that
the spectrum is Lebesgue with countable multiplicity
and that T is mixing of all orders. With an elegant
proof Sinaǐ shows that if Z' is absolutely continuous with respect to Z", and vice versa, then G'
$= G" = N$.

Unfortunately, more hypotheses are needed to
obtain K-flows. Sinaǐ finds sufficient conditions
in the concept of (mutual) nonintegrability of two
measurable foliations. The terms clearly goes
back to G. D. Birkhoff, who never made it precise.
Sinaǐ makes it precise with a vengeance, and I must
confess that I do not completely understand his
two-page, highly technical, definition. To motivate my next remarks, let me merely state that
here also the sum of the dimensions of the foliations is one less than that of the space.

4. There is a different approach to ad-
mittedly slightly weaker results, which I think
has some merit. It is motivated by the situation
in semisimple group spaces as treated by C. C.
Moore in [6].

Let X, H^1, H^2,...,H^m be C^1 vector fields on
a smooth compact manifold V, each of which is the
infinitesimal generator of a one-parameter group of
diffeomorphisms, denoted by $\{X_t\}$, $\{H_s^i\}$, $i = 1,...,m$,
respectively. Assume further that div X = 0, where
the divergence is taken with respect to a smooth
density which we also use to form $L^2(V)$.

GENERALIZED MAUTNER LEMMA. Suppose that $[X, H^i]$
$= \Sigma\ \lambda_k^i\ H^k$, where the matrix of functions (λ_k^i) is
uniformly positive definite. Then, for each s and
i,

$$\lim_{t\to\infty} X_{-t}H_s^i X_t = I$$

strongly in $L^2(V)$.

This is the function-analytic analogue of
part of Sinaǐ's Theorem 4.1 which we quoted above.
Notice that an immediate corollary is

COROLLARY. If f is an eigenvector of $\{X_t\}$ in
$L^2(V)$, then $H_s^i f = f$ for all s and i.

The connection with the Sinaǐ-Anosov theory
of geodesic flows is as follows. We take V to be

the principal bundle of orthonormal frames on a

compact n-dimensional Riemannian manifold of

strictly negative sectional curvature. $\{X_t\}$ is

the lift of the geodesic flow in the tangent

bundle to V. Let B^k, k = 1, 2,...,n - 1, be vector

fields of other "geodesic" frame flows based on

parallel transport along the geodesic determined

by the kth vector of the frame, just as X arose

from the nth vector. Then it is possible to find

vector fields H^k of the form $B^k + E^k$, where the

fields E^k are tangent to the fibers, which satisfy

the Lie bracket relations needed for the above

theorem. These fields generate the generalized

horocycle flows, and there are n - 1 of them for

which (λ_k^i) is positive definite, and n - 1 more

with a negative definite matrix. Thus the distri-

butions they span correspond to expanding and

contracting transverse fields.

It is possible to project this situation

down to the (2n - 1)-dimensional unit tangent

bundle to obtain transverse horospherical fields,

the sum of whose dimensions is one less than that

of the space. These fields define the C-system

which Anosov uses to prove ergodicity of the

geodesic flow. But the dimension of V, the principal bundle, is $\frac{1}{2}(n^2 + n)$, and it seems that there
are too few horocycle fields even to imply
ergodicity of the frame flow. The idea which re-
deems the situation is the realization that the
principal bundle of an irreducible Riemannian
manifold behaves, qualitatively, somewhat like a
simple Lie group. The horocycle fields, in fact,
are analogues of root vectors with respect to the
"regular element" X. In the Lie case, Moore showed
that these root vectors generate the whole algebra,
so that an eigenvector of $\{X_t\}$, in virtue of the
above corollary, turns out to be invariant under
the whole Lie group, and hence constant. When the
curvature is not necessarily constant, that is,
when we are not in the symmetric space case, I
show that an eigenvector is also annihilated by
the horizontal fields B^k, and then use the holonomy
theorem which says essentially that these fields
generate the whole "algebra" of vertical and
horizontal vector fields associated with the
Riemannian connection.

The conclusion is that the geodesic frame
flow is weakly mixing. Such flows were first

considered by Arnol'd in the case of constant
curvature [2].

    5. The above point of view has many differ-
ential geometric implications, but it also raises
some interesting dynamical questions. Given T, to
return to the automorphism case for simplicity,
what groups of measure preserving transformations
can T normalize? Sinaǐ considers the implications
of the existence of such one parameter groups in
S, Section 7: $TZ_u = Z_{\bar{u}}T$, with $\bar{u} = \bar{u}(u, x)$. Such
a group $\{Z_u\}$ may be called a transversal flow, for
it defines a one-dimensional transversal field.
Sinaǐ proves that if an ergodic T normalizes $\{Z_u\}$,
the Z-periodic points form a null set or almost
all points have the same Z-period. (The last
possibility is inadvertently omitted in S.) Other
properties of the system can be deduced from the
mutual relationships of T and $\{Z_u\}$.

    In view of the fact that some transformations,
notably the horocycle flow, are transversals to
other flows, it is probably also important to ask
about the normalizers of the given transformation.
A start has been made in this direction by Adler
in [1], where T's with pure point spectrum and the

skew-product transformations are examined in some
detail.

But the horocycle fields constructed above
are not, in general, measure preserving, and they
are normalized by the geodesic flow only as a
class and in an infinitesimal sense. Nevertheless,
their existence raises the question of the extent
to which we may obtain a Lie-type structure theory
for smooth flows on manifolds. In particular, are
there reasonable definitions of regular and nilpotent elements? Such a definition will be useful
if it enables us to prove analogues of the Jacobson-
Morozov lemma and thereby make a start on a
structure theory. Having made such an audacious
proposal, I had better conclude my talk here.

REFERENCES

1. Adler, R. L., Generalized Commuting Properties
of Measure-Preserving Transformations, Trans. Am.
Math. Co., 115 (1965), pp. 1-13.
2. Arnol'd, V. L., Some Remarks on Flows of Line
Elements and Frames, Dokl. Akad. Nauk SSR, 138
(1961), pp. 255-257.

3. Arnol'd, V. L., and Avez, A., Problèmes
Ergodiques de la Méchanique Classique, Gauthiers-
Villars, Paris, 1967.

4. Auslander, L., and Green, L. W., G-Induced
Flows, Am. J. Math., 88 (1966), pp. 43-60.

5. Auslander, L., and Hahn, F., Flows on Homogeneous Spaces, Ann. Math. Stud., No. 53 (1963).

6. Moore, C. C., Ergodicity of Flows on Homogeneous Spaces, Am. J. Math., 88 (1966), pp. 154-
178.

7. Rohlin, V. A., On the Fundamental Ideas of
Measure Theory, Mat. Sbornik, 25 (1959), pp. 107-
150.

8. Sinaĭ, J. G., Classical Dynamical Systems with
Countable Lebesgue Spectrum II, Izv. Akad. Nauk SSR,
Ser. Math., 30 (1966), pp. 15-68.

9. Sinaĭ, J. G., Proof of the Ergodic Hypothesis
for a Dynamical System of Statistical Mechanics,
Dokl. Akad. Nauk SSSR, 153 (1963), pp. 1261-1264.

CATEGORIAL CONCEPTS IN DYNAMICAL SYSTEM THEORY[1]

Otomar Hájek

(Caroline University, Prague, and
Case Western Reserve University)

The aim of this paper is, first, to exhibit an elementary application of category-theoretical concepts to the theory of dynamical systems; and second, to indicate how this may influence the posing and solution of some rather interesting problems.

Categorial formulations seem to appear naturally in several basic problems of dynamical system theory (to be understood as including the global and local dynamical systems proper, and also the nonautonomous flows, systems without

[1]Acknowledgment: This work was supported by the National Science Foundation under Grant No. NSF-GP-7447.

unicity, and so on). In this context, the first
question seems to be how should one make these
objects into a category, that is, which transformations is one to allow. It is this question with
which the present paper is concerned; but first a
minor digression.

Once a suitable choice has been made, it turns
out that the standard representation of an autonomous differential equation in n-space (under the
usual conditions) is the action of a well-behaved
functor taking the category of autonomous differential equations into that of dynamical systems;
and analogously for other similar constructions,
applying, for example, to functional-differential
equations, differential equations in function
spaces, equations without unicity.

The advantage of this approach is that one
is then prompted to ask various questions, quite
elementary category-wise, but rather important as
far as dynamical system theory is concerned. To
give one illustration, one has a number of interesting subcategories (requiring significant properties of the objects concerned, for example, global
existence, or differentiability); a quite basic

and natural question is then whether the natural
inclusion functor between the categories

(global dynamical systems) ⟶ (local
        dynamical systems)

has an adjoint (that is, whether the subcategory
is reflective). In one setting the answer is as
follows (on eliminating categorial formulations;
see [1, Theorem 16]):

THEOREM. Every continuous local dynamical system
on P has an extension to a continuous global
dynamical system on a space $P^\wedge$ containing P as an
open subset. (In another setting an answer is
given by Vinograd's theorem on reparametrization
of differential equations [4, Chapter I, Theorem
7].)

Returning to the question of selecting the
class of morphisms for the dynamical categories,
it is obvious that any such definition will auto-
matically specify the isomorphisms (that is, the
ignorable differences between systems which are
"essentially the same"), and hence will also
restrict the properties invariant under these

isomorphisms; properly, the latter should be the
guiding criterion for the former. This is, of
course, not surprising: it is generally accepted
that the categorial approach is a direct descendant
of that explicitly described in Klein's Erlangen
program. In the context of dynamical systems, it
also shows that there can be no unique reasonable
choice of the (iso-)morphisms: thus in one situation one might be interested merely in the presence
of cyclic trajectories, while in another one might
actually wish to determine the primitive periods
(compare qualitative against quantitative problems).

Nevertheless, it is important at least to
list some reasonable choices of the class of
morphisms; a number of these fall under the following general scheme.

Consider two dynamical systems, π on a set P
and π' on P', and also an assignment $(x, \xi) \to (x', \xi'$
between phase-time pairs, yielding a map
$P \times R^1 \to P' \times R^1$. Then this assignment may be
termed a morphism between π and π' (or to map π
into π', or to be compatible with π and π', and
so on) if and only if the implication $\Longrightarrow$ in the
following diagram is valid:

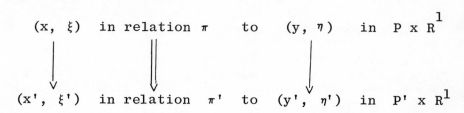

(If π is a dynamical system proper, then the first
line reads $x\pi\xi = y\pi\eta$, that is, $y = x\pi\theta$ for
$\theta = \xi - \eta$.) In the examples below, special types
of the assignment $(x, \xi) \rightarrow (x', \xi')$ are informally
described, and the compatibility condition exhibited
for the case of global dynamical systems (throughout, $\pi(x, \xi)$ is written as $x\pi\xi$).

Phase-space maps f x identity with $f:P \rightarrow P'$:

$$x' = f(x) \qquad \xi' = \xi \qquad f(x\pi\xi) = f(x)\pi'\xi$$

(Ad hoc term) phase-independent repara-
metrizations identity x φ with $\varphi:R^1 \rightarrow R^1$ a group
homomorphism:

$$x' = x \qquad \xi' = \varphi(\xi) \qquad x\pi\xi = x\pi'\varphi(\xi)$$

Topological morphisms f x φ with $f:P \rightarrow P'$
and $\varphi:R^1 \rightarrow R^1$ a group homomorphism (see [0]):

$$x' = f(x) \qquad \xi' = \varphi(\xi) \qquad f(x\pi\xi) = f(x)\pi'\varphi(\xi)$$

Reparametrizations (proj_1, φ):

$$x' = x \qquad \xi' = \varphi(x, \xi) \qquad x\pi\xi = x\,\pi'\,\varphi(x, \xi)$$

(Ad hoc term) phase-maps-with-reparametrization
$(f \circ \text{proj}_1, \varphi)$ with $f:P \to P'$:

$$x' = f(x) \qquad \xi' = \varphi(x, \xi) \qquad f(x\pi\xi)$$
$$= f(x)\pi'\varphi(x, \xi)$$

(Ad hoc term) time-preserving morphisms
(f, proj_2):

$$x' = f(x, \xi) \qquad \xi' = \xi \qquad f(x\pi(\xi - \eta), \eta)$$
$$= f(x, \xi)\pi'(\xi - \eta)$$

General morphisms (f, φ):

$$x' = f(x, \xi) \qquad \xi' = \varphi(x, \xi)$$

$$f(x, \xi)\pi'\varphi(x, \xi) = f(y, \eta)\pi'\varphi(y, \eta)$$

$$\text{for} \quad y = x\pi(\xi - \eta)$$

The list could, of course, be extended. Also,
some modifications are immediate: for example, in
the topological case, with all the mappings continuous, one may localize the compatibility condition to neighborhoods in P or in P x R^1; or

replace the mapping $P \times R^1 \to P' \times R^1$ by a general
relation between these sets, to describe, for
example, symmetry properties of a dynamical system,
or adjointness of linear systems. If local rather
than global dynamical systems are involved, further
changes should be made: for example, the compatibility condition for phase-space maps should be
augmented by the clause "whenever the left side is
defined," so as to read: $f \cdot \pi \subset \pi' \cdot (f \times$ identity). It may be noted that the morphism classes
exhibited are modeled after the interesting types
of transformation of variables in differential
equations.

Since the morphisms determine the isomorphisms, each choice of the class of morphisms
naturally raises the question of classification
and canonic objects (that is, of exhibiting repre-
sentative skeletal subcategories). A less ambitious
program would be to determine the interesting invariants to a given class of isomorphisms; or
conversely, given a property, to discover the isomorphism class to which it properly belongs. All
that follows consists of remarks to various cases
of these types of problems.

To be quite specific, consider the category
whose objects are the continuous global dynamical
systems on topological spaces, and whose morphisms
are continuous phase-space maps (using the terminology from our list). Evidently the isomorphisms
are precisely the homeomorphisms between the
corresponding phase spaces; so that as concerns
the classification problem, it would suffice to
solve it for each phase space individually. Unfortunately, at present, this seems over-difficult
even for R^2 as the phase space.

On the other hand, in R^1 the situation is
comparatively simple. Each (continuous global)
dynamical system π on R^1 determines the following
two objects:

(i)   a closed subset $C \subset R^1$, the set of
critical points of π, and

(ii)   a map $\delta: R^1 - C \to \{1, -1\}$ which assigns
± 1 to each component of $R^1 - C$, the orientation
of trajectories of π in the interval components.
These two objects constitute a complete set of invariants, in a sense possibly obvious from the
following assertions:

THEOREM. Two such dynamical systems π_1, π_2 are
isomorphic (in the exhibited category) if, and
only if, first, their critical point sets are
homeomorphically embedded in R^1 [that is, C_2
= $f(C_1)$ for some $f:R^1 \approx R^1$] and second, their
orientations either coincide or are opposite through-
out (that is, $\delta_2 = \delta_1 \circ f$ or $\delta_2 = -\delta_1 \circ f$).

THEOREM. To any closed $C \subset R^1$ and continuous
$\delta:R^1 - C \rightarrow \{1, -1\}$ there exists a dynamical system
π with C, δ as prescirbed invariants; furthermore,
one may even take π defined by a differential
equation. (For most of this see [3, Chapter VI,
4.13]; a related assertion was proved in [5].)

One quite trivial fact, which should nevertheless be stressed here, is that these problems
depend strongly on the category concerned: if,
for instance, the class of morphisms is enlarged,
there will be less nonisomorphic objects, and the
classification problem may lose some interest.
This seems to be the case in the following assertion, which covers even the nonautonomous flows
[2, Theorem 6]:

THEOREM. Every (global continuous) flow on a
differentiable n-manifold is isomorphic, in the
category with time-preserving morphisms, to an
"immobile" flow defined by $dx/d\theta = 0$ (in local
coordinates x on another n-manifold).

The next group of problems I wish to consider
concerns the so-called local behavior of dynamical
systems near isolated critical points. First, let
us describe the appropriate categories. The objects
are triples (P, π, x), where π is a continuous
dynamical system (global or local) on the topological space P, and x $\in$ P is an isolated critical
point of π. The morphisms f:(P, π, x) $\rightarrow$ (P', π', x')
are maps f with the following properties:

> (i)   the set G = domain f is an open subset
> of P and contains only one critical point of π,
> namely x;

> (ii) f:G $\rightarrow$ P' is continuous;

> (iii) f(x) = x';

> (iv) whenever yπI $\subset$ G with I an open interval
> containing 0, there is f(y$\pi\xi$) = f(y)π'ξ for all
> $\xi \in$ I.

[Remark. (iv) is precisely the morphism condition

for f, π', and the local dynamical system obtained
by relativizing π to G.]

This exhibits the category corresponding to
the "local" phase-space maps; the modifications
needed to obtain the remaining classes of morphisms
are perhaps obvious (thus, for example, Ura's
local isomorphisms [5] are precisely the isomorphisms in the category with local topological
morphisms).

For one type of critical point, the classification problem in this category is completely
solved [3, Chapter VIII, 4.6]:

THEOREM. Let π be a (continuous local) dynamical
system on a 2-manifold P, let $x \in P$ be an asymptotically stable point of π. Then, in the category
with local phase-space maps, (P, π, x) is isomorphic to (R^2, π', 0) with π' defined by the linear
differential equation $dz/d\theta = -z$ (in a complex
coordinate z).

In general terms, then, for planar systems
all stable focuses and nodes are (topologically at
least) locally the same. On the other hand, if
one considers the centers, a similar assertion is

no longer true. Indeed, in our category, the
primitive periods are invariants, so that the
planar systems defined by

$$\frac{dz}{d\theta} = iz \qquad \frac{dz}{d\theta} = 2iz$$

cannot be locally isomorphic at 0. Nevertheless,
they are extremely alike; this could probably be
best made precise by observing that they are isomorphic in the category with Ura's local morphisms
(use an appropriate group isomorphism $R^1 \approx R^1$ to
adjust the periods). But again, even in this
larger category, the planar systems defined by

$$\frac{dz}{d\theta} = iz \qquad \frac{dz}{d\theta} = i|z|z$$

are not locally isomorphic at 0. One of the best
positive results in this direction is the following
(private communcation by Prof. Ura):

THEOREM. Two (continuous local) dynamical systems,
in R^2 with 0 as center are isomorphic, locally at
0, in the category with Ura's local isomorphisms if:

    (i)   the primitive periods of cycles around

0, considered as functions of cycle position,
are strictly increasing (or strictly decreasing)
for both systems, near 0; and

(ii)   these two functions both tend either
to 0, or to finite limits, or to $+\infty$, as the
cycle is made to approach 0.

It would now seem reasonable to inquire to
which category in our list the concept of a center
properly belongs.   The search ends at the category
with local phase-maps-with-reparametrization (an
unpublished result of R. McCann):

THEOREM.   Let π be a (continuous local) dynamical
system on a 2-manifold P, let $x \in P$ be a center to
π.   Then there exists a homeomorphism $f:G \approx G'$
between disk neighborhoods, and a map $\varphi:G \times R^1 \to R^1$
continuous in $(G - (x)) \times R^1$, such that

$$y\pi\xi = f(y) \exp i\varphi(y, \xi) \quad \text{for} \quad (y, \xi) \in G \times R^1$$

(Thus $(f \circ proj_1, \varphi)$ maps (P, π, x) into $(R^2, \pi', 0)$
with π' defined by the equation $dz/d\theta = iz$.)

A number of formulations in the qualitative
theory involve various properties of the trajectories
(or semitrajectories) as a whole, and depend little

or not at all on the parametrizations implicit in
the specification of the dynamical system. This
naturally leads to inquiring for conditions of
"geometric equivalence," for example, between two
systems on the same space; the analogy with differential equations suggests that this may well involve significantly the category with reparametrizations as morphisms.

THEOREM [3, Chapter VI, 1.14]. Let π and π' be
(continuous global) dynamical systems on a Hausdorff
space P; the following properties are equivalent:

    (i)   every semitrajectory of π is a semi-
trajectory of π', and conversely;

    (ii) for every $x \in P$ there is a homeo-
morphism $\varphi_x : R^1 \approx R^1$ such that

$$x \pi \xi = x \pi' \varphi_x (\xi) \quad \text{for all} \quad \xi \in R^1$$

Evidently the last condition is precisely the
morphism condition in the category mentioned above.
However, it should be emphasized that (a priori at
least) it is not asserted that φ_x depends continuously on x. Note also that in (i) it is not
required that positive semitrajectories go into

precisely the positive semitrajectories. I have
been unable to prove a similar result involving
trajectories rather than semitrajectories; I have
the impression that this is again equivalent with
(ii) for R^2 as phase space, but not in R^3.

REFERENCES

0. Gottschalk, W. H., and Hedlund, G. A., Topological Dynamics, Am. Math. Soc. Colloq. Publ.
(1955).

1. Hájek, O., Structure of Dynamical Systems,
Comment. Math. Univ. Carol., 6,1 (1965), pp. 53-72.

2. Hájek, O., Differentiable Representation of
Flows, Comment. Math. Univ. Carol, 7,2 (1966),
pp. 219-225.

3. Hájek, O., Dynamical Systems in the Plane,
Academic Press, New York (in press).

4. Nemyckiǐ, V. V., and Stepanov, V. V.,
Qualitative Theory of Differential Equations,
Gostechizdat, Moscow-Leningrad, 1949.

5. Ura, T., Lecture Notes on Dynamical Systems
(unpublished), 1966-67.

TRANSFORMATIONS COMMUTING WITH
THE SHIFT[1]

G. A. Hedlund

(Yale University)

The dynamical system defined by the shift
transformation acting on the space of unending
sequences of symbols from some finite set has been
investigated in great detail, both in its topological and its measure-theoretic aspects. This
shift dynamical system contains a large variety of
subdynamical systems which have served as useful
models to indicate possible structures of dynamical
systems. The construction of a subdynamical system
with desired properties becomes the problem of
constructing symbolic sequences with corresponding
properties, and this reduces to combinatorial

---

[1]This research was partially supported by Army
Research Office (Durham).

problems which can often be attacked successfully.

A natural question in connection with any dynamical system is that concerning the existence and properties of continuous transformations which commute with the group action. In the shift dynamical system it is a question concerning continuous transformations of the space of unending sequences of symbols into itself which commute with the shift.

An obvious example of such a transformation is obtained by simply permuting the symbols. A generalization of this is to define a mapping of blocks (words) of symbols of a specified length into single symbols and extending this mapping in a natural manner to infinite sequences. It will be shown that these mappings essentially generate all continuous transformations which commute with the shift.

Now this class of mappings has been analyzed rather thoroughly during the past decade in work sponsored by the Institute for Defense Analyses, Communications Research Division, Princeton, New Jersey. Contributors to these developments include K. I. Appel, David Blackwell, W. A. Blankenship,

R. Creighton Buck, M. L. Curtis, J. D. Ferguson,
A. M. Gleason, G. A. Hedlund, R. C. Lyndon, O. S.
Rothaus, L. R. Welch, and probably others.

In this paper we describe a considerable
portion of these developments and use them to draw
conclusions about continuous transformations which
commute with the shift. Space limitations preclude
detailed proofs, which will be published at a later
date.

1. THE SHIFT DYNAMICAL SYSTEM

Let I denote the set of all integers. For
$i \in I$, let $I_i = \{j \,|\, j \in I,\ j \geq i\}$. The cardinal of
a set E will be denoted by crd E.

Let $S \in I_1$ and let S be a set with crd $S = S$.
The set S is the symbol set and any element of S
is a symbol. A convenient choice for S is the set
$\{0, 1, \ldots, S - 1\}$.

A bisequence over S is a function on I to S.
Let $X(S) = S^I$ denote the set of all bisequences
over S. The set $X(S)$ is the bisequence set over
S. If $x \in X(S)$ and $i \in I$, the value of x at i
will be denoted by x_i or $x(i)$ and x will often be

written ... $x_{-1}x_0x_1$... .

We define a metric d on $X(S)$. Let x, y $\in X(S)$. If x = y, then d(x, y) = 0. If x $\neq$ y, let k be the least nonnegative integer such that either $x_k \neq y_k$ or $x_{-k} \neq y_{-k}$. Then d(x, y) = $(1 + k)^{-1}$.

It is easily verified that d : $X(S) \times X(S) \to R$ defines a metric on $X(S)$ and that the metric topology induced by d coincides with the product topology induced by the discrete topology of S.

If S = 1, then X(S) contains just one point. We will assume throughout that crd S = S > 1.

If S > 1, then X(S) is homeomorphic to the Cantor discontinuum.

The metric space $X(S)$ is the <u>bisequence</u> <u>space</u> over S.

The <u>shift</u> or <u>shift</u> <u>transformation</u> is the mapping $\sigma : X(S) \to X(S)$ defined by $[\sigma(x)]_i = x_{i+1}$, x $\in X(S)$. It is known (see [1]) that σ is a topologically mixing, expansive homeomorphism of X(S) onto X(S).

The discrete flow $(X(S), \sigma)$ is called the <u>symbolic flow over</u> S or the shift <u>dynamical system</u> <u>over</u> S.

The shift dynamical system over S, crd S > 1,

contains a large variety of orbits (see [1]). The periodic points are everywhere dense, and the same is true for the set of points which are almost periodic but not periodic. There exist regularly almost periodic points which are not periodic and isochronous points which are not regularly almost periodic. The bilaterally transitive points, that is, those points for which each semiorbit is every-where dense, for a residual set.

2. A CLASS OF MAPPINGS WHICH COMMUTE WITH THE SHIFT

Let $n \in I_1$. An n-block over S is an ordered set $x_1 x_2 \ldots x_n$ where $x_i \in S$, $i = 1, 2, \ldots, n$. Let $A = a_1 a_2 \ldots a_n$ be an n-block over S and let $B = b_1 b_2 \ldots b_m$ be an m-block over S. Then A appears in B if and only if there exists an integer i such that $b_{i+1} b_{i+2} \ldots b_{i+n} = a_1 a_2 \ldots a_n$.

Let $x \in X(S)$ and let $B = b_1 b_2 \ldots b_n$ be an n-block over S. Then B appears in x if and only if there exists $i \in I$ such that $x_{i+1} x_{i+2} \ldots x_{i+n} = B$.

Let $n \in I_1$ and let $B_n(S)$ denote the set of all n-blocks over S. Let f be a mapping of $B_n(S)$

into $B_1(S) = S$. The set of all such mappings for

a given $n \in I_1$ and a given S will be denoted by

$F(S, n)$. We note that $\text{crd } B_n(S) = S^n$ and $\text{crd } F(S, n)$

$= S^{S^n}$.

Let $f \in F(S, n)$ and let $m \in I_1$. Corresponding

to f and m we define a mapping f_m of $B_{m+n-1}(S)$ into

$B_m(S)$. Let $B = b_1 \ldots b_{m+n-1} \in B_{m+n-1}(S)$ and let

$a_i = f(b_i b_{i+1} \ldots b_{i+n-1})$, $i = 1, 2, \ldots, m$. Then

$A = a_1 a_2 \cdots a_m \in B_m(S)$ and we define $f_m(B) = A$.

Let $f \in F(S, n)$. Corresponding to f we

define a mapping of $X(S)$ into $X(S)$. Let $x \in X(S)$

and let $y \in X(S)$ be defined by $y_i = f(x_i x_{i+1} \cdots x_{i+n-1})$

$i \in I$. By definition $f_\infty(x) = y$.

The following theorem is easily proved.

2.1 THEOREM. Let $f \in F(S, n)$. Then f_∞ is a

continuous map of $X(S)$ into $X(S)$ which commutes

with σ.

For convenience we will use the following

notations:

(2.2) $F(S) = \bigcup_{n=1}^{\infty} F(S, n)$

(2.3) $F_\infty(S) = \{ f_\infty | f \in F(S) \}$

(2.4) $F_\infty^*(S) = \{ \sigma^m f_\infty | m \in I, f \in F_\infty(S) \}$

(2.5) $\Phi(S)$ is the set of all continuous

mappings of $X(S)$ into $X(S)$ which commute with σ.

(2.6) $E(S)$ is the set of all continuous mappings of $X(S)$ onto $X(S)$ which commute with σ. These are the endomorphisms of $(X(S), \sigma)$.

(2.7) $H(S)$ is the set of all members of $\Phi(S)$ which are one-to-one.

(2.8) $A(S)$ is the set of all homeomorphisms of $X(S)$ onto $X(S)$ which commute with σ. These are the automorphisms of $(X(S), \sigma)$.

Clearly, $F_\infty^*(S) \subset \Phi(S)$. The basic result that these two classes are identical is due to M. L. Curtis, G. A. Hedlund, and R. C. Lyndon.

2.9 THEOREM. $F_\infty^*(S) = \Phi(S)$.

Proof. Let $S = \{0, 1, \ldots, S - 1\}$. Let $\varphi \in \Phi(S)$. For each $i \in S$, let $U_i = \{x \mid x \in X(S),\ x_0 = i\}$. Then U_i is open and closed, $U_i \cap U_j = \phi$ if $i \neq j$, and $X(S) = \bigcup_{i=0}^{S-1} U_i$. Let $V_i = \varphi^{-1}(U_i)$, $i \in S$. Then each V_i is open and closed, $V_i \cap V_j = \phi$ if $i \neq j$, and $X(S) = \bigcup_{i=0}^{S-1} V_i$.

From the properties of the sets V_i, there exists an integer k such that if $x \in V_i$ and $y \in V_j$ with $i \neq j$, then $d(x, y) \geq (1 + k)^{-1}$.

Let $x \in X(S)$ and let m be a nonnegative

integer. The <u>central</u> $(2m + 1)$-<u>block</u> of x is the
block $x_{-m} \cdots x_{-1} x_0 x_1 \cdots x_m$.

For each $i \in S$ let B_i be the collection of all
$(2k + 1)$-blocks B over S with the property that
there exists $x \in V_i$ such that B is the central
$(2k + 1)$-block of x. If $i \neq j$, then $B_i \cap B_j = \phi$.
For if $B \in B_i \cap B_j$, there exists $x \in V_i$, x with
central $(2k + 1)$-block B, and $y \in V_j$, y with central
$(2k + 1)$-block B. But then $d(x, y) < (1 + k)^{-1}$,
which is not the case. Since $X(S) = \bigcup_{i=0}^{S-1} V_i$, it
follows that $\bigcup_{i=0}^{S-1} B_i$ is the set A_{2k+1} of all
$(2k + 1)$-blocks over S.

Let $f : A_{2k+1} \to S$ be defined by $f(A_{2k+1}) = i$
provided $A_{2k+1} \in B_i$.

Let $x \in X(S)$, $\varphi(x) = y$, and $f_\infty(x) = z$. We
show that $y_0 = z_{-k}$. There exists a unique $i \in S$
such that $x \in V_i$, and hence if B is the central
$(2k + 1)$-block of x, then $B \in B_i$, $f(B) = i$, and
$z_{-k} = i$. But since $\varphi(x) = y$ and $x \in V_i = \varphi^{-1}(U_i)$,
we have $y = \varphi(x) \in U_i$ and $y_0 = i$. Thus $y_0 = i$
$= z_{-k}$.

Now let $u \in X(S)$, $\varphi(u) = v$, $f_\infty(u) = w$, and
let $n \in I$. Let $x = \sigma^n(u)$, $y = \sigma^n(v)$, $z = \sigma^n(w)$.
Then

$$\varphi(x) = \varphi\sigma^n(u) = \sigma^n\varphi(u) = y$$

and

$$f_\infty(x) = f_\infty\sigma^n(u) = \sigma^n f_\infty(u) = \sigma^n(w) = z$$

We have shown that $y_o = z_{-k}$. Since $y = \sigma^n(v)$,

$y_o = \left[\sigma^n(v)\right]_o = v_n$. Since $z = \sigma^n(w)$, z_{-k}

$= \left[\sigma^n(w)\right]_{-k} = w_{-k+n}$. We conclude that $v_n = w_{n-k}$

for all $m \in I$ and hence

$$\varphi(u) = v = \sigma^{-k}(w) = \sigma^{-k}f_\infty(u)$$

Since u was arbitrary, it follows that $\varphi = \sigma^{-k}f_\infty$,

which is a member of $F_\infty^*(S)$. Thus $\Phi(S) \subset F_\infty^*(S)$.

Since $F_\infty^*(S) \subset \Phi(S)$, the proof is completed.

It follows from Theorem 2.1 that crd $\Phi(S)$

$= \aleph_o$. For crd $F(S, n) = S^{S^n}$, hence $F_\infty(S)$ and

$F_\infty^*(S)$ are countable sets. Since $\sigma^n \in F_\infty^*(S)$,

$n \in I$, and $\sigma^n \neq \sigma^m$ if $n \neq m$, it follows that

crd $F_\infty^*(S) = \aleph_o$.

3. MULTIPLICITIES OF THE MAPPINGS f_m AND f_∞

Let $f \in F(S, n)$. The condition that f_∞ be

onto, that is, $f_\infty \in E(S)$, puts strong restrictions

on the mappings f_m. The situation is particularly

simple in the case n = 1, that is, when f is a
mapping of S into S.

3.1 THEOREM.   Let f $\in$ F(S, 1).   Then the following
statements are equivalent:

(1) f_∞ is onto;

(2)   f is a permutation of S;

(3)   crd f_m^{-1}(B) = 1 for every m $\in$ I_1 and
every B $\in$ B_m(S);

(4) f_∞ is a homeomorphism of X(S) onto X(S).

3.2 THEOREM.   Let f $\in$ F(S, 1).   If f_∞ is not onto
then there exists x $\subset$ X(S), x a fixed point under
σ, such that the set f_∞^{-1}(x) is of the power of the
continuum.

From Theorem 3.1 it follows that if f $\in$ F(S, 1)
then f_∞ is onto if and only if each of the mappings
f_m is onto.   The same result holds for arbitrary n.

3.3 THEOREM.   Let n $\in$ I_1 and let f $\in$ F(S, n).   Then
f_∞ is onto if and only if each f_m : B_{m+n-1}(S) $\rightarrow$ B_m(S)
is onto, m $\geq$ 1.

For n > 1, it cannot be expected that f_∞
onto implies condition (3) of Theorem 3.1.   The

following theorem, due to W. A. Blankenship and
O. S. Rothaus, yields the equivalence of conditions
(1) and (3) of Theorem 3.1 as a special case.

3.4 THEOREM. Let $n \in I$, $f \in F(S, n)$. Then the
following statements are equivalent:

(1) f_∞ is onto;

(2) crd $f_m^{-1}(B) = S^{n-1}$ for each $B \in B_m(S)$
and for all $m \geq 1$.

Given an $f \in F(S, n)$, $n > 1$, it is a difficult
task to determine whether or not f_∞ is onto, and
the question arises as to whether there is any
finite process for making this determination. The
following theorem, due to David Blackwell, answers
this question.

3.5 THEOREM. Let $n \in I_1$, $f \in F(S, n)$. Then the
following statements are equivalent:

(1) f_∞ is onto;

(2) crd $f_m^{-1}(B) = S^{n-1}$ for each $B \in B_m(S)$,
$1 \leq m \leq S^{n-1}$.

When n or S is large, the number of compu-
tations required to verify ontoness is large, but
the Blackwell criterion has been successfully used

to determine all members of $F(S, 4)$ and $F(S, 5)$,
crd $S = S = 2$, which determine onto maps.

From Theorem 3.4 we can draw conclusions
concerning the mappings f_∞ which are onto and
hence concerning the members of $E(S)$.

3.6 THEOREM. Let $n \in I_1$, $f \in F(S, n)$, and let f_∞
be onto. Then crd $f_\infty^{-1}(x) \leq S^{n-1}$ for all $x \in X(S)$.

This follows from the fact that if there
exists $x \in X(S)$ with crd $f_\infty^{-1}(x) > S^{n-1}$, then there
exists an m-block B with crd $f_m^{-1}(B) > S^{n-1}$.

This result and Theorem 2.9 together imply
the following theorem.

3.7 THEOREM. Let $\varphi \in E(S)$. Then there exists a
constant $M(\varphi)$ such that crd $\varphi^{-1}(x) \leq M(\varphi)$ for all
$x \in X(S)$.

Theorem 3.2 becomes valid for $n > 1$ provided
the condition that x be fixed under σ is replaced by
the condition that x be periodic. The proof of
this depends on several lemmas which are useful in
other contexts.

3.8 LEMMA. Let $m \in I_1$ and let B be an m-block over

S . For $q \geq m$, let $\mathcal{D}(B, q)$ be the set of all q-blocks over S in which B appears and let $N(B, q)$ = crd $\mathcal{D}(B, q)$. Then

$$\lim_{q \to \infty} \frac{N(B, q)}{S^q} = 1$$

3.9 LEMMA. Let $n \in I_1$, $f \in F(S, n)$, and suppose that f_∞ is not an onto map. Let k and t be positive integers. Then there exists an m-block A with $m \geq t$ such that crd $f_m^{-1}(A) > k$.

3.10 LEMMA. Let $n \in I_2$ and let E be a collection of $(m + 2n - 2)$-blocks over S such that crd $E > S^{2n-2}$. Then there exist distinct blocks E and E* in E and $(n - 1)$-blocks A and B such that $E = ADB$, $E^* = AD^*B$.

3.11 LEMMA. Let $n \in I_2$, $f \in F(S, n)$, and let $m \in I_1$. Let there exist an $(m + n - 1)$-block C such that crd $f_{m+n-1}^{-1}(C) > S^{2n-2}$. Then there exist distinct $(m + n - 1)$-blocks P and P* and an $(n - 1)$-block A such that

$$f_{m+2(n-1)}(APA) = f_{m+2(n-1)}(AP^*A)$$

The generalization of Theorem 3.2 is the following.

3.12 THEOREM. Let $n \in I_1$, $f \in F(S, n)$, and let f_∞ be not onto. Then there exists $x \in X(S)$, x a fixed point under some power of σ, such that the set $f_\infty^{-1}(x)$ is of the power of the continuum.

From this and Theorem 2.9 we obtain:

3.13 THEOREM. Let $\varphi \in \Phi(S)$ but $\varphi \notin E(S)$. Then there exists $x \in X(S)$, x periodic, such that the set $\varphi^{-1}(x)$ is of the power of the continuum.

If $\varphi \in \Phi(S)$ and φ is a one-to-one mapping, it follows from Theorem 3.13 that $\varphi \in E(S)$.

3.14 COROLLARY. $H(S) = A(S)$.

4. A FUNDAMENTAL PROPERTY OF INVERSES IN THE CASE
   OF AN ONTO MAPPING

If f_∞ is onto, then the members of $f_\infty^{-1}(x)$ display certain fundamental separation properties. These properties carry over to any member of $\Phi(S)$ and enable us to show that many properties carry over to inverses.

Let x, y $\in$ X(S), x $\neq$ y. Then x and y are
negatively (positively) asymptotic provided there
exists N $\in$ I such that $x_i = y_i$ for i $\leq$ N (i $\geq$ N);
x and y are bilaterally asymptotic provided they
are both negatively and positively asymptotic.

Let x $\in$ X(S), let m $\in$ I_1, and let i $\in$ I.
The m-block $x_i x_{i+1} \cdots x_{i+m-1}$ will be denoted by
B(x, i, m).

Let x, y $\in$ X(S) and let m $\in$ I_1. Then x and
y are totally m-separated provided B(x, i, m)
$\neq$ B(y, i, m) for all i $\in$ I; x and y are negatively
(positively) m-separated provided there exists an
integer N such that B(x, i, m) $\neq$ B(y, i, m) for
i $\leq$ N (i $\geq$ N).

4.1 THEOREM. Let n $\in$ I_2, let f $\in$ F(S, n), and let
f_∞ be onto. Let there exist y, z $\in$ X(S), y $\neq$ z,
such that f_∞(y) = f_∞(z). Then one and only one of
the following statements is valid:

(1) y and z are positively asymptotic and
negatively (n - 1)-separated;

(2) y and z are negatively asymptotic and
positively (n - 1)-separated;

(3)   y and z are both positively and
negatively (n - 1)-separated.

By virtue of Theorem 2.9 we can draw conclusions concerning the endomorphisms of the shift
dynamical system over S, that is, $(X(S), \sigma)$.

4.2 THEOREM.   Let $\varphi \in E(S)$, let y, z $\in X(S)$,
y $\neq$ z, and suppose $\varphi(y) = \varphi(z)$.   Then the orbits
of y and z are either separated in both senses, or
asymptotic in one sense and separated in the
other.

The proof of Theorem 4.1 depends on a simple
form of a general lemma which is useful in other
connections.

Let f $\in$ F(S, n), n $\geq$ 2, let m, k, q $\in I_1$
with m > n - 1, and let B be a collection of blocks
over S.   Then B has <u>property</u> P(m, k, q, f) provided
the following conditions are fulfilled:

(1)   each member of B is an m-block;

(2)   crd B = k+q;

(3)   the collection A of initial (n - 1)-
blocks of the members of B is identical with the
collection of terminal (n - 1)-blocks of B and
crd A = k;

(4)   there exists an $(m - n + 1)$-block D

such that $f_{m-n+1}(B) = D$ for each $B \in \mathcal{B}$.

4.3 LEMMA. Let $n \in I_2$, let $f \in F(S, n)$, and let there exist a collection $\mathcal{B}$ of blocks with property $P(m, k, q, f)$. Then there exists a positive integer r and a collection $\mathcal{B}*$ of blocks with property $P(2m - n + 1, k, q + r, f)$.

4.4 THEOREM. Let $f \in F(S, n)$ where $n \in I_2$. If there exists a collection $\mathcal{B}$ of blocks with property $P(m, k, p, f)$, then f_∞ is not onto.

5. INVARIANCE OF ORBIT PROPERTIES

Orbit properties of a dynamical system such as periodicity, almost periodicity, positive or negative recurrence, and bilateral recurrence are preserved under homomorphisms of such systems. Thus, in particular, if $\varphi \in \Phi(S)$ and $x \in X(S)$ are periodic, almost periodic, positively recurrent, negatively recurrent, or bilaterally recurrent, then $\varphi(x)$ has the corresponding property.

On the other hand, if $\varphi \in \Phi(S)$, $\varphi(y) = x$,

and x has some one of these properties, it does
not necessarily follow that y has any of these
properties. This is illustrated by letting
$\varphi : X(S) \to X(S)$ be defined by $\varphi(y) = u$, $y \in X(S)$,
where $u_i = 0$, $i \in I$. Thus $\varphi(X(S))$ is a single
point which is fixed under σ.

We can put the question in a somewhat less
restrictive fashion and ask if there exists some
$y \in \varphi^{-1}(x)$ which exhibits a given property of x.
The following theorems give some answers.

5.1 THEOREM. Let $\varphi \in \Phi(S)$, let x be a periodic
point (under σ), and suppose $\varphi^{-1}(x) \neq \phi$. Then there
exists $y \in \varphi^{-1}(x)$ such that y is periodic.

5.2 THEOREM. Let $\varphi \in \Phi(S)$, let x be negatively
(positively) recurrent (under σ), and let
$0 < \mathrm{crd}\ \varphi^{-1}(x) < \infty$. Then there exists $y \in \varphi^{-1}(x)$
such that y is negatively (positively) recurrent.

5.3 THEOREM. Let $\varphi \in \Phi(S)$, let x be almost
periodic (under σ), and suppose $\mathrm{crd}\ \varphi^{-1}(x) > 0$.
Then there exists $y \in \varphi^{-1}(x)$ such that y is almost
periodic.

In the preceding theorem it is not assumed that the mapping φ is necessarily onto. If this is assumed, much stronger conclusions concerning inverses can be obtained. These results are first proved for the onto members of $F_\infty(S)$ and carry over readily to the members of $E(S)$ by means of Theorem 2.9.

The following theorem, due to L. R. Welch, yields a basic property of the inverses of recurrent points in the case of an onto map. A point $x \in X(S)$ is <u>recurrent</u> (under σ) provided that corresponding to any neighborhood U of x, there exists an infinite sequence of integers $\cdots < n_{-1} < n_0 < n_1 \leq \cdots$ such that $\sigma^{n_i}(x) \in U$, $i \in I$.

5.4 THEOREM. Let $f \in F(S, n)$ with $n \geq 2$, and let f_∞ be onto. Let $x \in X(S)$, let x be recurrent, and let there exist y, z $\in X(S)$, $y \neq z$, such that $f_\infty(x) = x = f_\infty(z)$. Then y and z are totally $(n - 1)$-separated.

This theorem, combined with Theorem 2.9, yields:

5.5 THEOREM. Let $\varphi \in E(S)$, let x be recurrent,
and let $\varphi(y) = x = \varphi(z)$ with $y \neq z$. Then y and z
are separated (distal) under σ.

Here, y and z separated under δ means that
$\inf_{p \in I} d(\sigma^p(z), \sigma^p(y)) > 0$.

Now, many properties of points carry over to
inverses in the case of an endomorphism.

5.6 THEOREM. Let $\varphi \in E(S)$ and let x, y $\in X(S)$ with
$\varphi(y) = x$. If x is periodic (almost periodic;
recurrent) then y is periodic (almost periodic;
recurrent).

In the shift dynamical system $(X(S), \sigma)$, a
point x is <u>transitive</u> (<u>negatively</u> <u>transitive</u>;
<u>positively</u> <u>transitive</u>; <u>bilaterally</u> <u>transitive</u>)
provided the orbit of x is dense in $X(S)$　the
negative semiorbit of x is dense in $X(S)$; the
positive semiorbit of x is dense in $X(S)$; both
semiorbits of x are dense in $X(S)$.

5.7 THEOREM. Let $\varphi \in E(S)$ and let x, y $\in X(S)$ with
$\varphi(y) = x$. If x is transitive (negatively transitive;
positively transitive; bilaterally transitive) then
y is transitive (negatively transitive; positively

transitive; bilaterally transitive).

6. THE NUMBER OF INVERSES

If $f \in F(S, n)$ and f_∞ is onto, according to
Theorem 3.6, crd $f_\infty^{-1}(x) \leq S^{n-1}$ for all $x \in X(S)$,
while if f_∞ is not onto, by Theorem 3.12 there
exists a periodic point x such that the set
$f_\infty^{-1}(x)$ is of the power of the continuum.

For the case f_∞ onto, it is true that
crd $f_m^{-1}(B) = S^{n-1}$ for every positive integer m and
every m-block B. This exactness of the mappings
f_m does not, however, imply exactness of the
mapping f_∞, only that crd $f_\infty^{-1}(x)$ has S^{n-1} as an
upper bound. Examples can be constructed for which
crd $f_\infty^{-1}(x)$ assumes various values. However, for
almost all x, crd $f_\infty^{-1}(x)$ is constant. It has been
proved, both by A. M. Gleason and L. R. Welch,
using dissimilar methods, that if f_∞ is onto, then
there exists an integer $k \geq 1$ such that crd $f_\infty^{-1}(x)$
$= k$ for every bilaterally transitive $x \in X(S)$. We
prove slightly more than this.

6.1 THEOREM. Let $f \in F(S, n)$, $n \geq 2$, and let f_∞

be onto. Let $x \in X(S)$, let x be bilaterally
transitive, and let crd $f_\infty^{-1}(x) = M(x)$. Then
crd $f_\infty^{-1}(y) \geq M(x)$ for every $y \in X(S)$ and $f_\infty^{-1}(y)$
has $M(x)$ members which are mutually totally $(n - 1)$-
separated.

From this we readily obtain:

6.2 THEOREM. Let $f \in F(S, n)$, $n \geq 2$, and let f_∞
be onto. Then there exists an integer $M(f)$ such
that if $x \in X(S)$ and x is bilaterally transitive,
then crd $f_\infty^{-1}(x) = M(f)$.

The integer $M(f)$ can be characterized in
terms of the inverses of finite blocks. For given
$f \in F(S, n)$ and an m-block B, let $M(B, f)$ be the
number of blocks in a maximal subset of $(n - 1)$-
separated members of $f_m^{-1}(B)$.

6.3 THEOREM. Let $f \in F(S, n)$, $n \geq 2$, and let f_∞
be onto. Let B be the collection of all finite
blocks over S. Then

$$M(f) = \inf_{B \in B} M(B, f)$$

By applying Theorem 2.9, we obtain information
concerning endomorphisms of $(X(S), \sigma)$.

6.4 THEOREM. Let $\varphi \in E(S)$. There exists a
positive integer $M(\varphi)$ such that if x is bilaterally
transitive, then crd $\varphi^{-1}(x) = M(\varphi)$. For any
$y \in X(S)$, crd $\varphi^{-1}(y) \geq M(\varphi)$, and the set $\varphi^{-1}(y)$
contains $M(\varphi)$ members which are mutually separated.

The following theorem, due to L. R. Welch,
shows that there are restrictions on the branching
behavior of the inverses of a point which is
transitive in at least one sense.

6.5 THEOREM. Let $f \in F(S, n)$ $n \geq 2$, and let f_∞
be onto. Let x be positively (negatively)
transitive and let $f_\infty(y) = x = f_\infty(z)$ with $y \neq z$.
Then y and z are negatively (positively) $(n - 1)$-
separated.

7. COMPOSITIONS

Let m and n be positive integers and let
$f \in F(S, m)$, $g \in F(S, n)$. Then g_m maps $B_{m+n-1}(S)$
into $B_m(S)$ and f maps $B_m(S)$ into $B_1(S) = S$, so fg_m
is a well-defined mapping of $B_{m+n-1}(S)$ into S. The
mapping fg_m will also be denoted by fg. It is easy
to show that $(fg)_\infty = f_\infty g_\infty$.

If f_∞ and g_∞ are both onto maps, then so is their composition $f_\infty g_\infty$. The converse of this is true and this result holds generally for members of $\Phi(S)$.

7.1 THEOREM. Let $\varphi, \Psi \in \Phi(S)$. Then $\varphi\Psi$ is onto if and only if both φ and Ψ are onto.

In Section 6 there was associated with any $\varphi \in E(S)$ a positive integer $M(\varphi)$ characterized by the property that crd $\varphi^{-1}(x) = M(\varphi)$ for every bilaterally transitive x. In view of this characterization and Theorem 5.7, the following theorem is easily derived.

7.2 THEOREM. Let $\varphi, \Psi \in E(S)$. Then $\varphi\Psi \in E(S)$ and $M(\varphi\Psi) = M(\varphi)M(\Psi)$.

Little is known about the commuting properties of members of $E(S)$. If $\varphi, \Psi \in E(S)$, and either is a power of σ, then $\varphi\Psi = \Psi\varphi$. But if neither φ nor Ψ is a power of σ, then the study of a number of examples makes it appear unlikely that φ and Ψ commute.

8. MAXIMAL COMPATIBLE EXTENSIONS

With any onto f_∞ defined by $f \in F(S, n)$ there has been associated an integer $M(f)$ which is multiplicative under composition. We associate with any onto f_∞ two integers $R(f)$ and $L(f)$ which, likewise, are multiplicative under composition. The definition and development of their properties is in large part due to L. R. Welch.

Let A be an m-block over S and let $p \in I_1$. A <u>right</u> (<u>left</u>) p-<u>extension</u> of A is a block AB (BA) where B is an arbitrary p-block.

Let $f \in F(S, n)$, $n > 1$, let A be an m-block, $m \geq n - 1$, and let AB, AC be right p-extensions of A. Let $q = m + p - n + 1$. Then AB and AC are f-<u>compatible</u> provided $f_q(AB) = f_q(AC)$. Similarly, the left p-extensions BA, CA of A are f-<u>compatible</u> provided $f_q(BA) = f_q(CA)$. Let B be a collection of p-blocks. Then the set $AB = \{AB | B \in B\}$ is f-<u>compatible</u> provided each pair of members of AB is f-compatible. The definition of an f-compatible set BA of left p-extensions is analogous.

If the set AB is f-compatible then all members have the same image under f_q. Thus, if f_∞ is onto, then crd $AB \leq S^{n-1}$. The collection of all f-com-

patible sets of right p-extensions of A has finite
cardinality, so there is one, $AB(A, p, f)$, of
maximum cardinality. Let $R(A, p, f) = \text{crd } B(A, p, f)$
Now $R(A, p, f) \leq S^{n-1}$ for all $p \in I_1$ and we let
$R(A, f) = \sup_{p \in I_1} R(A, p, f)$. Then $R(A, f) \leq S^{n-1}$.

It is easy to show that if A and C are any
blocks, each of length at least n - 1, then
$R(A, f) = R(C, f)$. We define $R(f) = R(A, f)$, where
A is any block of length at least n - 1. The
integers $L(A, p, f)$, $L(A, f)$, and $L(f)$ are defined
analogously for left extensions.

Let D be a d-block over S. A <u>connected</u>
<u>maximal</u> f-<u>covering</u> <u>of</u> D is a set CAB of $(d + n - 1)$-
blocks where A is an m-block, $m \geq n-1$, AB is an
f-compatible set of right p-extensions of A such
that crd $AB = R(f)$, CA is an f-compatible set of
left q-extensions of A such that crd $CA = L(f)$
and $CAB \subset f_d^{-1}(D)$.

It is easy to show that there exists a block
D which has a connected maximal f-covering. The
following theorem gives a global picture of the
set of inverses of certain blocks.

8.1 THEOREM. Let $f \in F(S, n)$ with n > 1, and let

f_∞ be onto. Let $k \in I_1$. There exists a d-block D
and a positive integer M such that $d > k$ and

$$f_d^{-1}(D) = \left\{ C_i A_i B_i \,\middle|\, i = 1, 2, \ldots, M \right\}$$

where each $C_i A_i B_i$ is a connected maximal f-covering
of D. If $i \neq j$, then each member of $C_i A_i B_i$ is
$(n - 1)$-separated from each member of $C_j A_j B_j$.
Moreover, $M = M(f)$.

It follows from this theorem that crd $f_d^{-1}(D)$
$= L(f)M(f)R(f)$. But since f_∞ is onto, from Theorem
3.4 we have crd $f_d^{-1}(D) = S^{n-1}$.

8.2 COROLLARY. $L(f)M(f)R(f) = S^{n-1}$.

This result is still valid when $f \in F(S, 1)$
and f_∞ is onto. For in this case, $L(f) = M(f)$
$= R(f) = 1$.

Corollary 8.2 imposes restrictions on the
values which $L(f)$, $M(f)$, $R(f)$ can assume for a
given S. If S is a power of a prime P then each
of the integers $L(f)$, $M(f)$, $R(f)$ is a power of P.

8.3 THEOREM. Let $f \in F(S, m)$, $g \in F(S, n)$, with
both f_∞ and g_∞ onto mappings. Then
$fg \in F(S, m + n - 1)$ and

$$L(fg) = L(f)L(g) \qquad R(fg) = R(f)R(g)$$

Interesting results concerning the roots of powers of σ can be drawn from Theorem 8.3.

8.4 THEOREM. Let $\varphi \in \Phi(S)$ and let there exist $p, q \in I_1$ such that $\varphi^p = \delta^q$. Then p divides q. Hence, in particular, σ has no proper roots.

9. POLYNOMIAL MAPPINGS

Let $S = \operatorname{crd} S$ be a prime, let $n \in I_1$ and let $P(x_1, x_2, \ldots, x_n)$ be a polynomial in $(x_1, x_2, \ldots, x_n)$ over GF(S). Then P defines a mapping of $B_n(S)$ into $B_1(S) = S$ and hence $P \in F(S, n)$. It is not difficult to show that the collection of all such polynomials is identical with $F(S, n)$.

9.1 THEOREM. Let $S = \operatorname{crd} S$ be a prime, let $n \in I_1$ and let $f \in F(S, n)$. Then there exists a unique polynomial $P(x_1, x_2, \ldots, x_n)$ over GF(S) such that

$$f(x_1 x_2 \cdots x_n) = P(x_1, x_2, \ldots, x_n)$$

for all $x_1 x_2 \cdots x_n \in B_n(S)$.

This representation of f by a polynomial has

been useful in classifying the functions f and in
the determination of the properties of f_∞.

The polynomial $P(x_1,\ldots,x_n)$ is <u>linear</u> <u>in</u>
x_1 $[x_n]$ provided it is of the form $x_1 + Q(x_2,\ldots,x_n)$
$[Q(x_2,\ldots,x_n) + x_n]$. It is not difficult to show
that if $f = P$ is linear in either x_1 or x_n, then f_∞
is onto.

If f is linear in both x_1 and x_n, then f_∞ is
not only onto but is an exactly S^{n-1}-to-one map of
$X(S)$ onto $X(S)$. Thus there are many members of
$E(S)$ which are exactly k-to-one mappings, k a power
of a prime.

O. S. Rothaus has proved the converse result,
namely, that if $f \in F(S, n)$ and f_∞ is an exactly
S^{n-1}-to-one mapping, then f is linear in both x_1
and x_n. It is an open question as to whether the
same conclusion follows under the assumption that
f_∞ is onto and crd $f_\infty^{-1}(x) = S^{n-1}$ for some $x \in X(S)$.

Let $L(S, n) = \{f | f \in F(S, n)$, f linear in an
end variable$\}$ and let $L(S) = \{f_\infty \sigma^m$ $m \in I$, $f \in L(S, n)$
for some n$\}$. Then $L(S) \subset E(S)$. If $f \in F(S, m)$
with f linear in x_1 and $g \in F(S, n)$ with g linear
in x_n, then f_∞ and g_∞ are both onto mappings; hence
$(fg)_\infty$ is onto, but fg is not necessarily linear in

an end variable. Thus L(S) is a proper subset of
E(S).

Let C(S) denote the class of mappings
obtained by composing members of L(S). Then
L(S) ⊂ C(S) ⊂ E(S). But the class C(S) by no
means exhausts the class E(S). Large subsets of
E(S) have been constructed which are disjoint from
C(S).

The group A(S) of homeomorphisms of X(S)
onto X(S), which commute with σ, contains the
powers of σ, and many additional members as well.
In the case crd S = 2, Curtis, Hedlund, and Lyndon
have shown that every finite group is isomorphic
to some subgroup of A(S); also that A(S) contains
two elements of order two whose product is of
infinite order. A deeper analysis of the structure
of A(S) would be of interest.

Finally, O. S. Rothaus has obtained an interesting result concerning the existence of a cross
section for the mappings f_∞. A mapping φ of a
topological space X onto a topological space Y <u>has</u>
<u>a cross section</u> provided there exists a continuous
map Ψ of Y into X such that $\varphi(\Psi(y)) = y$ for all
y ∈ Y. His result is the following theorem:

9.2 THEOREM. Let $n \in I_2$, let $f \in F(S, n)$ with crd $S = 2$, and let f_∞ be onto. Then the following statements are equivalent:

    (1) f_∞ is open;

    (2) f_∞ has a cross section;

    (3) for each $x \in X(S)$ the members of $f_\infty^{-1}(x)$ are $(n - 1)$-separated;

    (4) f_∞ is an exactly μ-to-one map for some integer μ.

REFERENCES

1. Gottschalk, W. H., and Hedlund, G. A., Topological Dynamics, Am. Math. Soc. Colloq. Pub., 36 (1955).

TWO COMMUTING CONTINUOUS FUNCTIONS
FROM THE CLOSED UNIT INTERVAL ONTO
THE CLOSED UNIT INTERVAL WITHOUT
A COMMON FIXED POINT

John Philip Huneke

(Wesleyan University and
University of Minnesota)

The object of this paper is to define two
continuous Lipschitzian functions mapping the
closed unit interval onto itself which commute under
composition and which have no common fixed point.

DEFINITIONS.

   1.   Let s be the real number $3 + \sqrt{6}$.

   2.   For any real-valued function f defined on
a real set D, call f s-Lipschitzian provided that
$|f(x) - f(y)| \leq s \cdot |x - y|$ for all x, y in D.

   3.   For any real-valued function f defined
on a real set D, define the function f* by:
f*(x) = 1 - f(1 - x) for each x in D.

   4.   Define h_1 on $[0, 1/s]$ by $h_1(x) = sx$,
define h_2 on $[1/s, 2/s]$ by $h_2(x) = 2 - sx$, and

define h_3 on $[2/s, \; 3/s]$ by $h_3(x) = sx - 2$.

    5. Considering a function as a set of ordered pairs, define the function h: h $= h_1 \cup h_2 \cup h_3$.

    6. Let L denote the set of all functions $f:[0, \; 1] \to [0, \; 1]$ such that $h \subset f$ and f is s-Lipschitzian.

    7. Let $I_0 = [0, \; 3/s]$, $I_1 = [3/s, \; h_2^{*-1}(h_2^{-1}(0))]$ and $I_2 = [h_2^{*-1}(h_2^{-1}(0)), \; 1]$.

    8. Define T (to be a map from L to L) by: for each f in L,

$$T(f)(x) = h(x) \qquad \text{for each} \quad x \quad \text{in} \quad I_0$$

$$T(f)(x) = h_1^{*-1} f(h^*(x)) \qquad \text{for each} \quad x \quad \text{in} \quad I_1$$

and

$$T(f)(x) = h_2^{*-1} f(h*(x)) \qquad \text{for each} \quad x \quad \text{in} \quad I_2$$

LEMMA 1. $T(f)$ is a well-defined function for each f in L.

Proof. To see that $T(f)$ is unambiguously defined at $3/s$ and at $h_2^{*-1}(h_2^{-1}(0))$, observe that $T(f)(3/s)$ $= 1$ and that $T(f)(h_2^{*-1}(h_2^{-1}(h_2^{-1}(0)))) = h_1^{*-1}(0)$

$= 1 - 1/s = h_2^{*-1}(0)$ for each f in L.

LEMMA 2. $T(f)$ is s-Lipschitzian for each f in L.

Proof. Let f be in L and let x, y be in $[0, 1]$; we must show that $\left| T(f)(x) - T(f)(y) \right| \leq s \cdot \left| x - y \right|$. This is clear when x, y are in I_0 as h is s-Lipschitzian. If x, y are in I_i with $i = 1$ or 2, then

$$\left| T(f)(x) - T(f)(y) \right|$$
$$= \left| h_i^{*-1} f(h^*(x)) - h_i^{*-1} f(h^*(y)) \right|$$
$$= \frac{1}{s} \cdot \left| f(h^*(x)) - f(h^*(y)) \right| \leq \left| h^*(x) - h^*(y) \right|$$
$$\leq s \cdot \left| x - y \right|$$

Without loss of generality assume $x \leq y$. If x is in I_1 and y in I_2, then

$$\left| T(f)(x) - T(f)(y) \right|$$
$$= \left| h_1^{*-1} f(h*(x)) - h_2^{*-1} f(h^*(y)) \right|$$
$$= \left| h_1^{*-1} f(h*(x)) - h_1^{*-1}(0) + h_2^{*-1}(0) \right.$$
$$\left. - h_2^{*-1} f(h*(y)) \right|$$
$$= \frac{1}{s} \cdot \left| f(h^*(x)) - f(h^*(y)) \right| \leq s \cdot \left| x - y \right|$$

If x is in I_0 and y in I_2, then

$$\left| T(f)(x) - T(f)(y) \right|$$
$$\leq 1 < s \cdot \left| \frac{3}{s} - (1 - \frac{1}{s} - \frac{2^2}{s}) \right|$$
$$= s \cdot \left| \frac{3}{s} - h_2^{*-1}(h_2^{-1}(0)) \right| \leq s \cdot \left| x - y \right|$$

If x is in I_0 and y in I_1 and $T(f)(x) \leq T(f)(y)$, then

$$\left| T(f)(x) - T(f)(y) \right| \leq \left| T(f)(x) - 1 \right|$$
$$= \left| h(x) - h(\frac{3}{s}) \right| \leq s \cdot \left| x - \frac{3}{s} \right| \leq s \cdot \left| x - y \right|$$

If x is in I_0 and y in I_1 and $T(f)(x) \geq T(f)(y)$, then

$$\left| T(f)(x) - T(f)(y) \right| \leq \left| 1 - T(f)(y) \right|$$
$$= \left| h_1^{*-1}(1) - h_1^{*-1}f(h*(y)) \right|$$
$$= \frac{1}{s} \cdot \left| 1 - f(h*(y)) \right|$$
$$= \frac{1}{s} \cdot \left| f(\frac{3}{s}) - f(h^*(y)) \right| \leq \left| \frac{3}{s} - h^*(y) \right|$$
$$= \left| h^*(\frac{3}{s}) - h^*(y) \right| \leq s \cdot \left| \frac{3}{s} - y \right| \leq s \cdot \left| x - y \right|$$

All possible positions of x, y have been considered.

Lemmas 1 and 2 yield the following proposition:

PROPOSITION 1.   T maps L into L.

To find a function f which agrees with the right-hand side of the equations in Definition 8 above, Dàvid Boyd [1] suggested finding a fixed

point of the mapping T as follows: supply L with
the supremum norm metric.

PROPOSITION 2. T is a contraction (with respect
to the constant $1/s$) of the complete metric space
L.

Proof. Clearly L is a complete metric space with
respect to the supremum norm metric. For any f, g
in L,

$$
\sup_{x} \left| T(f)(x) - T(g)(x) \right|
$$
$$
= \sup_{\substack{x \\ i=1,2}} \left| h_i^{*-1} f(h^*(x)) - h_i^{*-1} g(h^*(x)) \right|
$$
$$
= \frac{1}{s} \cdot \sup_{x} \left| f(h^*(x)) - g(h^*(x)) \right|
$$
$$
= \frac{1}{s} \cdot \sup_{y} \left| f(y) - g(y) \right|
$$

COROLLARY 1. There exists a unique f in L such
that $T(f) = f$.

PROPOSITION 3. Let f be the member of L such that
$T(f) = f$; then f and f^* commute under composition.

Proof. If x is in I_i for $i = 1$ or 2, then

$$
f^*(f(x)) = f^*(h_i^{*-1} f(h^*(x))) = f(h^*(x))
$$

$$= f(f^*(x))$$

since f^* coincides with h^* or h_i^* wherever h^* or
h_i^* are defined. If x is in $[1 - 3/s, 3/s]$, then
$f^*(f(x)) = f(f^*(x))$ because $f^*(f|_{[1-3/s,3/s]})$
$= h^*(h_3|_{[1-3/s,3/s]})$ and $f(f^*|_{[1-3/s,3/s]})$
$= h(h_3^*|_{[1-3/s,3/s]})$, and each of these functions
are full functions (with range $[0, 1]$) with slopes
$\pm s^2$, which agree at $3/s$, and hence they coincide.
If x is in $[0, 1 - 3/s]$, then $(1 - x)$ is in
$[3/s, 1]$ and so

$$f^*(f(x)) = 1 - f(f^*(1 - x)) = 1 - f^*(f(1 - x))$$
$$= f(f^*(x))$$

Therefore f and f^* commute under composition.

PROPOSITION 4. Let f be the member of L such that
$T(f) = f$; then f and f^* have no common fixed point.

Proof. If x is in $\left[\frac{1}{2}, 1\right]$, then $f^*(x) = h^*(x)$, and
the only fixed points of h^* are the fixed points
of h_i^* for $i = 1, 2$, or 3. The fixed point of h_1^*
is 1, and $f(1)$ is in the domain of definition of
h_2^*, which does not contain 1. The fixed point of
h_2^* is in I_1, and f maps points in I_1 into the

domain of definition of h_1^*, which is a subset of
I_2 disjoint from I_1. The fixed point of h_3^* is $3/s$,
and $f(3/s) = 1 \neq 3/s$. Thus f and f^* have no common
fixed points in $\left[\frac{1}{2}, 1\right]$; and hence f^* and f have no
common fixed points in $\left[0, \frac{1}{2}\right]$ since $f(x) = x$
$= f^*(x)$ implies that $1 - f^*(1 - x) = x = 1 - f(1 - x)$,
or that $f^*(1 - x) = 1 - x = f(1 - x)$.

Corollary 1 and Propositions 3 and 4 establish
a pair of commuting continuous functions from the
closed unit interval to itself which have no common
fixed point. Several of the unanswered questions
which remain in this area follow; for these
questions, let f, g be continuous commuting functions
from the closed unit interval to itself.

QUESTION 1. Does there exist an integer n such
that f and g^n have a common fixed point?

A. J. Schwartz [3] answered Question 1
positively, provided that f is continuously
differentiable.

QUESTION 2. Is there a differentiability condition
on f (or on f and g) which forces f and go to have
a common fixed point?

Observe that the functions established above are Lipschitzian; it can also be determined that they are differentiable almost everywhere.

QUESTION 3. If f is piecewise linear, then does f and g have a common fixed point?

QUESTION 4. What is the minimum number S such that f and g S-Lipschitzian implies that f and g have a common fixed point?

Ralph DeMarr [2] showed that $S \geq 1 + \sqrt{2}$, and the above example shows that $S \leq 3 + \sqrt{6}$.

REFERENCES

1. Boyd, D., personal correspondence with author, May 1967.

2. DeMarr, R., A Common Fixed Point Theorem for Commuting Mappings, Am. Math. Monthly, 70 (1963), pp. 536-537.

3. Schwartz, A. J., Common Periodic Points of Commuting Mappings, Michigan Math. J., 12 (1965), pp. 353-355.

FUNCTIONS BEHAVING LIKE ALMOST
AUTOMORPHIC FUNCTIONS[1]

A. W. Knapp

(Cornell University)

Let G be a discrete group and let ℓ^∞ be the
Banach algebra of all bounded complex-valued
functions on G with the supremum norm. A G-subalgebra of ℓ^∞ is a left-invariant conjugate-closed
subalgebra of ℓ^∞ which contains the constants and
is closed under uniform limits.

This paper is divided into two parts, and the
connection between the parts is indicated only at
the end. The first part gives some simple properties of a certain G-subalgebra L of ℓ^∞. The
functions in L arise naturally from Ellis' work in

[1]Supported while at MIT by the Air Force Office of
Scientific Research, Office of Aerospace Research,
USAF, under AFOSR Grant No. 335-63. The results
in Section 2 were joint work with H. Mirkil.

[2] and the author's in [5], and they seem to be
closely related both to the almost automorphic
functions of Veech [7] and to the distal functions
of [6].

▢ The second part of the paper contains a
theorem and an application about disjointness in
the sense of Furstenberg [4], together with some
remarks about how this theorem might apply to L if
more were known about L.

1.   THE ALGEBRA L

The notation we use is essentially that in
[5].   The maximal ideal space of a G-algebra B is
denoted M(B); M(B) is a flow in a natural way, and
G maps canonically onto a dense orbit of M(B).   If
$\{g_n\}$ is a net in G such that $\lim f(gg_n)$ exists for
all f in ℓ^∞ and all g in G, then $\{g_n\}$ converges in
$M(\ell^\infty)$ to some α and we write $T_\alpha f(g) = \lim f(gg_n)$.
T_α is called a shift operator.   Conversely, if $\{g_n\}$
converges to some α in $M(\ell^\infty)$, then $\lim f(gg_n)$
exists and depends only on α.   Thus the shift
operator T_α depends only on α and not on the net
which defines it.   Right translations are examples

of shift operators. The set of shift operators is a semigroup under composition, and the compact Hausdorff topology it inherits from $M(\ell^\infty)$ is such that the map $T_\alpha \to T_\alpha T_\beta$ for fixed T_β is continuous.

A shift operator T_u is minimal if it lies in a minimal left ideal, and T_u is idempotent if $T_u T_u = T_u$. Define

$$L = \left\{ f \,\middle|\, T_u f = f \quad \text{for every minimal idempotent} \quad T_u \right\}$$

L is the intersection of all the algebras A which arise in [5], or it is the intersection of all maximal G-subalgebras of minimal functions in the sense of [5], or it is the intersection of all the algebras $A(u)$ in the notation of Ellis [2]. Although no maximal G-subalgebra of minimal functions need be invariant under right translation, L is right-invariant because a right translate of such a maximal subalgebra is another such subalgebra.

We recall that an f in ℓ^∞ is distal if the equality $T_\alpha T_\beta f = T_\alpha T_\gamma f$ implies $T_\beta f = T_\gamma f$. Distal functions are exactly those functions lying in algebras whose maximal ideal spaces are distal

flows. Almost automorphic functions are defined
as follows. If a net $\{g_n\}$ defines a shift
operator T_α, then it is easy to see that $\{g_n^{-1}\}$ does
define a shift operator, and we call this operator
$T_{\alpha-1}$. Call an f in ℓ^∞ almost automorphic if
$T_{\alpha-1}T_\alpha f = f$ for all T_α. Almost periodic functions
are both almost automorphic and distal, and an
almost automorphic distal function is almost
periodic. L contains all almost automorphic
functions and all distal functions.

PROPOSITION 1.1. If f is in ℓ^∞, f is in L if and
only if the equality $T_\alpha T_\beta f = T_\alpha f$ implies $T_\beta f = f$.

Proof. If the condition holds and T_u is idempotent, then the equality $T_u T_u f = T_u f$ implies
$T_u f = f$. Conversely, let f be in L and let $T_\alpha T_\beta f$
$= T_\alpha f$. By Corollary 3-5 of $[5]$, there is a minimal
idempotent T_v, say in the left ideal I, such that
$T_v T_\beta f = T_\beta f$. Since $T_\alpha T_v$ is in I, find by Lemma 2
of $[1]$ members T_δ and T_u of I with $T_u(T_\alpha T_v) = T_\alpha T_v$
and $T_\delta(T_\alpha T_v) = T_u$. Since $T_v T_u = T_v$, we obtain

$$T_\beta f = T_v T_\beta f = T_v T_u T_\beta f = T_v(T_\delta T_\alpha T_v)T_\beta f$$
$$= T_v T_\delta T_\alpha(T_\beta f) = T_v T_\delta T_\alpha f = T_v T_\delta T_\alpha T_v f$$

$$= T_v T_u f = T_v f = f$$

as required.

We wish to point out some similarities between the role of functions in L relative to distal functions and the role of almost automorphic functions relative to almost periodic functions. In [7] Veech proved, among other things, the following five facts about almost automorphic functions. In them, (1a) and (1b) follow easily from each other, and (2), (3), and (4) are corollaries of (1b).

(1a) If G is given the relative topology from the orbit Ge in the universal equicontinuous flow, then the almost automorphic functions are exactly the bounded continuous functions on G.

(1b) A G-subalgebra A consists entirely of almost automorphic functions if and only if M(A) is proximally equicontinuous and the fiber above e in the equicontinuous quotient has just one point in it.

(2) f is almost periodic if and only if $T_\alpha f$ is almost automorphic for all T_α.

(3)   The composition of an almost automorphic function followed by a bounded continuous function on its range is again almost automorphic.

(4)   A nontrivial G-subalgebra of almost automorphic functions contains nonconstant almost periodic functions.

PROPOSITION 1.2.   Let $\{T_\alpha\}$ be a set of shift operators, and let A be the G-subalgebra of all f in ℓ^∞ for which $T_\alpha f = f$ for all the given α's. Then any bounded continuous function on the orbit Ge of M(A) is a member of A.   Conversely, if B is a G-subalgebra of ℓ^∞ and A is the G-subalgebra of all bounded continuous functions on the orbit Ge of M(B), then there is a set $\{T_\alpha\}$ of shift operators such that A is all functions in ℓ^∞ for which $T_\alpha f$ = f for all the α's.

Proof.   Let the set of shift operators be given, let T_α be in the set and be defined by a net $\{g_n\}$, and let f be bounded and continuous on the orbit Ge of M(A).   Every continuous h on M(A) satisfies

$$\lim h(g_n) = T_\alpha h(e) = h(e)$$

and it follows that $g_n e$ converges to e in $M(A)$.
Then $gg_n e \to ge$ also, and hence

$$T_\alpha f(g) = \lim f(gg_n e) = f(ge) = f(g)$$

the middle equality holding by the continuity of
f on Ge. Thus $T_\alpha f = f$.

Conversely let B and A be given, let $\{T_\alpha\}$ be
the set of all shift operators such that $T_\alpha h = h$
for all h in B, and suppose f is a function in ℓ^∞
with $T_\alpha f = f$ for all these α's. We are to show f
is in A or that f is continuous on the orbit Ge
in $M(B)$. To see f is continuous at e in $M(B)$, let
$\{g_n e\}$ be a net converging to e in $M(B)$ and suppose,
by taking a subnet if necessary, that $\{g_n\}$ defines a
shift operator T_α. Since $g_n e \to e$ in $M(B)$, we have
$T_\alpha h = h$ for all h in B and consequently $T_\alpha f = f$.
That is,

$$\lim f(g_n e) = T_\alpha f(e) = f(e)$$

Since $\{g_n\}$ is arbitrary, f is continuous at e. To
obtain continuity at ge in $M(B)$, we observe that
the left translate f_g satisfies $T_\alpha f_g = f_g$ and hence
f_g is continuous at e. In other words f is continuous at ge.

PROPOSITION 1.3. L has the following properties:

(1') If G is given the relative topology
from the orbit Ge in the universal distal flow,
then every bounded continuous function on G is
in L. There is a set of shift operators $\{T_\alpha\}$
such that the bounded continuous functions on
G in this topology are those functions in ℓ^∞
with $T_\alpha f = f$ for these α's.

(2') f is distal if and only if $T_\alpha f$ is in
L for every shift operator T_α.

(3') The composition of a function in L
followed by a bounded continuous function on
its range is again in L.

Proof. (1') is a special case of Proposition 1.2.
(2') is immediate from the definition of L and
from the fact that an f in ℓ^∞ is distal if and
only if $T_u T_\alpha f = T_\alpha f$ for every T_α and every minimal
idempotent T_u. This fact is Theorem 3.7 of [6].
(3') is a consequence of Proposition 1.2 and the
fact that the composition of continuous functions
is continuous.

For an example, $\cos 2\pi n^2 \theta$ is a well-known
distal function on the integers and its range does

not include 0 if θ is irrational. Since signum is
continuous on the line with 0 deleted, signum
cos $2\pi n^2 \theta$ is in L.

One might conjecture as a converse to the
first half of (1') that every member of L is continuous on G in the relative topology from the
universal distal flow. But Furstenberg pointed
out that M(L) should be closed under isometric
extensions (see Proposition 1.4), whereas this
closure property is not apparent for the algebra
of bounded functions on G continuous in this
relative topology. A safer conjecture would be
that there is an analogue to property (4), namely
that any nontrivial G-subalgebra of L contains
nonconstant distal functions. The answer to this
question is not known.

PROPOSITION 1.4. If B is a G-subalgebra of L and
A is a G-subalgebra of ℓ^∞ for which M(A) is an
isometric extension (see [3]) of M(B), then A is
contained in L.

Proof. Let ρ exhibit the isometric extension,
let u be an idempotent in the Ellis semigroup of

M(A), and let π be the projection of M(A) onto
M(B). Then π(u) is idempotent on M(B) and must
satisfy $\pi(u)\pi(e) = \pi(e)$ since B $\subseteq$ L. That is, ue
and e are in the same fiber and ρ(ue, e) is defined.
Since ρ is G-invariant and continuous,

$$\rho(ue,\ e)\ =\ \rho(u^2e,\ ue)\ =\ \rho(ue,\ ue)\ =\ 0$$

Since ρ is a metric on each fiber, ue = e. This
condition on M(A) means that A $\subseteq$ L.

2. A DISJOINTNESS THEOREM

We say that two flows X and Y under G have a
common factor if for some flow Z with more than one
point there are homomorphisms of X and Y onto Z.
The flows X and Y are disjoint if the only closed
G-invariant subset of X x Y which projects onto
all of X and all of Y is X x Y itself. If X and
Y are both minimal, it is easy to see that X and Y
are disjoint if and only if X x Y is minimal. In
particular, this observation applies to maximal
ideal spaces of G-subalgebras of minimal functions,
since these flows are minimal. The maximal ideal
spaces of G-subalgebras A and B have no common

factor if and only if $T_\alpha(A) \cap T_\beta(B)$ = constants
for every T_α and T_β. If $M(A)$ and $M(B)$ are minimal,
they have no common factor provided $A \cap T_\beta(B)$ =
constants for every T_β.

Disjointness of X and Y implies that X and
Y have no common factor, and Furstenberg asked in
[4, p. 25] about the converse. The converse is
false in general, and we give an example which
both settles the question and illuminates the
relation between the two notions.

EXAMPLE. Let G be a compact topological group,
and restrict attention to G-subalgebras of continuous functions. The maximal ideal spaces of
such algebras are left coset spaces of G and are
in one-to-one correspondence with the closed subgroups of G. Let H_1 and H_2 be two closed subgroups. Then G/H_1 and G/H_2 have no common factor
if and only if $[gH_1g^{-1}H_2]$, the closed subgroup
generated by gH_1g^{-1} and H_2, is all of G for each
g in G. Also, G/H_1 and G/H_2 are disjoint if and
only if H_1H_2, the set of products of a member of
H_1 by a member of H_2, is all of G.

If H_1H_2 = G, then $gH_1g^{-1}H_2$ = G also. Thus

the inclusion $[H_1 H_2] \supseteq H_1 H_2$ shows that disjointness
implies no common factor. The reverse implication
is false. For instance, take G to be the symmetric
group on four letters, let H_1 be the powers of a
4-cycle, and let H_2 be the powers of a 3-cycle.
Then $[H_1 H_2] = G$. Since $gH_1 g^{-1}$ is again the powers
of a 4-cycle, we have $[gH_1 g^{-1} H_2] = G$ for every g.
Hence G/H_1 and G/H_2 have no common factor. On the
other hand, $H_1 H_2$ has at most twelve elements and
therefore cannot be all of G. Thus G/H_1 and G/H_2
are not disjoint.

When G is compact, the Ellis semigroup (or
group, actually) of G/H is $G/ \underset{g \in G}{\cup} gHg^{-1}$. Let
$E(G/H)$ be the Ellis group of G/H. Even if G/H_1
and G/H_2 are disjoint, it does not follow that
$E(G/H_1)$ and $E(G/H_2)$ are disjoint. For an example,
take G to be the symmetric group S_n with $n > 2$,
H_1 to be the alternating group A_n, and H_2 to be
the identity and a transposition. Then $H_1 H_2 = G$,
$E(G/H_1)$ is a two-element group $\{+1, -1\}$ and
$E(G/H_2) = S_n$. The closed orbit of (+1, e) in
$E(G/H_1)$ x $E(G/H_2)$ contains no points of the form
(-1, even permutation), and $E(G/H_1)$ and $E(G/H_2)$
are therefore not disjoint.

Return to the case of a G not necessarily compact. The theorem to follow comes from an idea suggested by the above example. We know that $[H_1 H_2] = H_1 H_2$ when either H_1 or H_2 is normal. Now H is normal exactly when the algebra of functions lifted to G from G/H is right-invariant, and this condition suggests that we assume one of the flows is closed under the operation of all shift operators.

We say a G-subalgebra A is shift-invariant if $T_\alpha f$ is in A whenever f is in A and T_α is a shift operator. For M(A), shift-invariance of A means that there is a transitive set of homeomorphisms of M(A) commuting with G.

THEOREM 2.1. Let A and B be G-subalgebras of ℓ^∞ and suppose B is distal and shift-invariant. If M(A) and M(B) have no common factors and if M(A) is minimal, then M(A) and M(B) are disjoint and, consequently, M(A) x M(B) is minimal.

Proof. M(A) x M(B) is semisimple because all distal functions occur in every maximal G-subalgebra of minimal functions on G. Thus we are to prove that the orbit of (e_A, e_B) in M(A) x M(B) is dense.

Let C be the least G-subalgebra of ℓ^∞ containing both A and B. It is well known that M(C) is canonically isomorphic with the closure of the orbit of (e_A, e_B) in M(A) x M(B) and that e_C is identified with (e_A, e_B). Let E(C) be the Ellis semigroup of C, let π_A be the projection of M(C) on M(A) or E(C) on E(A), and define π_B analogously.

Define X_e to be the set of points $\pi_A(r)e_A$ in M(A) as r ranges through all members of E(C) for which $\pi_B(r)$ is the identity on M(B). We prove that if $X_e = M(A)$, then $G(e_A, e_B)$ is dense in M(A) x M(B) and that if X_e is not M(A), then M(A) and M(B) have a common factor.

If $X_e = M(A)$, let (x, y) be given in M(A) x M(B) and let U be any neighborhood of y. Since Ge_B is dense in M(B), we can choose $y' = ge_B$ in U for some g in G. Then $g^{-1}x$ is in M(A), hence in X_e. Hence $g^{-1}x = \pi_A(r)e_A$ with $\pi_B(r)$ equal to the identity on M(B), and

$$gr(e_A, e_B) = (g\pi_A(r)e_A, g\pi_B(r)e_B)$$
$$= (gg^{-1}x, ge_B) = (x, y')$$

That is, the closure of $G(e_A, e_B)$ meets (x, U).

Since U is arbitrary, the orbit of (e_A, e_B) is dense.

Now suppose X_e is not all of $M(A)$. For t in $E(B)$, we define X_t to be all points $\pi_A(r)e_A$ in $M(A)$ as r ranges through the members of $E(C)$ with $\pi_B(r) = t$. Every element of $M(A)$ is in some X_t. We claim that either $X_s = X_t$ or $X_s \cap X_t$ is empty. Let x be in $X_s \cap X_t$ and let y be in X_s. It suffices to show y is in X_t. Let

$$x = \pi_A(r_s)e_A = \pi_A(r_t)e_A \quad \text{and} \quad y = \pi_A(p_s)e_A$$

with

$$\pi_B(r_s) = \pi_B(p_s) = s \quad \text{and} \quad \pi_B(r_t) = t$$

Since $M(C)$ is minimal, we can find members u and r_s^{-1} of $E(C)$ such that $u^2 = u$, $ue_C = e_C$, and $r_s^{-1}r_su = u$. Then

$$y = \pi_A(p_s)e_A = \pi_A(p_s)\pi_A(u)e_A$$
$$= \pi_A(p_sr_s^{-1})\pi_A(r_s)\pi_A(u)e_A = \pi_A(p_sr_s^{-1})\pi_A(r_s)e_A$$
$$= \pi_A(p_sr_s^{-1})\pi_A(r_t)e_A = \pi_A(p_sr_s^{-1}r_t)e_A$$

Since $E(B)$ is a group, $\pi_B(u)$ is the identity and $\pi_B(r_s^{-1}) = s^{-1}$. Thus $\pi_B(p_sr_s^{-1}r_t) = ss^{-1}t = t$, and y is in X_t.

   If x and y are in $M(A)$, define $x \sim y$ if x
and y are in the same X_t. We have just proved that
this is an equivalence relation. There exist in-
equivalent pairs since X_e is not all of $M(A)$. The
equivalence relation is group-invariant since
$gX_t = X_{gt}$. To see the relation is closed, let
x_n be in X_{t_n}, let $x_n \to x$, and let $t_n \to t$. We are
to show x is in X_t. For suitable r_n we have

$$x_n = \pi_A(r_n)e_A \quad \text{and} \quad \pi_B(r_n) = t_n$$

Passing to a subnet if necessary, we may assume r_n
converges, say to r. Then by continuity of π_A
and π_B we obtain

$$x = \pi_A(r)e_A \quad \text{and} \quad \pi_B(r) = t$$

That is, x is in X_t.

   Let $(Y, G) = \sigma_A(M(A), G)$ be the quotient.
(Y, G) is not the one-point flow. It is straightforward to verify that (Y, G) is a quotient flow of
$(E(B), G)$ under the definition $\sigma_B(t) = \sigma_A(X_t)$ for
t in $E(B)$. Since B is shift-invariant, $E(B)$ and
$M(B)$ are isomorphic flows. Therefore $M(A)$ and
$M(B)$ have Y as a common factor. The proof is

complete.

COROLLARY 2.2.   If C is a G-subalgebra of minimal
functions, then any directed system of G-subalgebras
of C with no nonconstant distal functions has an
upper bound.

Proof.   Let D be the algebra of all distal functions.
It is shift-invariant. By the theorem, M(D) is
disjoint from the maximal ideal space of each
member of the system. An easy calculation shows
that Furstenberg's definition (in [4]) of disjointness from a given flow is preserved under inverse
limits. The inverse limit of the system in
question is therefore disjoint from M(D) and can
have no common factors with it. That is, the
closure of the union of the given algebras has no
distal functions other than the constants, and the
proof is complete.

Let A and B be G-subalgebras of minimal
functions and distal functions, respectively. By
the theorem and Proposition II.1 of [4], M(A) and
M(B) are disjoint if A contains no nonconstant
distal functions. This fact may help settle the

question whether every nontrivial G-subalgebra of
L contains nonconstant distal functions. If the
answer to the question is yes, is the M(A) in the
statement above disjoint from M(L)?

REFERENCES

1. Ellis, R., A Semigroup Associated with a
Transformation Group, Trans. Am. Math. Soc., 94
(1960), pp. 272-281.

2. Ellis, R., Group-Like Extensions of Minimal
Sets, Trans. Am. Math. Soc., 127 (1967), pp. 125-
135.

3. Furstenberg, H., The Structure of Distal Flows,
Am. J. Math., 85 (1963), pp. 477-515.

4. Furstenberg, H., Disjointness in Ergodic
Theory, Minimal Sets, and a Problem in Diophantine
Approximation, Math. Systems Theory, 1 (1967), pp.
1-49.

5. Knapp, A. W., Decomposition Theorem for Bounded
Uniformly Continuous Functions on a Group, Am. J.
Math., 88 (1966), pp. 902-914.

6. Knapp, A. W., Distal Functions on Groups, Trans.
Am. Math. Soc., 128 (1967), pp. 1-40.

7. Veech, W. A., Almost Automorphic Functions on
Groups, Am. J. Math., 87 (1965), pp. 719-751.

EMBEDDING A HOMEOMORPHISM IN A FLOW

SUBJECT TO DIFFERENTIABILITY

CONDITIONS

Ping-Fun Lam

(Wesleyan University)

1. INTRODUCTION

Very often we find theorems on continuous
flows related to theorems on homeomorphisms. This
relation, however, is nonsymmetrical. For a continuous flow $(X, \mathbf{R}, \pi)$[1] the study of the homeomorphism π^1 often recovers information for the
flow; while for a homeomorphism f of X (onto X),
information can be obtained from the study of continuous flows only when f can be <u>embedded</u> in a
flow in the sense that a flow $(X, \mathbf{R}, \pi)$ can be
found such that $f = \pi^1$. It is the embeddability

---

[1]Notation and terminology coincides with that
of [5].

of f that we are interested in. This problem is
completely solved when X is a line or a circle [3,
4]; for spaces of higher dimension the problem seems
to be difficult, even for a plane [1]. Our problem
here is this embedding problem on the line taking
continuous differentiability into account. More
precisely, we study the embeddability of a homeomorphism $f \in C^1$ of the line in a flow $(X, \mathbf{R}, \pi)$
such that $\pi^t \in C^1$ for all $t \in \mathbf{R}$. The results to be
shown in the following are part of the results
published in the author's dissertation [9]. Due to
shortage of space, the proof of theorems will not
be given.

2. C^1-HOMEOMORPHISMS OF THE LINE WITH AT MOST ONE
   FIXED POINT

In the following X will generally be a
connected subset of the line. A flow $(X, \mathbf{R}, \pi)$
such that $\pi^t \in C^1$ for all $t \in \mathbf{R}$ will simply be
called a C^1-flow. If a homeomorphism f of X can
be embedded in a C^1-flow, it is necessary that
$f \in C^1$ and $f'(x) > 0$ for all $x \in X$. If, in addition, f does not have a fixed point in X, this

constitutes also a sufficient condition by a theorem of Bödewadt [2]; and for such an f there are uncountably many distinct C^1-flows in which f can be embedded. A proof for this, similar to that for the embedding problem without differentiability conditions, can be given.

If f has one fixed point in X, the condition $f \in C^1$ and $f'(x) > 0$ for all $x \in X$ is insufficient. An example of such a homeomorphism not embeddable in a C^1-flow was given in [9]. However, if f has exactly one fixed point, $f. \in C^2$, and $f'(x) > 0$ for all $x \in X$, then f can be embedded in a unique C^1- flow (see Szekeres [12]). In this direction Fort [4] has shown that if the condition $f \in C^1$ and f' is nonincreasing is substituted for $f \in C^2$, then the same conclusion holds. In fact, Fort proved a slightly stronger result than the uniqueness of such an embedding:

THEOREM (M. K. Fort, Jr. [4]). Let X = (a, b], $- \infty \ a < b < \infty$; $f \in C^1$, $f'(x) > 0$ for all $x \in X$ and f (x) > x for a < x < b. If f' is nonincreasing then there exists a unique C^1-flow in which f can be embedded. Moreover, if g is any continuously

differentiable homeomorphism of X into X which
commutes with f, then g is some transition homeomorphism of the flow.

In case $f'(b) \neq 1$, there is a more general
theorem concerning the uniqueness of C^1-embedding:

THEOREM (H. Michel [10]). Let X = (a, b],
$-\infty < a < b < \infty$; f a homeomorphism of X which
satisfies f (x) $\neq$ x for a < x < b, and $f'(b)$ exists
with $f'(b) \neq 1$. Then f can be embedded in at most
one flow, every transition homeomorphism of which
has a derivative at b.

We now extend the results of Szekeres and
Fort. We observe that in order to study the C^1-
embeddability of a homeomorphism f on a connected
subset of the line with exactly one fixed point,
it suffices to consider X = (a, b], $-\infty < a < b < \infty$.
In the remainder of this section we let X = (a, b],
and let f be a homeomorphism of X which satisfies
the following hypothesis.

HYPOTHESIS 2.1. $f \in C^1$, $f'(x) > 0$ for all $x \in X$,
f (x) > x for a < x < b.

Let f^n denote the nth iterate of f, n = 0,

$\pm$ 1, $\pm$ 2,... . For x $\in$ X we write x_n for $f^n(x)$, and (x_n') for $(f^n)'(x)$.

HYPOTHESIS 2.2. x_n'/y_n', n = 1, 2,..., converges for all (x, y) $\in$ (a, b) x (a, b), and uniformly on compact subsets.

HYPOTHESIS 2.3. For some a < c < b, x_n'/c_n', n = 1, 2,..., converges for all a < x < b, and uniformly on compact sets.

HYPOTHESIS 2.4. For any ϵ > 0 there is a < θ < b such that $\Sigma_{n=0}^{\infty} \left| f'(x_n) - f'(y_n) \right|$ < ϵ for all θ < x < b and for all x $\leq$ y $\leq$ f(x).

HYPOTHESIS 2.5. There exists a < u < b such that the restriction of f' on (u, b) is a function of bounded variation.

It can be shown that Hypothesis 2.5 implies 2.4, which in turn implies 2.3. Clearly Hypotheses 2.2 and 2.3 are equivalent.

The main theorem of this section is the following:

THEOREM 2.1. Let $X = (a, b]$ and let f be a homeomorphism which satisfies Hypothesis 2.1. If f also
satisfies Hypothesis 2.2 (such is the case if f
satisfies Hypothesis 2.5), f can be embedded in a
unique C^1-flow.

Consider the following two properties which a
function $g: X \to X$ may satisfy:

(α) $g'(b)$ exists and $g(x_o) \neq b$ for some $x_o \in X$.

(β) $g'(x)$ exists in (γ, b) for some $a < \gamma < b$,
    g' continuous at b and $g(x_o) \neq b$ for
    some $x_o \in X$.

The following theorem is an elaboration of the
uniqueness part of Theorem 2.1.

THEOREM 2.2. Let $X = (a, b]$ and f be a homeomorphism of X which satisfies Hypotheses 2.1 and
2.2. Let $(X, \mathbf{R}, \pi)$ be the unique C^1-flow in which
f is embedded. The following properties hold:

(a) If $f'(b) \neq 1$ and if $g : X \to X$ is any
function which commutes with f and which satisfies
(α), then

$$g = \pi^\gamma \quad \text{with} \quad r = \frac{\log g'(b)}{\log f'(b)}$$

(b)   If $f'(b) = 1$ and if $a < c < b$, then there exists a continuous function h on (a, b). If $g : X \to X$ is any function which commutes with f and which satisfies (β), then

$$g = \pi^S \qquad s = h\,(g(c))$$

The proof of Theorem 2.1 included the solving of the following Abel functional equation:

$$A(f(x)) = A(x) + 1 \qquad a < x < b \qquad\qquad (1)$$

where the unknown A is assumed to be a C^1 function with nonzero derivative defined on (a, b). The proof of Theorem 2.2 is easy once the explicit formula for A is established.

The next theorem is an easy consequence of Theorems 2.1 and 2.2.

THEOREM 2.3.   Let $X = (a, b]$. Let M denote the set of all homeomorphisms f of X which satisfy Hypotheses 2.1 and 2.2. Let $G(f)$ denote the group of transition homeomorphisms of the unique C^1-flow in which f is embedded. Let I be the identity map of X. Then

(a) $M \cup \{I\} = \underset{f \in M}{\cup}\, G(f)$

(b)   For f, g $\in$ M, then f$\circ$g = g$\circ$f if and
only if G(f) = G(g)

(c)   For f, g $\in$ M, then G(f) $\cap$ G(g) = $\{I\}$
or G(f) = G(g)

(d)   For f, g, h $\in$ M, if f$\circ$g = g$\circ$f, g$\circ$h
= h$\circ$g then f$\circ$h = h$\circ$f

This sums up some interesting properties of
homeomorphisms which satisfy Hypotheses 2.1 and 2.2.

3. C^1-HOMEOMORPHISMS OF THE LINE WITH FIXED POINTS

Let X be a connected subset of the line.   In
this section we are exclusively interested in homeomorphisms f of X which satisfy the following
hypotheses:

HYPOTHESIS 3.1. $f \in C^1$, $f'(x) > 0$ for all $x \in X$.

HYPOTHESIS 3.2. F_f, the set of fixed points of f,
is nonempty.

HYPOTHESIS 3.3.   For every $x \in F_f$ there is a
neighborhood U_x in which f' is a function of bounded
variation.   Such is the case if X is a finite closed

interval, $f \in C^2$ and $f'(x) > 0$ for all $x \in X$.

THEOREM 3.1. Let $X \subset \mathbf{R}$ be connected. Let f be a homeomorphism of X which satisfies Hypotheses 3.1, 3.2, and 3.3. Let T_1, T_2,... be the component intervals of $X - F_f$, the set of nonfixed points. A necessary and sufficient condition for f to be embeddable in a C^1-flow is that the restrictions of f to all $\overline{T}_i \cap X$, $i = 1, 2,...$, have such a property.

It follows from Theorems 2.1 and 3.1 that if the embedding in Theorem 3.1 exists, then it is unique. Theorem 3.1 reduces the C^1-embedding problem of f to that of the restriction of f to $\overline{T}_i \cap X$. The restrictions are homeomorphisms on (possibly infinite) half-closed intervals with one fixed point, or homeomorphisms of a finite closed interval with two fixed points. The former case has already been discussed in Section 2. It remains to consider $X = [a, b]$, $-\infty < a < b < \infty$, and the following hypothesis.

HYPOTHESIS 3.4. $f(x) > x$ for $a < x < b$. (If $f(x) < x$ for all $a < x < b$ we consider f^{-1}.)

THEOREM 3.2. Let $X = [a, b]$, $-\infty < a < b < \infty$. Let
f be a homeomorphism of X which satisfies Hypotheses
3.1, 3.3., and 3.4. A necessary and sufficient
condition for f to be embeddable in a C^1-flow is
that the following equation is satisfied for some
(then all) c, $a < c < b$,

$$\lim_{n \to \infty} \frac{x_n'(x_{-n} - a)}{c_n'(c_{-n} - a)} = \lim_{n \to \infty} \frac{x_{-n}'(x_n - b)}{c_{-n}'(c_n - b)},$$

$$a < x < b$$

(2)

In case $f'(a) \neq 1$ and $f'(b) \neq 1$, Eq. (2) can
be simplified:

THEOREM 3.3. Let $X = [a, b]$, $-\infty < a < b < \infty$. Let
f be a homeomorphism of X which satisfies Hypotheses
3.1, 3.3, and 3.4. Suppose $f'(a) \neq 1$ and $f'(b)$
$\neq 1$. A necessary and sufficient condition for f
to be embeddable in a C^1-flow is that the following
equation is satisfied for some (then all) c,
$a < c < b$,

$$\log f'(b) \cdot \log \left(\lim_{n \to \infty} \frac{x_{-n} - a}{c_{-n} - a}\right)$$

(3)

$$= \log f'(a) \cdot \log \left(\lim_{n \to \infty} \frac{x_n - b}{c_n - b}\right), \quad a < x < b$$

EXAMPLE 1. Let $X = [0, 1]$ and let $F(x)$

$$= \frac{\gamma x}{(r - 1)x + 1}, \quad r > 0, \quad r \neq 1. \quad \text{Then}$$

$$\lim_{n \to \infty} \frac{x_{-n} - 0}{c_{-n} - 0} = \frac{x(1 - c)}{c(1 - x)}$$

$$0 < c, \ x < 1$$

$$\lim_{n \to \infty} \frac{x_n - 1}{c_n - 1} = \frac{c(1 - x)}{x(1 - c)}$$

$F'(0) = \gamma$, $F'(1) = \frac{1}{r}$. Hence Eq. (3) holds. In this case it is also easy to see by inspection that the flow $(X, \mathbf{R}, \pi)$ in which F is embedded is given by

$$\pi^t(x) = \frac{\gamma^t x}{(\gamma^t - 1)x + 1} \quad x \in X \quad t \in \mathbf{R}$$

Let g be a homeomorphism of $X = [0, 1]$ which is a C^1-conjugate of a homeomorphism f, that is, there exists a homeomorphism ψ of X onto X such that ψ, $\psi^{-1} \in C^1$ and such that $g = \psi^{-1} \circ f \circ \psi$. If f can be embedded in a C^1-flow, then so can g. Any C^1-conjugate g of F in the example can therefore be

embedded in a C^1-flow. However, since we must
have $g'(0) \ F'(1) = F'(0) \ g'(1)$, we have $g'(0)$
$= 1/g'(1)$. By this restriction and by the next
example, we see that the set of C^1-conjugates of
the F's in Example 1 are far from exhausting the
set of all homeomorphisms of X without interior
fixed points which can be embedded in a C^1-flow.

EXAMPLE 2. Let $0 < a < 1 < \beta$ and $\tau = 1 - \log a/\log \beta$.
There exists one and only one homeomorphism f of
$[0, 1]$ which satisfies

   (a) $f(x) = ax$ $0 \le x \le 1/\tau a$

   (b) $f(x) = 1 + \beta(x - 1)$ $1/\tau \le x \le 1$

   (c) f has no interior fixed points.

   (d) f can be embedded in a C^1-flow.

   The proof of Example 2 makes use of Theorem
3.3.

   Another application of Theorem 3.1 is to study
the C^1-embeddability of analytic functions. Making
use of the fact that analytic functions only have
isolated fixed points, we have:

THEOREM 3.4. Let $X \subset \mathbf{R}$ be connected. Let f be an
analytic homeomorphism of X which satisfies:

(a) $f' > 0$; (b) f is not the identity map, and

(c) F_f, the set of fixed points of f, is nonempty.

Let g be an analytic homeomorphism of X which has

the same properties and which commutes with f.

Then f can be embedded in a C^1-flow if and only if

g has this property.

When a homeomorphism has one or no fixed point,

we have shown that sufficient degree of smoothness

of f has something to do with the C^1-embeddability

of f. Such is not the case when f admits more than

one fixed point.

Let $X = [a, b]$, $-\infty < a < b < \infty$. Let $C_{(k)}$

$(2 \leq k \leq \infty)$ be the set of all C^k-homeomorphisms f

of X such that f' is positive. For an integer n,

$2 \leq n \leq k$, the c^n-topology on $C_{(k)}$ is the topology

induced by the metric.

$$d_n(f, g) = \max_{i = 0, 1, \ldots, n} \left\{ \sup_{x \in X} |f^{(i)}(x) - g^{(i)}(x)| \right\}$$

The C^∞-topology on $C_{(\infty)}$ is defined to be the (least)

topology which is generated by all C^n-topology,

$2 \leq n \leq \infty$. If $m \leq n$, then the C^n-topology, is

stronger than the C^m-topology. The following

theorem shows, roughly, that <u>most</u> elements in $C_{(k)}$

$(2 \le k \le \infty)$ cannot be embedded in a C^1-flow.

THEOREM 3.5.   Let $X = [a, b]$, $-\infty < a < b < \infty$.   In $C_{(k)}$ $(2 \le k \le \infty)$ there exists a subset $\cup_k$ which is open with respect to the C^2-topology and which is dense with respect to the C^k-topology such that no member of $\cup_k$ can be embedded in a C^1-flow.

REFERENCES

1.   Andrea, S., On Homeomorphisms of the Plane, and Their Embedding in Flows, Bull. Am. Math. Soc., 71 (1965), pp. 381-383.

2.   Bödewadt, U. T., Zur Iterationreeller Funktionen, Math. Z., 49 (1944), pp. 497-516.

3.   Foland, N., and Utz, W., The Embedding of Discrete Flows in Continuous Flows, Ergodic Theory, New York, 1963, pp. 121-134.

4.   Fort, Jr., M. K., The Embedding of Homeomorphisms in Flows, Proc. Am. Math. Soc., 6 (1955), pp. 960-967.

5.   Gottschalk, W., and Hedlund, G., Topological Dynamics, Am. Math. Soc. Colloq. Publ. (1955).

6.   Hadamard, J., Two Works on Iteration and

Related Questions, Bull. Am. Math. Soc., 50 (1944), pp. 67-75.

7. Kuczma, M., A Remark on Commutable Functions and Continuous Iterations, Proc. Am. Math. Soc., 13 (1962), pp. 847-850.

8. Kuczma, M., On the Schroder Equation, Rozprawy Mat., 34 (1963), pp. 1-50.

9. Lam, P. F., The Problem of Embedding a Homeomorphism in a Continuous Flow Subject to Differentiability Conditions, dissertation, Yale University, 1967.

10. Michel, H., Untersuchungen über stetige, monotone Iterationsgruppen reeller Funktionen ohne Differenzierbarkeitsvoraussetzungen, Publ. Math. Debrecen, 9 (1962), pp. 13-46.

11. Sternberg, S., Local C^n Homeomorphisms of the Real Line, Duke Math. J., 24 (1957), pp. 97-102.

12. Szekeres, G., Regular Iteration of Real and Complex Functions, Acta Math., 100 (1958), pp. 203-258.

VIRTUAL GROUPS

George W. Mackey

(Harvard University)

Much of what I shall have to say today will
be found explained in greater detail in items [6]
and [7] of the bibliography. It seems to require
about three hours to give a properly motivated
account of the notion of virtual group. Since I
have only one hour I shall concentrate on talking
about the notion and about why I think it is a
useful one. However, I shall take advantage of
this opportunity to describe an extension of the
development in [7], which occurred to me after [7]
was published, as well as an example which I have
known about for many years but which has never
been published.

Let me begin by describing the context in
which we shall develop the notion of virtual group.

Of course we shall be talking about the system
consisting of a space S and a homomorphism of a
group G into the group of all one-to-one transformations of S into itself. However, we shall be
dealing with systems S, G whose further structure
is measure theoretic rather than topological, and
I shall introduce the measure theory in a slightly
unorthodox fashion. To be specific, we shall
assume that S is what I have elsewhere [4] called
a "standard Borel space," that G is a separable
locally compact topological group, that the mapping
s, x $\longrightarrow$ sx is a Borel function from S x G to S,
and that we are given a "measure class" C in S
which is invariant under the action of G.

We add a few paragraphs in explanation of the
less familiar of these definitions. A Borel space
is just a set together with a σ-field of subsets
called Borel sets. The Borel spaces of greatest
interest are those obtained from topological spaces
by distinguishing the σ-field generated by the
open and closed sets, that is, the classical Borel
sets. One may develop a theory of Borel spaces
which in many respects is analogous to that of
topological spaces. In particular, one may speak

of subspaces, product spaces, subspaces, and so on.
The analogue of a continuous function is a "Borel
function"; that is, a mapping ϕ from the Borel space
S_1 to the Borel space S_2 such that $\varphi^{-1}(E)$ is a
Borel set in S_1 whenever E is a Borel set in S_2.
The analogue of a homeomorphism is a Borel isomorphism; that is, a one-to-one function from S_1
into S_2 such that both φ and φ^{-1} are Borel functions.

One important respect in which the theory of
Borel spaces differs from the theory of topological
spaces lies in the fact that barring pathology, the
interesting Borel spaces are almost all mutually
isomorphic. Specifically, a result in [3] may be
reformulated to read as follows. Let S_1 and S_2 be
Borel subsets of separable complete metric spaces
M_1 and M_2. Then S_1 and S_2 are isomorphic as Borel
spaces if and only if S_1, S_2 have the same cardinal
number. Moreover, this cardinal number must either
be finite, or $\aleph_o$. With this in mind, we define
a standard Borel space to be a Borel space which is
isomorphic to a Borel subset of a separable complete
metric space.

Let S and G be as above and let μ be a measure
in S; that is, a function from Borel sets to the

nonnegative real numbers and ∞ which is countably
additive and such that S is a sum of countably many
sets of finite measure. For each x ∈ G let $\mu_x(E)$
= $\mu(Ex)$. Then μ_x is also a measure. If $\mu = \mu_x$
for all x we say that μ is <u>invariant</u>, while if μ
and μ_x have the same sets of measure zero for all
x we say that μ is <u>quasi-invariant</u>. Let us say
that two measures belong to the same <u>class</u> if they
have the same sets of measure zero and let C_μ
denote the set of all measures in the same class
as μ. By a <u>measure class</u> we shall mean a set of
measures of the form C_μ. If C is a measure class
then Cx is the set of all μ_x with $\mu \in$ C. Clearly,
Cx is also a measure class and Cx = C if and only
if some (and here every) member of C is quasi-
invariant. Thus, a measure class is <u>invariant</u>
in the sense that Cx = C for all x if and only if
it is the class of a quasi-invariant measure.

As justification for generalizing from invariant measures to invariant measure classes we
point out the following. First of all if H is a
closed subgroup of the separable locally compact
group G, and S^H is the set of all right H cosets
Hx, then we may make G act on S^H by setting (Hx)y

= Hxy. S^H has a natural Borel structure (inherited

from G via x ——►Hx) which is such that the system

S, G satisfies the conditions laid down above.

Indeed, to within the obvious equivalence, it is

the most general example which is <u>transitive</u> in

the sense that every orbit is the whole space. Now

S^H may or may not admit an invariant measure, but

it always admits a <u>unique</u> invariant measure class.

Secondly, suppose that S is the standard Borel

space underlying a C manifold and that for each

x ∈ G x, s——► sx is a diffeomorphism. Then S

admits a canonical measure class which is neces-

sarily invariant, but this class need not contain

an invariant measure. This canonical class is, of

course, the unique class which coincides in each

coordinatizable neighborhood with the Lebesgue

measure class associated with a coordinatization.

The latter is, of course, independent of the co-

ordinatization chosen and mild conditions on the

global behavior of S are sufficient to ensure the

existence of a measure class on S having the indi-

cated local behavior.

These preliminaries attended to, let us turn

our attention to the analysis of the systems S, G,

C defined above. In obvious generalization of the
classical case (in which C is replaced by an invariant measure) we say that C is ergodic or that
the action of G on S is ergodic with respect to C
if it is impossible to find a Borel subset E of S
having the following properties: (1) Ex = E for
all x $\in$ G; (2) E is not a measure zero with
respect to C; (3) S - E is not of measure zero with
respect to C.

Extending a classical theorem of von Neumann
one can prove that an arbitrary system S, G, C may
be decomposed in an essentially unique manner into
a direct sum or "direct integral" of systems S^λ,
G, C^λ in such a fashion that each system S^λ, G, C^λ
is ergodic. In this way one can, to a large extent,
reduce the analysis of general systems S, G, C to
a study of the ergodic case. This case can be
further subdivided as follows. Consider the orbits
of the action of G on S. It follows from the
definition of ergodicity that at most one of these
can be of positive measure, and that the complement
of an orbit of positive measure must be of measure
zero. Thus, either (a) every orbit is of measure
zero, or (b) one can discard an invariant set of

measure zero and obtain an action which is trivally
ergodic in the sense that there is only one orbit;
that is, the action is transitive. In the first
case, we shall say that the action is properly
ergodic, and in the second, that it is essentially
transitive (we used the term "strictly ergodic" in
[7], but this term is already in use to describe a
rather different concept). Since we are not interested in distinguishing systems which differ from
one another by an invariant set of measure zero,
we are reduced to studying transitive systems and
properly ergodic systems.

Now we have already remarked that the transitive systems are just the systems S^H, G, C, where
H is a closed subgroup of G, S^H is the space of all
right H cosets, and C is the unique invariant
measure class. To obtain H we simply choose a
point $s_0 \in S$ and let H be the subgroup of all
$x \in G$ such that $s_0 x = s_0$. It turns out that this
subgroup is necessarily closed in spite of the fact
that s, x $\longrightarrow$ sx is only assumed to be a Borel
function. Of course, H depends upon the choice of
s_0, but it is easy to see that changing s_0 simply
replaces H by one of its conjugates yHy^{-1}. Con-

versely, if H_1 and H_2 are conjugate, there is a
Borel isomorphism ϕ of S^{H_1} on S^{H_2} such that $\varphi(sx)$
$= \varphi(s)x$ for all s in S^{H_1} and all x in G. Thus,
studying the possible transitive actions of G is
equivalent to studying the possible conjugacy classes
of closed subgroups of G. While this problem can be
quite difficult there are many interesting groups
for which S is trivial and many others for which S
can be completely solved. For example, if G is the
additive group of the real line, the most general
possible H (other than G itself) is the set of all
integer multiples of λ where λ is a fixed nonnegative real number.

The position for properly ergodic actions is
completely different. Compact groups do not have
properly ergodic actions and the "simplest" separable locally compact group which is not compact
is the additive group of the integers. Even for
this group one has nothing approaching a complete
classification of all possible properly ergodic
actions. One has only a fairly extensive collection
of examples and a few invariants for distinguishing
one example from another.

A "virtual group" is a rather complicated
mathematical object which shows promise of being

useful in studying the problem of classifying the properly ergodic actions. This object plays the role for a properly ergodic action of G played by the group H in the transitive action of G on the coset space S^H = G/H. Indeed, it can be shown that an ergodic action of G determines and is determined by a pair consisting of a "virtual group" and an "injection" of this "virtual group" into G. Moreover, "virtual groups" have properties closely analogous to those of groups. It thus appears that the analogy between transitive and properly ergodic actions is much closer than at first appears to be the case. In particular, one can think of the family of all properly ergodic actions of a given group G as having a structure similar to that of the family of all conjugacy classes of subgroups of G. As we have already indicated, we shall not attempt to give a formal definition of virtual group at this time. The reader will find a carefully motivated one in [7]. However, it may be useful to point out one thing that a virtual group is not. If G acts in a properly ergodic fashion on S, C, one can consider for each s ∈ S the subgroup H_s of all x in G for which sx = s. The H_s

will be conjugate for all s in a given orbit and
we thus obtain a mapping from orbits into conjugacy
classes of subgroups of G. One might at first
suppose that this mapping would serve as a substitute for the H of the transitive case. That this
is false can be seen from the fact that, in all
properly ergodic actions of the additive group of
the integers, the subgroup H_s reduces to the identity for almost all s.

Now let me be more specific about some of the
ways in which the introduction of the notion of
"virtual group" is or can be useful in studying
the problem of classifying ergodic actions. First
of all it breaks the problem into two parts and one
of these parts does not involve the group G. One
part is the problem of classifying the virtual
groups, the other is that of classifying the different ways of "injecting" a given "virtual group"
into a given group G. To the extent that a given
"virtual group" admits "injections", into different
groups G, one obtains significant relationships
between properly ergodic actions of different
groups.

Secondly, the "virtual group" notion suggests

new invariants for ergodic actions. As we shall
see below it makes sense to talk about the "homomorphisms" of virtual groups into groups, and about
the "kernels" and "ranges" of such "homomorphisms."
In particular, for each finite or compact group F
and each properly ergodic action of G, one has the
following definite "yes or no" question. Does
there exist a "homomorphism" of the "virtual subgroup" of G defining the action whose "range" is
all of F? There are concrete examples in which
questions of this type can be answered, but by no
means trivially. In somewhat the same way it is
possible to extend the theory of group representations to "virtual groups" and then pose such "yes
or no" questions as: Does the "virtual group"
underlying a given properly ergodic action admit
"irreducible unitary representations" of a given
order? Does it admit an "irreducible unitary
representation" whose tensor product with itself
has this or that kind of decomposition into irre-
ducibles? And so on, and so on.

Thirdly, the "virtual group" concept turns
out to be useful in explaining certain familiar
constructions in ergodic theory in a unified way

and suggesting generalizations of them. For
example, as already remarked, it turns out to be
possible to define "homomorphisms" of "virtual subgroups" into groups and to consider the "kernels"
and "ranges" of such homomorphisms. These "kernels"
and "ranges" are themselves virtual subgroups, and
hence define ergodic actions. The well-known "flow
built under a function" construction of an ergodic
action of the real line turns out to be the range
of such a "homomorphism," and the skew products of
Anzai [2] turn out to be "kernels." We shall give
details below.

We remark finally that via the virtual group
notion one achieves a fairly thoroughgoing unifi-
cation of ergodic theory with the theory of unitary
group representations in which "virtual subgroups"
act like subgroups, and the spectrum of an ergodic
action is a special case of an "induced representation." In fact the author was led to the notion
of virtual subgroup by studying what happened in a
branch of the theory of group representations when
certain transitive actions were (of necessity)
replaced by properly ergodic ones (see [5, No. 7]).

It is time to proceed to somewhat more detailed

considerations. Let G_1 and G_2 be separable locally compact groups and let C be an invariant measure class in the standard Borel G-space S. Let us define a (one) cocycle from S, G_1, C to G_2 as a Borel function from S x G_1 to G_2, which satisfies the identities,

$$\pi(s, e) = e$$
$$\pi(s, x_1 x_2) = \pi(s, x_1)\pi(sx_1, x_2)$$

(*)

for all $s \in S$, x_1, $x_2 \in G_1$ x G_1. Further, let us say that the two cocycles π_1 and π_2 are cohomologous if there exists a Borel function a from S to G_2 such that

$$\pi_2(s, x) = a(s)\pi_1(s, x)a(sx)^{-1}$$

(**)

We note that if π_1 is a cocycle and a is any Borel function, then the function π_2 defined by (**) is necessarily a cocycle. Now suppose that C is ergodic with respect to the G_1 action so that we think of the action as defined by a "virtual sub-group" of G_1. Considerations developed at length in [7] then suggest that a "homomorphism" of this "virtual subgroup into G_2 be defined to be a cohomology class[1] of (one) cocycles from S, G_1, C

to G_2. The reader will find it easy to verify
that when $S = G_1/H$, these cohomology classes
correspond one-to-one in a natural way to the
conjugacy classes of continuous homomorphisms of H
into G_2.

Let π be a (one) cocycle from $S \times G_1$ to G_2.
We may make $S_1 \times G_2$ into a $(G_1 \times G_2)$-space by
setting

$$(s, y)(x, z) = sx, z^{-1}y\,\pi(s, x)$$

By restriction to $e \times G_2$ this $(G_1 \times G_2)$-space may
be considered as a G_2-space, and it is clear that
the G_2 action maps each $G_1 \times e$ orbit into another.
Suppose that the space $\widetilde{S}$ of all $G_1 \times e$ orbits is a
standard Borel space. Then $\widetilde{S}$ will be a standard
Borel G_2-space. Moreover, if C_{G_2} is the Haar
measure class in G_2, then $C \times C_{G_2}$ will define an
invariant measure class $\widetilde{C}$ in $\widetilde{S}$ which will be

---

[1]In order to avoid distracting technical compli-
cations we are oversimplifying here and throughout
the paper. Actually, we should identify cocycles
which are almost everywhere equal and permit the
cocycle identity to fail on suitable null sets.
See [6] for a correct formulation. At some points
our invariant measure class is only relevant if we
make these identifications.

ergodic if C is. Thus π defines an ergodic action
of G_2 and this action (up to the usual equivalence)
depends only on the cohomology class of π. In the
special case in which $S = G_1/H$ so that π is defined
by a homomorphism ϕ of H into G_2, it can be shown
that $\tilde{S}$ is a standard Borel space if and only if
$\phi(H)$ is closed and that the ergodic action of G_2
defined by ϕ is just the transitive action defined
by the closed subgroup $\phi(H)$. Thus, in the general
case we think of the virtual subgroup defined by
the resulting ergodic action of G_2 as being the
range of the homomorphism defined by the cocycle π.

The construction fails if $\tilde{S}$ is not a standard
Borel space but can be replaced by the following
modification. Instead of considering the G_1 x e
orbits, consider the decomposition of the G_1 x e
action into ergodic parts. The technical details
are more complicated but it can be shown that we
always obtain a standard Borel G_2-space and an
ergodic invariant measure class. In the special
case in which $S = G_1/H$ so that π is defined by a
homomorphism φ as above, it can be shown that the
ergodic G_2 action is transitive and is that defined
by the closure of $\varphi(H)$. More generally then, we think

of our ergodic action of G_2 as defining a virtual
subgroup of G_2 which is the closure of the range of
the homomorphism defined by π.

As an example consider the special case in
which $G_1 = Z$, the group of all integers under addition. In this special case the cocycles (but of
course not the corresponding cohomology classes)
correspond one-to-one to the Borel functions from
S_1 to G_2. Indeed

$$\pi(s, n) = \pi(s, n - 1 + 1)$$
$$= \pi(s, n - 1)\pi(s)(n - 1), 1)$$

and by induction π is uniquely determined for all
positive n by $\pi(s, 1)$. Also

$$\pi(s, 0) = 1 = \pi(s, -n + n)$$
$$= \pi(s, -n)\pi((s)(-n), n)$$

so that π is also uniquely determined for all
negative n by $\pi(s, 1)$. A further computation
shows that (s, 1) may be taken to be an arbitrary
Borel function from S_1 to G_2. It follows that we
have a method for constructing an ergodic action of
an arbitrary separable locally compact group G_2
whenever we are given an ergodic action of the

integers on a space S_1 and a Borel function from S_1
to G_2. In the special case in which G_2 is the
additive group of the real line and our Borel
function takes on only positive values, it can be
shown that our construction reduces to the classical
construction of a "flow built under a function."
Thus the notion of virtual subgroup has led us in
a natural way to a far-reaching generalization of
this construction. In view of the results of
Ambrose about the universality of flows built under
functions [1] one can hope that a fairly broad sub-
class of the ergodic actions of general groups may
be obtained by our construction.

In a similar fashion we may construct new
ergodic actions out of old by exploiting the
concept of the kernel of a homomorphism. However,
there are difficulties except when G_2 is compact,
and we shall restrict ourselves to this case. Let
π then be a cocycle from $S_1 \times G_1$ to the compact
group G_2 and consider the ergodic action of G_2
defined by the range of the corresponding homomorphism. Since G_2 is compact this action is
essentially transitive and hence is of the form
G_2/H, where H is a closed subgroup of G_2. It can

be shown that π is cohomologous to a cocycle π'

having values in H and that if we replace π, G_2 by

π', H, then the action of G_1 x e on S_1 x H is

ergodic. We call the virtual subgroup of G_1 defined

by this ergodic action the kernel of the homo-

morphism defined by π and π'. We do so because

when S_1 is a transitive G_1-space, so that π is

defined by an honest homomorphism φ, then the

transitive action of G_1 defined by the kernel of ρ

coincides with that provided by the above con-

struction.

When G_1 is the group of all integers under

addition, then π is defined by a Borel function g

from S_1 to G_2. In the very special case in which

G_2 is the multiplicative group of all complex

numbers of modulus unity, $S = G_2$, and s $\longrightarrow$ sn is

rotating through n times an irrational angle β, we

obtain what Anzai [2] calls the skew product of G_2

and β. Thus, in the notion of the kernel of a

homomorphism, we have a considerable generalization

of this construction of Anzai.

As mentioned above one of the "yes or no"

questions one can ask about virtual subgroups is

whether or not they admit homomorphisms onto various

particular finite (or compact) groups. We can now be more definite. Given S_1, C_1, G_1 and given a compact group G_2, the question is as to whether there exists a cocycle π from $S_1 \times G_1$ to G_2 which is not cohomologous to a cocycle having values in a proper subgroup of G_2. We show next[2] that this question has a positive answer in the special case in which S_1 is the unit circle $|z| = 1$, G_1 is the group of integers, $zn = ze^{in\pi a}$ for some irrational a, and G_2 is a certain noncommutative group of order 8. This will have the startling consequence that a virtual subgroup of a commutative group can have a noncommutative homomorphic image and admits irreducible two-dimensional unitary representations.

Let G_2 be the group of order 8 generated by the quaternionic units 1, i, j, k. We recall that $i^2 = j^2 = k^2 = -1$, $ij = k$, $jk = i$, $ki = j$, $ji = -ij$, $jk = -kj$, $ik = -ki$, and that ± 1 commutes with everything. Let M be the subset of all $z \in S_1$ with z in

---

[2]The argument which follows is a simplification and adaptation of one appearing in a twenty-year-old unpublished manuscript of the author. This older argument owes much to the collaboration of A. M. Gleason who provided the author with a key example.

the right half-plane and let π be the unique cocycle from $S_1 \times G_1$ to G_2 such that $\pi(s, 1) = j$ if
$s \in M$ and $\pi(s, 1) = k$ if $s \in S_1 - M$. We shall show
that π is not cohomologous to a cocycle taking
values in any proper subgroup of G_2. Let H be a
proper subgroup of G_2 and suppose that π is
cohomologous to π_1 where π_1 takes it values in H.
If $H \neq \{e\}$, it contains -1. Hence H is normal.
Moreover, j and k generate G_2. Hence there exists
a homomorphism ψ of G_2 on the two-element group
Z_2 which takes H into the identity but does not
take both i and j into the identity. Let π^0
$= \psi \circ \pi$. Then π^0 is a cocycle from $S_1 \times G_1$ to Z_2.
If π is cohomologous to a cocycle π_1 with values
in H, then $\pi_1(s, x) = a(s)\pi(s, x)a(sx)^{-1}$ for all x
and s and some Borel function a from S_1 to G_2.
Hence

$$\psi \circ \pi_1(s, x) = (\psi \circ a(s))(\psi \circ \pi(s, x))$$
$$(\psi \circ a)(sx)^{-1}$$

But $\psi \circ \pi_1(s, x) \equiv e$ because $\pi_1(s, x) \in H$. Thus
$\pi^0 = \psi \circ \pi$ is cohomologous to a cocycle all of
whose values are e. In other words, π^0 is a
trivial cocycle. Thus it will suffice to show that

π^o is not the trivial cocycle. That is, it will suffice to show that we do not have

$$\pi^o(s, x) = b(s) \, b(sx)^{-1} \qquad \text{for all} \quad s \quad \text{and} \quad x$$

and some Borel function b from S_1 to Z_2. Since $\pi^o(s, x)$ is determined by $\pi^o(s, 1)$ it will suffice to show that we do not have

$$\pi^o(s, 1) = b(s)b(s \cdot 1) \qquad \text{for all} \quad s$$

and some Borel b from S_1 to Z_2. Let τ be the transformation $z \longrightarrow -z = zb^{\pi i}$; that is, let τ be rotation through π. Let f be the element of Z_2 which is different from e so that $f^2 = e$. Then $\pi^o(s \cdot \tau, 1) = f\pi^o(s, 1)$ unless $\pi^o(s, 1) \equiv f$. Now the identity $\pi^o(s, 1) = b(s)b(s \cdot 1)$ implies $\pi^o(s\tau, 1) = b(s\tau)b(s\tau \cdot 1)$. Thus $b(s\tau)b(s\tau \cdot 1) \equiv f \, b(s)b(s \cdot 1)$ unless $\pi^o(s, 1) \equiv f$, and in that case $b(s)b(s \cdot 1) \equiv f$. Let $c(s) \equiv b(s)b(s\tau)$. Then

$$c(s \cdot 1) = b(s \cdot 1)b(s \cdot 1 \cdot \tau)$$
$$= f(bs)b(s \cdot 1) = fc(s)$$

unless $\pi^o(s, 1) \equiv f$. Hence, unless $\pi^o(s, 1) \equiv f$, we have $c(s \cdot 2) = f^2c(s) = c(s)$. Since $2a$ is also irrational, it follows from ergodicity that c is

almost everywhere constant. But if c is almost
everywhere constant then $c(s \cdot 1) = c(s)$ almost
everywhere. Thus, unless $\pi^0(s, 1) \equiv f$ we have
$c(s \cdot 1) = fc(s)$ for all s, and $c(s \cdot 1) = c(s)$ for
almost all s. Since these last two statements
conflict we conclude that $\pi^0(s, 1) \equiv f$ and hence
that $b(s)b(s \cdot 1) \equiv f$. Let A be the set on which
$b(s) = f$. Then if $s \in A$, we have $b(s \cdot 1) \in S_1 - A$
and if $s \in S_1 - A$, we have $s \cdot 1 \in A$. Hence
$(A) \cdot 1 = S_1 - A$ and vice versa, and, in particular,
(a) and $S_1 - A$ have equal nonzero measure. Hence
$(A) \cdot 2 = A$ and we have a contradiction to the
ergodicity of rotation through $2a$. This contradiction shows that no b exists, and establishes our
contention that π defines a homomorphism onto the
noncommutative group G_2.

To show that the virtual subgroup of G_1
defined by the indicated action on S_1 has irreducible representations in a two-dimensional vector
space, we have only to choose such a representation
of G_2 and "compose it" with π.

Let us now give some brief indications as to
how one actually defines the notion of "virtual
group." Given a cocycle π from $S_1 \times G_1$ to G_2, it

defines an ergodic action of G_2 which we have shown
is natural to call the closure of the range of the
homomorphism defined by π. Analysis of this situation leads without difficulty to the notion of a
homomorphism from a "virtual subgroup" of G_1 to a
virtual subgroup of G_2. This object turns out to
be defined by a pair consisting of a cocycle π from
$S_1 \times G_1$ to G_2 and a Borel function ϕ from S_1 to S_2
related by the condition that

$$\varphi(sx) \equiv \varphi(s)\pi(s, x)$$

Moreover, it turns out that π_1, φ_1 and π_2, φ_2
"define the same" homomorphism if and only if there
exists a Borel function a from S_1 to G_2 such that
$\varphi_1(s) \equiv \varphi_2(s)a(s)$ and

$$a(s)\pi_1(s, x) \equiv \pi_2(s, x)a(sx)$$

Now let H_1 and H_2 be closed subgroups of G_1 and G_2,
respectively. It is easy to see that H_1 and H_2 are
isomorphic as topological groups if and only if
there exist Borel homomorphisms ψ_1 and ψ_2 from H_1
to H_2 and H_2 to H_1, respectively, such that $\psi_1 \circ \psi_2$
is the identity in H_2 and $\psi_2 \circ \psi_1$ is the identity
in H_1. This suggests that we say that S_1, G_1 and

S_2, G_2 define isomorphic "virtual subgroups" of G_1
and G_2, respectively, if there exist homomorphisms
of these "virtual subgroups" into one another whose
"compositions" in either order are the identity.
Quite apart from the still undefined notion of
virtual subgroup we obtain a perfectly well-defined
equivalence relation for triples S, C, G, where C
is an ergodic invariant measure class in S. It is
then natural to define a virtual group to be an
equivalence class of such triples. For further
details we refer the reader to [7].

Actually, the notion of virtual group defined
in this way turns out to be too restrictive. One
can generalize it in a natural way so as to obtain
virtual groups which need not (at least a priori)
be virtual subgroups of actual groups. The idea
behind this generalization can be seen most clearly
in a special case. Let the system S, C, G be such
that G acts freely on S; that is, let sx = s imply
x = e for all s. Then the mapping s, x ⟶ s, sx
from S x G to S x S is one-to-one, and we may
identify S x G with a certain subset E of S x S.
This subset is just the set of ordered pairs s_1,
s_2 in S x S such that s_1 and s_2 are in the same G

orbit. In other words, "is" the equivalence
relation in S defined by the action of G? Furthermore, and this is the interesting point, the notion
of cocycle from S x G to G_2, as well as the cohomology notion for these cocycles, can be defined
entirely in terms of E without reference to G and
its action on S. Using the one-to-one map of S x G
on E defined above, every Borel function π from
S x G to G_2 has a unique corresponding function $\pi\sim$
from E to G_2, and vice versa: $\pi(s, x) = \pi\sim(s, sx)$.
Moreover, as the reader may verify without difficulty, a necessary and sufficient condition that
π be a cocycle is that

$$\pi\sim(s_1, s_2)\pi\sim(s_2, s_3) = \pi\sim(s_1, s_3)$$

whenever s_1, $s_2 \in E$ and s_2, $s_3 \in E$. Similarly,
π_1 and π_2 are cohomologous cocycles if and only if
there exists a Borel function a from S to G_2 such
that

$$\pi_2(s_1, s_2) = a(s_1)\pi_1(s_1, s_2)a(s_2)^{-1}$$

Thus we can replace ergodic actions of groups by
abstract "ergodic equivalence relations" and
develop a corresponding theory of virtual groups.

We refer the reader to [6, 7] for further details,
and in particular for an account of what one
replaces an "ergodic equivalence relation" by in
order to generalize ergodic actions in which the
action is not free.

As an example of an ergodic equivalence
relation defining a virtual group which is not
obviously a virtual subgroup of a group start with
a system S, C, G where C is ergodic with respect
to the G action and the G action is free. Then let
S_1 be a Borel subset of S in which neither S_1 nor
$S - S_1$ is a set of measure zero. Let E be the set
of all pairs s_1, s_2 where s_1 and s_2 are both in S_1
and $s_1 x = s_2$ for some x in G. Let C_G be the Haar
measure class in G and let C' be the restriction of
C to S_1. Then $C' \times C_G$ transferred to E by the
mapping s, x $\longrightarrow$ s, sx will be a measure class C''
in E and the triple S_1; C'' is an ergodic equivalence
relation as defined in [6, 7].

Each point s_1, $s_2 \in E$ is associated in a
natural way with an element x of G, namely the
unique x such that $s_1 x = s_2$. If we set $\pi(s_1, s_2)$
= x, it is easy to see that π is a cocycle. It is
interesting to notice that the system S, C, G can

be reconstructed from S_1, E, C'' once we are given
π , and that this construction is a general one
which enables us to assign an ergodic action of G
to the system consisting of an abstract ergodic
equivalence relation and a cocycle on E with values
in G.   Indeed, let $S_2 = S_1 \times G$ and let E_1 denote
the set of all pairs s, x; s, x' $\in S_2 \times S_2$ such
that $x\pi(s, s') = x'$.   Let us make S_2 into a G-space
by setting $(s, x)y = s, y^{-1}x$.   It is easy to verify
that E_1 defines an equivalence relation in S_2 and
that the action of G permutes the equivalence
classes among themselves.   Let $\tilde{S}_2$ denote the space
of all E_1 equivalence classes in S_2 and give to it
the Borel structure which it inherits as a quotient
space of S_2.   If $\tilde{S}_2$ is analytic[3] it is easy to see
that the action of G on the equivalence classes
makes it into an analytic Borel space.   Moreover,
the image in S_1 of C'' is a measure class in S_1
whose product with the Haar measure class is a
measure class in S_2.   The image of this in $\tilde{S}_2$ is
easily seen to be invariant and ergodic with

---

[3]Analytic Borel spaces are slightly more general
than standard ones.   See [4] for a definition.

respect to the G action. Thus S_1, E, C'', and π
define an ergodic action of G whenever $\tilde{S}_2$ is a
standard Borel space.

Now consider the special case in which S_1,
E, C'', and π come to us by restricting the equivalence relation defined by a free ergodic action of
G on S to a subset S_1 of positive measure as described above. For each s, $x \in S_2 = S_1 \times G$ let
$\psi(s, x) = sx^{-1}$. Then ψ is a Borel map of S_2 into
S and $\psi(s_1, x_1) = \psi(s_2, x_2)$ if and only if $s_1 x_1^{-1}$
$= s_2 x_2^{-1}$; that is, if and only if $s_1 x_1^{-1} x_2 = s_2$.
But this is equivalent to saying that s_1, $s_2 \in E$
and $x_1^{-1} x_2 = r(s_1, s_2)$; that is, s_1, x_1; s_2, $x_2 \in E$
and $x_1^{-1} x_2 = \pi(s_1, s_2)$; that is, s_1, x_1; s_2, $x_2 \in E_1$.
In other words, ψ is one-to-one on the E_1 equiva-
lence classes in S_2 and sets up a Borel isomorphism
between $\tilde{S}_2$ and a subset of S. Moreover

$$\psi(s, x)y = \psi(s, y^{-1}x) = sx^{-1}y = \psi(s, x)y$$

Thus the range of ψ is invariant and ψ sets up an
equivalence between the action of G on $\tilde{S}_2$ and that
in an invariant analytic subset of S. It follows
that $\tilde{S}_2$ is an analytic Borel space and one can show
that modulo invariant null sets the action of G on

$\tilde{S}_2$ is equivalent to that in S. Moreover, the subset S_1 may be identified with the image under ψ of
the set of all s, e. Thus we may recover the G
action from S_1, E, C'', and π as claimed. We leave
it to the reader to verify that the measure classes
come out right.

In conclusion we remark that our construction
can be modified so as to work even if the abstract
ergodic equivalence relation and the cocycle π are
such that $\tilde{S}_2$ is not a well-behaved Borel space.
Instead of forming the space of E_1 equivalence
classes in $S_1 \times G = S_2$, one collects these into
"ergodic pieces" using a construction analogous to
that described in the bottom one-third of page 194
of [7]. We shall not give details here. From the
virtual group point of view the virtual subgroup
of G defined by the G action on $\tilde{S}_2$ (or the associated space of "ergodic pieces") is just the closure
of the range of the homomorphism defined by the
cocycle π.

REFERENCES

1. Ambrose, W., Representation of Ergodic Flows,

Ann. Math., 42 (1941), pp. 723-739.

2.　Anzai, H., Ergodic Skew Product Transformations on the Torus, Osaka Math. J., 3 (1951), pp. 83-89.

3.　Kuratowski, C., Topologie I, espaces metrisables, especes complets, 2nd edition, Warsaw, 1948.

4.　Mackey, G. W., Borel Structures in Groups and Their Duals, Trans. Am. Math. Soc., 84 (1957), pp. 134-165.

5.　Mackey, G. W., Infinite Dimensional Group Representations, Bull. Am. Math. Soc., 69 (1963), pp. 628-686.

6.　Mackey, G. W., Ergodic Theory, Group Theory, and Differential Geometry, Proc. Nat. Acad. Sci. U. S., 50 (1963), pp. 1184-1191.

7.　Mackey, G. W., Ergodic Theory and Virtual Groups, Math. Ann., 1966 (1966), pp. 187-207.

HOMEOMORPHISMS OF THE CIRCLE WITHOUT
PERIODIC POINTS[1]

Nelson G. Markley

(University of Maryland)

Homeomorphisms of the circle without periodic points go back to Poincaré's work on differential equations on the torus [3]. He divided them into two classes -- transitive and intransitive, according as to whether there is a dense orbit or no orbit is dense. He also discovered an invariant for them called the rotation number. For the transitive case the rotation number is a complete invariant.

The purpose of this paper is to announce the existence of a complete set of invariants for the

---

[1]This work was partially supported by Research Grant No. GP-6864 from the National Science Foundation.

class of all homeomorphisms of the circle without

periodic points. It turns out that for this purpose

we need only consider one additional invariant,

which is essentially the set of distal points.

From this point of view the transitive case is the

special case in which the second invariant is

trivial. In addition, we give a characterization

in terms of the proximal relation of the minimal

sets which arise from homeomorphisms of the circle

without periodic points.

Let S be the circle. For convenience we

represent S as the set of complex numbers of

modulus one and use $|z - z'|$ as a metric. Let

$\{(a, b)\} \{[a, b]\}$ denote the $\{$open$\}$ $\{$closed$\}$

counterclockwise interval from a to b on S where

$a \neq b$. By a Cantor set in S we shall mean a

perfect nowhere dense subset of S. For any Cantor

set C we have

$$C = S - \bigcup_{i=1}^{\infty} (a_i, b_i)$$

where $[a_i, b_i] \cap [a_j, b_j] = \phi$ when $i \neq j$. Set

$$C(II) = S - \bigcup_{i=1}^{\infty} [a_i, b_i]$$

and

$$C(I) = C - C(II)$$

We define a closed equivalence relation $R(C)$ on S by $(x, y) \in R(C)$ if $x = y$ or $x, y \in [a_i, b_i]$ for some i. Let p_o denote the canonical map of S onto $S/R(C)$ and let $S/R(C)$ be topologized by the quotient topology.

LEMMA 1. (a) The restriction of p_o to $C(II)$ maps $C(II)$ homeomorphically onto the complement of a countable dense subset of $S/R(C)$. (b) The space $S/R(C)$ is homeomorphic to S.

The following extension theorem is the basic tool used in establishing the classification scheme:

THEOREM 2. Let C_1 and C_2 be two Cantor sets in S. Let p_i map S continuously onto S such that $p_i(x) = p_i(y)$ if and only if $(x, y) \in R(C_i)$, $i = 1, 2$. Let φ be a continuous map of S onto S such that $\varphi^{-1}(x)$ is finite for all x in S and

$$\varphi \cdot p_1[C_1(II)] \subset p_2[C_2(II)] \tag{1}$$

Then there exists a continuous map ψ of S onto S
such that $\psi(C_1) = C_2$ and $p_2 \cdot \psi = \varphi \cdot p_1$. Moreover,
when φ is a homeomorphism ψ can be a homeomorphism
if and only if equality holds in (1).

A discrete flow (X, φ) is a topological space
together with a self-homeomorphism φ. Given two
discrete flows (X, φ) and (Y, ψ), an {isomorphism}
{homomorphism} of (X, φ) onto (Y, ψ) is a
{homeomorphism} {continuous map} θ of X onto Y such
that $\theta \cdot \varphi = \psi \cdot \theta$. When X = Y and $\varphi = \psi$ we speak of
automorphisms and endomorphisms. The orbit of
$x \in X$ under φ, denoted by $o(x, \varphi)$, is $\{\varphi^n(x): n$ is
an integer$\}$. A subset A of X is a minimal set of
(X, φ) if it is nonempty, closed, invariant
$[\varphi(A) = A]$, and contains no proper subset with
these properties.

A generator of S is an element $g \in S$ such that
$[g] = \{g^n: n$ is an integer$\}$ is dense in S. For any
a in S we denote left multiplication by a by L_a,
that is, $L_a(z) = az$.

REMARK 3. Let g and h be generators of S. The
following statements hold:
    (a)   S is minimal under L_g.

   (b) ψ is an automorphism of (S, L_g) if and
only if $\psi = L_z$ for some $z \in S$.

   (c) (S, L_g) and (S, L_h) are isomorphic if
and only if $g = h$ or $g = h^{-1}$.

   (d)   If ψ is an endomorphism of (S, L_g), then
ψ is an automorphism.

   (e)   If ψ is a homomorphism of (S, L_g) on
(S, L_h), then $\psi(z) = z_o z^{\pm N}$ for some positive
integer N and some $z_o \in S$, and $g^{\pm N} = h$.

THEOREM 4.   Let φ be a self-homeomorphism of S
without periodic points.   If $\overline{0(z, \varphi)} = S$ for some
$z \in S$, then S is minimal under φ and (S, φ) is
isomorphic to (S, L_g) for some generator g of S.

Proof.   See E. R. van Kampen [2].

THEOREM 5.   Let φ be a self-homeomorphism of S
without periodic points.   If $\overline{0(z, \varphi)} \neq S$ for some
$z \in S$, then there exists a Cantor set C which is
the only minimal set under φ and such that
$\overline{0(z, \varphi)} - 0(z, \varphi) = C$ for all $z \in S - C$.

Proof.   See E. R. van Kampen [2].

   Let φ be as in the preceding theorem.   We

note that if (a, b) is a complementary interval of
C, then $\varphi[(a, b)]$ is also a complementary interval
and $\varphi^n[(a, b)] \neq (a, b)$ for $n \neq 0$. Hence
$(x, y) \in R(C)$ if and only if $(\varphi(x), \varphi(y)) \in R(C)$.
Consequently φ induces a homeomorphism ψ of $S/R(C)$
onto itself and the canonical map is a homomorphism
of (S, φ) onto $(S/R(C), \psi)$. Clearly $S/R(C)$ is
minimal under ψ. Therefore, there exists a continuous map p of S onto S and a generator g of S such
that p is a homomorphism of (S, φ) onto (S, L_g)
and $p(x) = p(y)$ if and only if $(x, y) \in R(C)$. If
we choose g so that Im g > 0, it is uniquely determined and we call it $r(\varphi)$. From Theorem 4 it is
clear how to define $r(\varphi)$ when S is minimal under
φ. It is not hard to show that $r(\varphi) = e^{2\pi ai}$ or
$e^{-2\pi ai}$ where a is the rotation number.

We now introduce the other invariant. When
(S, φ) has a minimal Cantor set C, set $T(\varphi)$
$= p[C(II)]$ where p is as above. For the transitive
case set $T(\varphi) = S$. We say two sets X and Y are
equivalent modulo S if $X = L_z(Y)$ for some z in S.
If p_1 and p_2 are two homomorphisms of (S, φ) onto
$(S, L_{r(\varphi)})$ such that $p_i(x) = p_i(y)$ if and only if
$(x, y) \in R(C)$, then clearly $T_1(\varphi) \equiv T_2(\varphi)$ (mod S).

THEOREM 6. Let T be a subset of S and g a generator of S with Im g > 0. If S - T is countable and $L_g(T)$ = T, then there exists a self-homeomorphism ψ of S without periodic points such that $r(\psi) = g$ and $T(\psi) \equiv T$ (mod S).

THEOREM 7. Let φ_1 and φ_2 be self-homeomorphisms of S without periodic points. Then (S, φ_1) is isomorphic to (S, φ_2) if and only if $r(\varphi_1) = r(\varphi_2)$ and $T(\varphi_1) \equiv T(\varphi_2)$ (mod S).

Theorems 6 and 7 imply that $r(\varphi)$ and $T(\varphi)$ form a complete system of invariants.

It is also possible to read off information about homomorphisms, endomorphisms, and automorphisms from these invariants. The next two theorems show how this is done.

THEOREM 8. Let φ_1 and φ_2 be homeomorphisms of S without periodic points. There exists a homomorphism ψ of (S, φ_1) onto (S, φ_2) if and only if for some nonzero integer N

$$[r(\varphi_1)]^N = r(\varphi_2)$$

and

$$[T(\varphi_1)]^N \subset T(\varphi_2) \quad (\text{mod } S)$$

THEOREM 9. Let φ be a homeomorphism of S without periodic points and let M be the minimal set of (S, φ). The group of automorphisms of $(M, \varphi \mid M)$ is isomorphic to $\{z \in S: L_z[T(\varphi)] = T(\varphi)\}$ as a subgroup of S. The semigroup of endomorphisms of $(M, \varphi \mid M)$ is isomorphic to $\{z: L_z[T(\varphi)] \subset T(\varphi)\}$ as subsemigroup of S.

It follows that there exist φ and M as in Theorem 9 such that $\varphi \mid M$ has an endomorphism which is not an automorphism.

Let X be a topological space and let A be a subset of X. By A' we mean the derived set of A, that is, $x \in A'$ if every neighborhood of x contains a point of A different from x. Let (X, φ) be discrete flow with X compact Hausdorff. We define a relation P in X called the proximal relation by $(x, y) \in P$ if given an index a of the unique uniformity on X there exists an integer n such that $(\varphi^n(x), \varphi^n(y)) \in a$. The proximal relation is not necessarily transitive or closed. It is invariant in the sense that $(x, y) \in P$ if and only if $(\varphi(x), \varphi(y)) \in P$. Ellis and Gottschalk [1] have shown that there is a least invariant closed equivalence relation R on X such that the proximal relation of (X/R, φ/R) is trivial. This system is called the distal structure transformation group of (X, φ). Clearly P $\subset$ R. We denote the diagonal of X x X by Δ. Let (Y, ψ) be another discrete flow. We say (X, φ) can be embedded in (Y, ψ) if there exists a homeomorphism θ mapping X into Y such that $\theta \cdot \varphi = \psi \cdot \theta$.

THEOREM 10. Let (X, φ) be a minimal discrete flow where X is a compact Hausdorff space. Then (X, φ) can be embedded in some (S, ψ) where ψ has no periodic points if and only if P' $\subset \Delta$, P - Δ is countable, and the proximal structure transformation group of (X, φ) is (S, L_g) where g is a generator of S.

REFERENCES

1. Ellis, R., and Gottschalk, W. H., Homomorphisms of Transformation Groups, Trans. Am. Math. Soc., 94 (1960), pp. 258-271.

2. Van Kampen, E. R., The Topological Transfor-

mation of a Simple Closed Curve into Itself, Am. J. Math., 57 (1935), pp. 142-152.

3. Poincaré, H., Sur les Courbes Defines par les Équations Differentielles, J. Math. Pures Appl. (4), 1 (1885), pp. 167-244.

GENERALIZED HAMILTONIAN MECHANICS

(SUMMARY)

J. E. Marsden

(Princeton University)

As my paper is quite long, I can present here only a brief description of some of the main results.

One of the main problems is the following:

PROBLEM. Suppose M is a manifold and X is a generalized vector field (here, think of a vector field with distributional coefficients; for details see my notes: distributions on manifolds). Then:

(a) Can we in any reasonable sense say that X has a flow F_t?

(b) If so, can we find conditions guaranteeing existence?

(c) If div X = 0, will F_t be measure preserving?

Divergence here is with respect to a volume (orientation) Ω on M.

This problem first arose in connection with Hamiltonian flows, where there was considerable optimism, for simple examples do indeed have flows. In this case we answer (a), (b), (c) affirmatively and can even do much better than (c).

It is instructive to consider an example corresponding to a particle moving past a potential step: Here $M = R^2$, and $X(q, p) = p \, \partial/\partial q - \delta(q) \, \partial/\partial p$ where δ is the delta function. This X is Hamiltonian with energy $H(q, p) = p^2/2 + V(q)$, where $V(q) = 0$ if $q \leq 0$ and 1 if $q > 0$. Approximating H by smooth Hamiltonians we see that the flows converge to the following discontinuous flow:

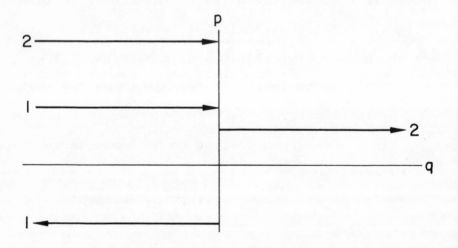

The resulting flow is measure preserving and conserves energy. Returning to the main problem, (a) is answered as follows:

DEFINITION. Let X be a generalized vector field. Suppose X_i are smooth vector fields with (complete) flows F_t^i and $X_i \longrightarrow X$ in the sense of distributions. We say X has a flow F_t if and only if

    (i) $F_t^i \longrightarrow F_t$ a. e. for each $t \in R$

    (ii) for each $t \in R$ and compact set C there is a compact set K so $F_t^i(C) \subset K$ for all i

    We have two main theorems [answering (b) and (c)]:

THEOREM 1. If F_t is defined by the above, then F_t is a flow. That is, $F_{t+s} = F_t \circ F_s$ a. e. for all t, s $\in$ R.

THEOREM 2. Suppose X has compact support and $X_i \longrightarrow X$ satisfy:

    (i) div X_i, div X are uniformly bounded;

    (ii) the singular support of X has measure zero.

    Then X has a flow. (The X_i may be modified.)

Further, if the X_i are divergence free [so (i) is vacuous], then F_t is measure preserving.

The restriction that X has compact support is not a severe one. Otherwise we would obtain a local flow only.

This theorem is particularly well adapted to the Hamiltonian case. Then we are dealing with a symplectic manifold (M, ω); that is, a manifold M with a closed, nondegenerate 2-form ω; $d\omega = 0$. To each smooth function H there is associated a smooth vector field X_H by lifting dH by ω. Similarly, for every distribution H we have associated a generalized vector field X_H. Further

$$H_i \longrightarrow H \quad \text{implies} \quad X_{H_i} \longrightarrow X_H$$

THEOREM 3. Suppose dH has compact support and singular support of measure zero. Suppose $H_i \longrightarrow H$ with dH_i all having supports in a compact set (no restriction). Then the flows (or a subsequence) of X_{H_i} converge to that of X_H. Further:

(i)   the flow is measure preserving (Liouville's theorem);

(ii)   energy is conserved in the following

sense: for a. e. $m \in M$, we have

$$H(F_t(m)) = H(m)$$

for all $t \in R$ for which $F_t(m)$ does not lie in
the singular support of H [so $H(F_t(m))$ makes
sense].

Further results can be obtained in the
Hamiltonian case which we now sketch. Suppose
T^*M is a cotangent bundle with its natural
symplectic structure and Φ is a smooth action of a
Lie group on M, and Φ^* is the corresponding action
induced on T^*M (functorial). Then we have:

THEOREM 4 (CONSERVATION LAW). Suppose H is
invariant under Φ^*; that is, $(\Phi^*)_*H = H$, where
H is a distribution on T^*M. Suppose there are
smooth $H_i \longrightarrow H$, and the H_i are invariant under
Φ^*. Then each of the functions $P_X : T^*M \longrightarrow R$,
$P_X(a_m) = a_m \cdot X(m)$, $a_m \in T_m^*M$, is invariant under
the flow of X_H obtained from the H_i, where X is
an infinitesimal transformation of Φ (X is a
vector field on M).

Actually, the condition on the existence of
H_i invariant under Φ^* is not severe and simple

conditions (for example, that the group be compact)
can remove it. The theorem is of some practical
importance.

There are numerous applications (to statistical mechanics especially) I have not mentioned.
There is one application to smooth flows I would
like to mention, for it answers an open problem:

THEOREM 5. Suppose X is a divergence-free smooth
vector field with complete flow F_t. Then the
(generalized) spectrum of X completely determines
the flow. That is, two flows with the same spectra
are equal (smoothness is essential).

This follows quite easily from Gelfand's
spectral theorem and an extension of the Lie
derivative to generalized forms ("courants").

REFERENCES

1. Abraham, R., and Marsden, J., Foundations of
Mechanics, W. A. Benjamin, New York, 1967.
2. Marsden, J., Generalized Hamiltonian Mechanics
(to be published; this talk condenses this paper).

3. Marsden, J., Hamiltonian One Parameter Groups (thesis, Princeton University).

4. Marsden, J., and Wightman, A. S., Lectures on Statistical Mechanics (mimeographed).

5. Marsden, J., Distributions on Manifolds (mimeographed). (A preliminary and incomplete version of 2.)

(A complete Bibliography may be found in [2].)

ZERO ENTROPY OF DISTAL AND RELATED

TRANSFORMATIONS

William Parry

(University of Sussex)

0. INTRODUCTION

It is not too difficult, as others are aware,
to prove that distal homeomorphisms of compact
metric spaces which preserve a normalized Borel
measure have zero entropy, if one uses Furstenberg's
deep structural theorem [1]. By means of this
theorem one obtains a distal minimal homeomorphism
as a transfinite inverse limit of isometric extensions of the trivial homeomorphism of a single
point. For each extension one verifies that the
entropy is zero and by a limit theorem the proof
is concluded.

The purpose of this note is to establish the
theorem by a direct simple argument and to comment

on a generalization which leads to a purely measure
theoretic class of transformations analogous to
distal homeomorphisms.

It should be noted that totally ergodic
transformations with quasidiscrete spectra are
representable as totally minimal affine transformations with quasidiscrete spectra, and these
latter are distal [2, 3]. Moreover, the nilflows
of [4] are distal. These two types of transformation are, in general, distinct [5].

1.   THE MAIN THEOREM AND GENERALIZATIONS

Let (X, d) be a compact metric space and let
T be a distal homeomorphism of X onto itself, that
is, if $\inf_n d(T^n x, T^n y) = 0$ then $x = y$. T is said
to be minimal if $TK = K$, and K closed implies
$K = \phi$ or X.

THEOREM 1.   If T is distal and minimal and preserves
a normalized measure m, then the entropy of T with
respect to m is zero $(h(T) = 0)$. (The minimality
condition will be dropped in Section 2.)

Proof.   The case of an atomic m is dealt with

easily. We assume m is nonatomic. Let X

$= S_o \supset S_1 \supset \ldots, \bigcap_n S_n = \{z\}$, S_i open, $d(S_n) \to 0$,

$m(S_n) \leq r^n$ where $r < 1/e$. Let $\xi = (A_o, A_1, \ldots)$

where $A_i = S_i - S_{i-1}$, $i \geq 1$, $A_o = \{z\} \cup (S_o - S_1)$.

Then ξ is a partition of X. Suppose $T^n x$, $T^n y \in A_{i_n}$

for some sequence $(i_1, i_2, \ldots)$ then for each N

there exists n such that $T^n x \in S_N$, by the minimality

of T, and therefore $T^n y \in A_{i_n} \subset S_N$ (if $N \neq 0$). In

other words, $d(T^n x, T^n y)$ has infinum zero; that is,

$x = y$ by the distal property. Hence $V_{i=0}^{\infty} T^{-i} \xi = \epsilon$,

the partition of X into one-point sets, and

$$h(T) = h(T, \xi) \leq H(\xi) = \sum_{i=0}^{\infty} -m(A_i) \log m(A_i)$$

$$\leq - mA_o \log mA_o + \sum_{n=1} -nr^n \log r$$

$$\leq -\log(1 - \sum_{n=1} r^n) - \frac{r}{(1 - r)^2} \log r \tag{1.1}$$

$$= \log \frac{(1 - r)}{(1 - 2r)} - \frac{r}{(1 - r)^2} \log r$$

(Here we have used the monotonicity of $-x \log x$ on

$(0, 1/e)$ and the relations $A_i \subset S_i$.) Since (1.1)

is true for all $r < 1/e$ we have $h'(T) = 0$. (Actu-

ally this also follows from the fact that $H(\xi) <$

and $V_{i=0} T^{-i} \xi = \epsilon$.)

  Only a weak form of the distal property was

used in this proof. Let us call z a <u>separating</u>
<u>point for T</u> if $T^{m_n}x \to z$ and $T^{m_n}y \to z$ implies $x = y$.
The above proof yields:

THEOREM 2. If T is a homeomorphism with a separating point and if T preserves a normalized Borel
measure with respect to which T is ergodic, then
$h(T) = 0$.

A measure theoretic analogue of the above
may be achieved as follows: Let $X = S_o \supset S_i \supset \cdots$
be a decreasing sequence of measurable sets of
positive measure such that $m(S_n) \to 0$. Such a
sequence will be called a <u>separating sieve</u> for a
measure preserving transformation T if there exists
a set M of measure zero with the following property:
if x, $y \in X - M$ and if for each N there exists n
such that $T^n x$, $T^n y \in S_N$, then $x = y$; equivalently,

$$\left[\bigcap_{N=0}^{\infty} \bigcup_{n=0}^{\infty} (T \times T)^{-n}(S_N \times S_N) \right] \cap (X - M) \times (X - M)$$
$$= \text{diag}(X \times X) \cap (X - M) \times (X - M) \quad (1.2)$$

THEOREM 3. An ergodic transformation T of a
Lebesgue space with a separating sieve has zero
entropy and possesses a nonconstant eigenfunction

(that is, T is not weakly mixing).

Proof. The first part is similar to the proof of
Theorem 1. By (1.2) we have

$$m \times m \bigcup_{n=0}^{\infty} (T \times T)^{-n}(S_N \times S_N) \underset{N}{\to} 0$$

since diag$(X \times X)$ cannot have positive measure.
Consequently the $T \times T$ invariant set
$\bigcup_{n=0}^{\infty} (T \times T)^{-n}(S_N \times S_N)$ is nontrivial for some N
and $T \times T$ is not ergodic, that is, T is not weakly
mixing.

The second part of this theorem was achieved
by Furstenberg [1] for minimal distal homeomorphisms.
For that case Furstenberg's method has the advantage
of producing a continuous eigenfunction.

2.   A DISTAL HOMEOMORPHISM HAS ZERO ENTROPY

Ellis [6] has shown that a compact metric
space, on which a distal homeomorphism acts,
decomposes into minimal sets; that is, $X = \cup_{\alpha \in A} X$
where $X_\alpha \cap X_\beta = \phi$ if $\alpha \neq \beta$ and X_α are closed minimal
sets. However, $\{X_\alpha\}$ is not always a Hausdorff
partition. Nevertheless, if $U_1, U_2, \ldots$ is a

countable basis for the open sets then V_1, V_2, . . .
($V_n = \cup T^i U_n$) form a countable basis for this
partition in the sense that for $\alpha \neq \beta$ there exists
n such that either

$$X_\alpha \subset V_n \quad X_\beta \subset X - V_n \quad \text{or} \quad X_\beta \subset V_n$$
$$X_\alpha \subset X - V_n$$

This is enough to ensure that:

(i) $\{X_\alpha\}$ is a measurable partition;

(ii)   there exists a canonical system of
measures m_α [7].

By virtue of [7] we have

$$h(T) = \int_{X_\zeta} h_\alpha(T_\alpha) \; dm_\zeta \qquad (2.1)$$

In (2.1) X_ζ is the factor space of X with
respect to $\zeta = \{X_\alpha\}$, m_ζ is the factor measure on
X_ζ, $T_\alpha = T|X_\alpha$, and h_α is the entropy of T_α with
respect to m_α, which, by virtue of Theorem 1, is
zero.

Consequently we have the following:

THEOREM 4.   If T is a distal homeomorphism of a
compact metric space X preserving a normalized
Borel measure, then T has zero entropy.

REFERENCES

1. Furstenberg, H., The Structure of Distal Flows,
Am. J. Math., 85 (1963), pp. 477-515.

2. Abranov, L. M., Metric Automorphisms with
Quasi-Discrete Spectrum, Izv. Akad. Nauk. Ser. Mat.,
26 (1962), pp. 513-530. Am. Math. Soc. Transl., 2,
39, pp. 37-56.

3. Hahn, F., and Parry, W., Minimal Dynamical
Systems with Quasi-Discrete Spectrum, J. London
Math. Soc., 40 (1965), pp. 309-323.

4. Auslander, L., Green, L., and Hahn, F., Flows
on Homogeneous Spaces, Ann. Math. Stud., No. 53.

5. Hahn, F., and Parry, W., Some Characteristic
Properties of Dynamical Systems with Quasi-Discrete
Spectra, Math. Systems Theory (to be published).

6. Ellis, R., Distal Transformation Groups,
Pacific J. Math., 8, No. 3 (1958), pp. 401-405.

7. Rohlin, V. A., On the Entropy of a Metric
Automorphism, Dokl. Akad. Nauk. SSSR., 124, No. 5
(1959), pp. 980-983 (in Russian).

CONCERNING TWO METHODS OF DEFINING
THE CENTER OF A DYNAMICAL SYSTEM

Coke S. Reed

(Auburn University)

1. INTRODUCTION

G. D. Birkhoff [1], G. D. Birkhoff and P. A.
Smith [2], and A. G. Maier [3] defined three
processes which describe the center (the closure
of the set of all points stable in the sense of
Poisson) of a dynamical system T defined on a
compact metric space S (a continuous mapping from
(- ∞, ∞) x S onto S such that if x is a number, y
is a number, and p is a point of S, $T[x, T(y, p)]$
= $T[x + y, p]$ and $T[0, p]$ = p). In each of these
processes a monotonic (perhaps transfinite)
sequence x of point sets in S is defined so that
the center of T is the closure of the common part
of all of the members of x. This paper deals with

the process of Birkhoff and Smith and the process of Maier.

Suppose T is a dynamical system defined on a compact metric space S. The sequence $(x_1, x_2, \ldots)$ used in the process of Birkhoff and Smith is the one with the following three properties:

(1) x_1 is the set of all points of S;

(2)   if α is an ordinal number, then there is a term x_α if and only if x_β exists for each ordinal number $\beta < \alpha$ and $cl(\bigcap_{\beta < \alpha} x_\beta)$ is not the center of T;

(3)   if α is an ordinal number such that x_α exists, x_α is the set to which p belongs if and only if p is an ω-limit point of a trajectory of T in $cl(\bigcap_{\beta < \alpha} x_\beta)$.

The sequence $(x_1, x_2, \ldots)$ used in the process of Maier is the sequence with properties (1) and (2) above and with property (3) above, except with "$cl(\bigcap_{\beta < \alpha} x_\beta)$" replaced by "$\bigcap_{\beta < \alpha} x_\beta$."

V. V. Nemyckiǐ [4] has asked if there exists an example of a dynamical system T defined on a compact subspace S of E^3 such that the sequence of Birkhoff and Smith has more terms than the sequence of Maier. The purpose of this paper is to describe

an elementary effective example of such a dynamical
system.

2.   DESCRIPTION OF THE EXAMPLE

The set of all rest points of the system
consists of the points of the closed intervals
$[(0, -1, 0), (0, -1, 1)]$, $[(0, -1, 1), (0, 1, 1)]$,
and $[(0, 1, 1), (0, 1, 0)]$, all of the points of
the form $(0, 0, n/(n + 1))$, where n is an integer
larger than 3, and all points of the form

$$(-1/4n^2, -\sum_{p=4}^{n} 2(p + 2)]/[1 + \sum_{p=4}^{n} 2(p + 2)],$$

$$1/(n + 1) + 1/4n^2)$$

where n is an integer greater than 3.

Two points, p and q, and two sequences of
points, $(p_4, p_5, p_6, \ldots)$ and $(q_4, q_5, q_6, \ldots)$,
will be defined such that every nonrest point of
the system will be on a trajectory through one and
only one point of $\{p, q, p_4, p_5, p_6, \ldots, q_4, q_5, q_6, \ldots\}$.
The system will have the property that if n is an
integer, x is a number in $(0, 1)$, and t is a point
of $\{p, q, p_4, p_5, \ldots, q_4, q_5, \ldots\}$, then

$$T(n + x, t) = (1 - x) \cdot T(n, t)$$
$$+ x \cdot T(n + 1, t)$$

The entire system will therefore be completely described by defining $T(n, t)$ for each integer n and each point t in $\{p, q, p_4, p_5, \ldots, r_4, r_5, \ldots\}$.

Let $p = (0, 0, 0)$. $T(J, p)$ will now be defined for each integer J. Define the number sequence $(x_0, x_1, x_2, \ldots)$ as follows: $x_0 = 0$, and if n is a positive integer, $x_n = \sum_{p=1}^{n} 2(p + 2)$.

For each nonnegative integer n, set $T(x_n, p)$ $= (0, n/(n + 1), 0)$ and define $T(m, p)$ for each of the $2n + 5$ integers m between x_n and x_{n+1} as follows: if K is a positive integer $\leq n$ and J is a positive integer such that $n + 5 \leq J \leq 2n + 5$, set

$$T(x_n + k, p) = \left[-\frac{1}{(n + 3 - k)}, \frac{n}{(n + 1)}, 0\right]$$

$$T(x_n + n + 1, p) = \left[-\frac{(n + 1)}{(n + 2)}, \frac{n}{(n + 1)}, 0\right]$$

$$T(x_n + n + 2, p) = \left[-\frac{(n + 1)}{(n + 2)}, \frac{1}{(n + 2)} - 2, 0\right]$$

$$T(x_n + n + 3, p) = \left[\frac{(n + 1)}{(n + 2)} \quad \frac{1}{(n + 2)} - 2, 0\right]$$

$$T(x_n + n + 4, p) = \left[\frac{(n + 1)}{(n + 2)}, \frac{(n + 1)}{(n + 2)}, 0\right]$$

and

$$T(x_n + J, \ p) = \left[\frac{1}{(J - n - 2)}, \ \frac{(n + 1)}{(n + 2)}, \ 0 \right]$$

For each negative integer L, set $T(L, \ p)$
= $[0, \ L/(1 - L), \ 0]$. Set $q = [-1, \ -2, \ 0]$. $T(J, \ q)$
will now be defined for each integer J in such a
way that each point of $T[(-\infty, \ \infty), \ q]$ is an ω-limit
of $T[(-\infty, \ \infty), \ p]$. Set $T(1, \ q) = (1, \ -2, \ 0)$ and
$T(2, \ q) = (1, \ 1, \ 0)$. For each positive integer J
greater than 2, set $T(J, \ q) = (1/J, \ 1, \ 0)$. Set
$T(-1, \ q) = (-1, \ 1, \ 0)$. If n is an integer less
than -1, set $T(J, \ q) = (1/(J - 1), \ 1, \ 0)$.

Suppose that n is an integer greater than 3.
$T(J, \ p_n)$ will now be defined for each integer J in
such a way that each point of $T[(-\infty, \ \infty), \ p]$ is a
limit point of $\sum_{p=4} T[(-\infty, \ \infty), \ p_n]$, but so that
if L is an integer greater than 3, no point of
$T[(-\infty, \ \infty), \ p]$ is an ω-limit point of $T[(-\infty, \ \infty), \ p_L]$.
If $|J| \le x_n$, set

$$T[J, \ p_n] = T[J, \ p] + \left[0, \ 0, \ \frac{1}{(n + 1)} \right]$$

If $x_n < J \le x_n + n - 1$, set

$$T[J, p_n] = T[x_n, p_n] + \left[0, 0, \frac{(J - x_n)}{(n + 1)}\right]$$

If $x_n + n - 1 < J \leq x_n + 2n - 2$, set

$$T[J, p_n] = T[x_n + n - 1, p_n]$$
$$+ \left[0, \frac{(x_n + n - 1 - J)}{(n + 1)}, 0\right]$$

If $x_n + 2n - 2 < J$, define $T(J, p)$ recursively by the formula

$$T[J, p_n] = \frac{T(J - 1, p_n) + \left[0, 0, \frac{n}{(n + 1)}\right]}{2}$$

If $-x_n - n + 1 \leq J < -x_n$, set

$$T[J, p_n] = T[-x_n, p_n] + \left[0, 0, \frac{(-x_n - J)}{(n + 1)}\right]$$

If $-2x_n - n + 2 \leq J < -x_n - n + 1$, set

$$T[J, p_n] = T[-x_n - n + 1, p_n]$$
$$+ \left[0, \frac{(-x_n - n + 1 - J)}{(x_n + 1)}, 0\right]$$

If $J < -2x_n - n + 2$, define $T(J, p)$ recursively by the formula

$$T[J, p_n] = \frac{T(J + 1, p_n) + \left[0, 0, \frac{n}{(n + 1)}\right]}{2}$$

Suppose that J is a positive integer greater than 3. $T(L, q_J)$ will now be defined for each integer L in such a way that each point of $T[(-\infty, \infty), p_J]$ is an ω-limit point of $T[(-\infty, \infty), q_J]$. Define the sequence y_0, y_1, y_2, ... as follows: $y_0 = 0$ and if n is a positive integer, $y_n = 2nx_J + 2nJ - 3n + \sum_{p=1}^{n} 2p$. For each nonnegative integer n, set $T(y_n, q_J) = p_J + [1/(4J^2 + n), 0, 1/(4J^2 + n)]$. $T(m, q_J)$ will now be defined for each of the $2x_J + 2J + 2n - 2$ integers m between y_n and y_{n+1}. If K is a positive integer less than $x_J + J + n$, then set

$$T(y_n + K, q_J) = T(K, p_J)$$

$$+ \left[\frac{1}{(4J^2 + n)}, \ 0, \ \frac{1}{(4J^2 + n)} \right]$$

If K is a positive integer between $x_J + J + n - 1$ and $2x_J + 2J + 2n - 1$, then set

$$T(y_n + K, q_J) = T(K - 2x_J - 2J - 2n + 1, p_J)$$

$$+ \left[\frac{1}{(4J^2 + n)}, 0, \frac{1}{(4J^2 + n)} \right]$$

If m is a negative integer greater than $-x_J$, set

$T(m, q_J) = T(m, p_J) + (-1/4J^2, 0, 1/4J^2)$. If m is a negative integer less than $-x_J + 1$, then define $T(m, q_J)$ recursively by

$$T(m, q_J) = \frac{T(m - 1, q_J) + \left[T(-x_J, p_J) + (\frac{1}{4J^2}, 0, \frac{1}{4J^2})\right]}{2}$$

This completes the description of the example.

Let R denote the set of all rest points of T and for each point s of the system, let t(s) denote $T[(-\infty, \infty), s]$.

The sequence $[B_1, B_2, \ldots]$ of Birkhoff and Smith, which is associated with T, has four members, but the sequence $[M_1, M_2, \ldots]$ of Maier, which is associated with T, has only three members. This fact is demonstrated below:

$$B_1 = R + t(p) + t(q) + \sum_{J=4}^{\infty} t(p_J)$$
$$+ \sum_{J=4}^{\infty} t(q_J) = cl(B_1)$$

$$B_2 = R + t(q) + \sum_{J=4}^{\infty} t(p_J)$$

$$cl(B_2) = R + t(q) + \sum_{J=4}^{\infty} t(p_J) + t(p)$$

$$B_3 = R + t(q) = cl(B_3)$$

$$B_4 = R$$

$$M_1 = R + t(p) + t(q) + \sum_{J=4}^{\infty} t(p_J + \sum_{J=4}^{\infty} t(q_J))$$

$$M_2 = R + t(q) + \sum_{J=4}^{\infty} t(p_J)$$

$$M_3 = R$$

REFERENCES

1. Birkhoff, G. D., Uber gewisse Zentralbewegungen dynamischer Systeme, Nachr. Ges. Wiss. Gottingen. Math.-Phys. Kl. (1926), pp. 81-92.

2. Birkhoff, G. D., and Smith, P. A., Structure Analysis of Surface Transformations, J. Math. Pures Appl., (9), 7 (1928), pp. 345-379.

3. Maier, A. G., On Central Trajectories and Birkhoff's Problem, Mat. Sbornik N.S., 26 (68) (1950), pp. 266-290.

4. Nemyckii, V. V., Topological Problems of the Theory of Dynamical Systems, Am. Math. Soc. Transl., No. 103 (1954).

A CLASS OF NONHOMOGENEOUS MINIMAL

ORBIT-CLOSURES

F. Rhodes

(Wesleyan University and
University of Southampton)

1. INTRODUCTION

In [1], J. Auslander gave a geometrical
description of a nonhomogeneous minimal orbit-
closure which is related to one previously described by E. E. Floyd [3]. The structure group
of the minimal orbit-closure is the triadic group
[2]. In this note, I describe a general construction of nonhomogeneous minimal orbit-closures
under the action of discrete flows whose structure
groups are those compact zero-dimensional groups
which arise from sequences of finite cyclic groups.

2. NOTATION

The following notation will be used for

compact zero-dimensional limit groups. The symbols
$[m, n]$ and $[m, \infty)$ will denote the sets of integers
i such that $m \le i \le n$ and $m \le i$, respectively. The
symbol (i, j) will denote an ordered pair. Given
a function $\mu : [0, \infty) \to [2, \infty)$, denote by E_r^{μ} the
set of functions

$$\phi : [0, r - 1] \to [0, \infty) \times [0, \infty)$$
$$\phi : \quad i \to \phi_i \quad = (i, \phi_i')$$

such that $\phi_i' \in [0, \mu_i - 1]$. Define maps

$$\Phi_r^{\mu} : E_r^{\mu} \to E_{r-1}^{\mu}$$
$$\Phi_r^{\mu} : \quad \phi \to \phi \, | \, [0, r - 2]$$

If the sets E_r^{μ} are furnished with the discrete
topology, then the inverse limit system $\{E_r^{\mu}, \Phi_r^{\mu}\}$
has a nonempty compact limit space E^{μ}. An element
of E^{μ} is a function

$$\phi : [0, \infty) \to [0, \infty) \times [0, \infty)$$
$$\phi : \quad i \longrightarrow (i, \phi_i')$$

such that $\phi_i' \in [0, \mu_i - 1]$.

Define maps

$$a_r^{\mu} : E_r^{\mu} \to E_r^{\mu}$$

$$a_r^{\mu} : \quad \phi \longrightarrow \psi$$

where

$$\psi_i = \phi_i \quad \text{if} \; \exists \; j < i \quad \text{such that} \; \phi_j' < \mu_j - 1$$

$$\psi_i = (i, \; \phi_i' + 1 \bmod \mu_i) \quad \text{if} \; \forall \; j < i, \; \phi_j'$$

$$= \mu_j - 1$$

Then for every integer r

$$a_{r-1}^{\mu} \Phi_r^{\mu} = \Phi_r^{\mu} a_r^{\mu}$$

Hence the maps a_r^{μ} induce a homeomorphism

$$a^{\mu} : E^{\mu} \to E^{\mu}$$

Now E^{μ} is an almost periodic compact minimal orbit-closure under the action of the homeomorphism a^{μ}. Hence there is a unique group structure on E^{μ} which makes E^{μ} a topological group compactification of the infinite cyclic group generated by a^{μ}, and E^{μ} is itself the structure group of the discrete flow (E^{μ}, a^{μ}) [2].

3. NESTINGS

    In the construction of the examples use will be made of families of functions on compact metric spaces. The description will be facilitated by the following language.

DEFINITION 1. Given a function $\mu : [0, \infty) \to [2, \infty)$, a <u>nesting</u> <u>of</u> <u>characteristic</u> μ on a metric space X is a family of functions $\{f_{i,j}\}$, $i \in [0, \infty)$, $j \in [0, \mu_i - 1]$, such that for all i, j, $f_{i,j} : X \to X$ is a homeomorphism into.

A nesting is said to be

      (i) <u>convergent</u> if $\forall$ $\epsilon > 0$ $\exists$ r such that $\forall$ $\phi \in E_{r+1}^{\mu}$

$$\delta f_{\phi_0} \cdots f_{\phi_r} X < \epsilon$$

      (ii) <u>disjointed</u> if $\forall$ i, j_1, j_2

$$f_{i,j_1} X \cap f_{i,j_2} X = \Phi$$

      (iii) <u>a</u> <u>nested</u> <u>covering</u> if $\forall$ i $\quad \bigcup_j f_{i,j} X =$

Set $X_r = \bigcup f_{\phi_0} \cdots f_{\phi_{r-1}} X$, $\phi \in E_r^{\mu}$. The space $X_\infty = \bigcap_{r>0} X_r$ will be called the <u>limit</u> <u>space</u> of the nesting.

    It will prove convenient to augment some nestings by the introduction of identity functions in positions which depend on the occurrences of the value 2 in the sequence μ.

DEFINITION 2. Given $\mu : [0, \infty) \to [2, \infty)$, let $S = \{s_n\}$ be the sequence of integers such that $\mu_i = 2$ if and only if $i \in S$. Set $\nu_i = \mu_i$, $i \in S$, and $\nu_i = \mu_i - 1$, $i \notin S$. Let $\{f_{i,j}\}$ be a nesting of characteristic ν on a space X.

For $i \notin S$ set

$$g_{i,o} = f_{i,o} \qquad g_{i,1} = \text{id} \qquad g_{i,j} = f_{i,j-1}$$
$$j \in [0, \mu_i - 1]$$

For $i \in S = \{s_n\}$ set

$$g_{s_{2n},o} = f_{s_n,o} \qquad g_{s_{2n+1},1} = f_{s_n,1} \qquad g_{s_{2n},1}$$

$$= g_{s_{2n+1},o} = \text{id}$$

The family of functions $\{g_{i,j}\}$ will be called the augmentation of the nesting $\{f_{i,j}\}$. If the nesting $\{f_{i,j}\}$ is a convergent nested covering, then the nesting $\{g_{i,j}\}$ will be called an augmented convergent nested covering of characteristic μ.

It is easy to see that the closed unit interval admits a convergent disjointed nesting and also a convergent nested covering of any prescribed characteristic. Other spaces also admit nestings of the kinds required to construct the examples.

For example, the Sierpinski universal curve admits a convergent nested covering with characteristic μ where, for all i, $\mu_i = 8$. The functions are

$$f_{i,j} : (x, y) \to (\frac{1}{3}(x + a_j), \frac{1}{3}(y + b_j))$$

where the pairs (a_j, b_j) are pairs of integers between 0 and 2 with the exception of the pair (1, 1).

In the following proposition conditions are given which ensure that the map α^{μ} induces a homeomorphism of the limit space of a nesting of characteristic μ.

PROPOSITION. If $\{f_{i,j}\}$ is a disjointed nesting of characteristic μ on a compact metric space X such that

$$\bigcap_{r>o} f_{o,o} \cdots f_{r,o} X \quad \text{and}$$

$$\bigcap_{r>o} f_{o,\mu_o-1} \cdots f_{r,\mu_r-1} X$$

are single points, then α^{μ} induces a homeomorphism of X_∞.

Proof. Let the two points specified in the statement of the proposition be denoted by x_o and x_1, respectively.

Suppose that $x \in X_\infty$. Then given $r > 0$ there exists an element ϕ in E^μ_{r+1} such that $x \in f_{\phi_o} \cdots f_{\phi_r} X$, and since the nesting is disjointed, ϕ is unique. Hence there exists a unique element ϕ in E^μ such that for every $r > 0$, $x \in f_{\phi_o} \cdots f_{\phi_r} X$. If $x \neq x_1$, there exists j such that $\phi'_i = \mu_i - 1$ wherever $i < j$, and $\phi'_j < \mu_j - 1$. Let $\psi = a^\mu \phi$. Then $\psi'_i = 0$ wherever $i < j$, and $\psi'_j \leq \mu_j - 1$, while $\psi'_i = \phi'_i$ wherever $i > j$. Define

$$\beta x = f_{\psi_o} \cdots f_{\psi_j} f_{\phi_j}^{-1} \cdots f_{\phi_o}^{-1} x \qquad x \neq x_1$$

$$\beta x_1 = x_o$$

The function $f_{\psi_o} \cdots f_{\psi_j} f_{\phi_j}^{-1} \cdots f_{\phi_o}^{-1}$ is a homeomorphism from the set $f_{\phi_o} \cdots f_{\phi_j} X$ to the set $f_{\psi_o} \cdots f_{\psi_j} X$.

Since the nesting is disjointed and X is a compact metric space there exists $\epsilon_j > 0$ such that for every element θ of E^μ_{j+1} other than ϕ, $\rho(f_{\theta_o} \cdots f_{\theta_j} X, f_{\phi_o} \cdots f_{\phi_j} X) > \epsilon_j$. Hence if $\rho(x, x') < \epsilon_j$, $x' \in f_{\phi_o} \cdots f_{\phi_j} X$. It follows that β is continuous at every point $x \neq x_1$.

Moreover, given $\epsilon > 0$ there exists r such that $f_{o,o} \cdots f_{o,r} X \subseteq S(x_o, \epsilon)$, and with this value of r there exists $\delta > 0$ such that $X_\infty \cap S(x_1, \delta)$ $\subseteq f_{o,\mu_o-1} \cdots f_{r,\mu_r-1} X$. If $x' \in X_\infty \cap S(x_1, \delta)$, then $\beta x' \in f_{o,o} \cdots f_{r,o} X \subseteq S(x_o, \epsilon)$. Hence β is also continuous at x_1.

The map β is bijective, and by similar arguments to those above β^{-1} is also continuous. Hence β is a homeomorphism.

4. NONHOMOGENEOUS MINIMAL ORBIT-CLOSURES

A nesting $\{f_{i,j}\}$ of characteristic μ on a space X and a nesting $\{g_{i,j}\}$ of the same characteristic on a space Y induce a nesting $\{F_{i,j}\}$ $= \{(f_{i,j} g_{i,j})\}$ on the product space $P = X \times Y$. The required examples arise from homeomorphisms of the limit spaces P_∞ when suitable restrictions are placed on the nestings on X and Y.

THEOREM. Let $\{f_{i,j}\}$ be a disjointed convergent nesting of characteristic μ on a compact metric space X, and let $\{g_{i,j}\}$ be an augmented convergent nested covering of characteristic μ on a compact metric space Y of dimension ≥ 1. Then the limit space P_∞ of the nesting $\{F_{i,j}\} = \{(f_{i,j} g_{i,j})\}$ on the product space $P = X \times Y$ is a nonhomogeneous minimal orbit-closure under a discrete flow whose structure group is E^μ.

<u>Proof.</u> The conditions ensure that the nesting $\{F_{i,j}\}$ is disjointed and that $\underset{r>0}{\cap} F_{0,0} \cdots F_{r,0} P$ is a single point (x_0, y_0), say, and that $\underset{r>0}{\cap} F_{0,\mu_0-1} \cdots F_{r,\mu_r-1} P$ is a single point (x_1, y_1), say. Hence α^μ induces a homeomorphism $\beta : P_\infty \to P_\infty$.

Let the convergent nested covering of which $\{g_{i,j}\}$ is the augmentation be denoted by N. Given $\epsilon > 0$, let r be an integer such that for every element ϕ in E^μ_{r+1}, we have $\delta f_{\phi_0} \cdots f_{\phi_r} X < \epsilon$ and for every element ϕ in E^μ_{r+1} such that for all i, $g_{\phi_i} \in N$, we have $\delta g_{\phi_0} \cdots g_{\phi_r} X < \epsilon$. Given $(x, y) \in P_\infty$ there exists an element ϕ in E^μ_{r+1} such that $(x, y) \in F_{\phi_0} \cdots F_{\phi_r} P$. Let t be the number of terms in $\phi_0 \cdots \phi_r$ such that $g_{\phi_i} \notin N$. Choose $\phi_{r+1} \cdots \phi_{r+t}$ such that $g_{\phi_i} \in N$ for $r + 1 \leq i \leq r + t$, and $y \in g_{\phi_0} \cdots g_{\phi_{r+t}} Y$. Then $(x, y) \in F_{\phi_0} \cdots F_{\phi_{r+t}} P \subset S(x, \epsilon) \times S(y, \epsilon)$. Let $\lambda = \mu_0 \mu_1 \cdots \mu_{r+t}$. The definition of the homeomorphism β ensures that if (x', y') is in $F_{\phi_0} \cdots F_{\phi_{r+t}} P$ then so also is $\beta^{\lambda}(x', y')$. Thus the transformation group (P_∞, β) is locally almost periodic. Moreover, if

$$\nu = \phi'_0 + \mu_0 \phi'_1 + \mu_0 \mu_1 \phi'_2 + \cdots + \mu_0 \cdots \mu_{r+t-1} \phi'_{r+t}$$

then $\beta^{\nu}(x_0, y_0) \in F_{\phi_0} \cdots F_{\phi_{r+t}} P$. Hence (x_0, y_0) is an almost periodic point whose orbit-closure P_∞ is minimal.

The proof given by Floyd [3] can be used to show that P_∞ is of dimension zero at some points and has the same dimension as Y at other points.

Since (P_∞, β) is a compact, locally almost periodic transformation group, its equicontinuous structure relation coincides with its proximal relation [2]. Two elements are proximal if and only if they belong to the same limit set $\bigcap_{r>0} F_{\phi_0} \cdots F_{\phi_r} P$ for some $\phi \in E_\mu$. Thus the equicontinuous structure transformation group arises from the action of β restricted to the sub-set X_∞ of P_∞. Since the nesting on X is convergent, X_∞ is homeomorphic to E^μ, and β restricted to X_∞ is equivariant with a^μ. It follows that the structure group of (P_∞, β) is the group E^μ.

REFERENCES

1.   Auslander, J., Mean-L-Stable Systems, <u>Ill. J.
Math.</u>, 3 (1959), pp. 566-579.

2.   Ellis, R., and Gottschalk, W. H., Homomorphisms
of Transformation Groups, <u>Trans. Am. Math. Soc.</u>, 94
(1960), pp. 258-271.

3.   Floyd, E. E., A Nonhomogeneous Minimal Set,
<u>Bull. Am. Math. Soc.</u>, 55 (1949), pp. 957-960.

POISSON STABLE ORBITS IN THE
INTERIOR OF THE SOLID TORUS[1]

A. J. Schwartz

(University of Michigan)

1. INTRODUCTION

This paper is a descendant of the so-called "Seifert conjecture," namely, every flow on S^3 contains a closed orbit [5]. Instead of S^3 we consider the solid torus $X = D^2 \times S^1$ which has certain characteristics making analysis somewhat easier, while still giving us some insight about S^3, since S^3 is the union of two solid tori intersecting in a two-dimensional torus. Whether or not X must contain a closed orbit is still a difficult question. Fuller [2] has constructed an example

[1]This research was supported by the National Science Foundation under Grant No. 01048.

where the only closed orbits in X are contractible, even though the flow on the boundary of X is the "irrational flow."

Our approach is to assume that the boundary of X contains no closed orbit and to try and derive the existence of an orbit in the interior of X which is "recurrent" in some sense. The strongest forms of recurrence are fixation and periodicity; that is, the orbit in question is closed. Unfortunately we are unable to prove the existence of such an orbit and must be content, at the present time, with the existence of a Poisson stable orbit. We define this concept as follows:

1.1 DEFINITION. Let (X, R, π) be a flow. Then a point x in X is called Poisson stable in case there exist sequences $\{s_n\}$ and $\{t_n\}$ such that $s_n \to -\infty$, $t_n \to \infty$, $\pi(x, s_n) \to x$, and $\pi(x, t_n) \to x$.

In order to obtain our result, we use the notions of center of attraction and minimal center of attraction which are defined below.

1.2 DEFINITION. Let x be a point of X, and K a nonempty compact subset of X. Let $\chi_\epsilon(x) = 1$ if dist$(x, K) < \epsilon$, and $\chi_\epsilon(x) = 0$ otherwise. Then if

$$\lim_{T \to \infty} \frac{1}{T} \int_0^T \chi_\epsilon(\pi(x, t))\, dt = 1$$

for every $\epsilon > 0$, we say K is a <u>center</u> <u>of</u> <u>attraction</u>
<u>for</u> <u>x</u>.

1.3 DEFINITION. If K is a center of attraction for
x and contains no proper subset which is also a
center of attraction for x, then K is called a
<u>minimal</u> <u>center</u> <u>of</u> <u>attraction</u> <u>for</u> <u>x</u>.

By means of Zorn's lemma and straightforward
arguments using the compactness of X we can prove
the following:

1.4 PROPOSITION. For every point x in X, there is
a unique minimal center of attraction. See [3,
p. 361 ff].

1.5 NOTATION. For a point x in X, M(x) denotes
the minimal center of attraction for x.

We will also need the following theorem:

1.6 THEOREM (G. D. BIRKHOFF). For every point x in

X, M(x) is contained in the closure of Poisson
stable orbits.

Proof. According to [1] M(x) is contained in the
center of (X, R, π). However the center of the flow i
contained in the closure of Poisson stable orbits;
see [3, Theorem 5.08, p. 358].

2. STATEMENT OF KEY THEOREM -- DERIVATION OF
    MAIN THEOREM

2.1 NOTATION. ∂X denotes the two-dimensional torus
which forms the boundary of X.

    The key result is the following:

2.2 THEOREM. If for every point x in X, $M(x) \subset \partial X$,
then ∂X contains a closed orbit.

    We shall prove the above theorem in Section 3.

2.3 THEOREM. If ∂X contains no closed orbit, then
X - ∂X contains a Poisson stable point.

Proof. It follows from 2.2 that there exists a
point x_0 such that $N = M(x_0) - \partial X \neq \Phi$. Let y be in
N and dist$(y, \partial X) = \delta > 0$. According to 1.6 there

exists a Poisson stable point z such that dist$(z, y) < \delta$, whence it follows that z belongs to $X - \partial X$.

3.   PROOF OF THEOREM 2.2

Let $\widetilde{X} = D^2 \times R$, let $p : \widetilde{X} \rightarrow X$ be given by $p(d, r) = (d, e^{2\pi i r})$, and let $(\widetilde{X}, R, \widetilde{\pi})$ be the unique flow such that $p(\widetilde{\pi}(\widetilde{x}, t)) = \pi(p(\widetilde{x}), t)$. Finally, for a point (d, r) in $\widetilde{X}$ we denote $(d, r)_3 = r$.

Now assume that $M(x) \subset \partial X$ for every x in X and that ∂X contains no closed orbit.

3.1 LEMMA.   There exists a number t_0 such that: either (a) $\left[\pi(x, t_0)\right]_3 - \left[x\right]_3 \geq 2$ for every x in $\partial\widetilde{X}$, the two-dimensional cylinder bounding $\widetilde{X}$; or (b) $\left[x\right]_3 - \left[\widetilde{\pi}(x, t_0)\right]_3 \geq 2$ for every x in $\partial\widetilde{X}$.

Proof.   See [4, 2.11].

We shall assume, without loss of generality, that (a) holds.

3.2 LEMMA.   For every x in $\widetilde{X}$ and $\epsilon > 0$,

$$\lim_{T \to \infty} \frac{1}{T} \int_0^T \tilde{\chi}_\epsilon(\pi(x, t)) \, dt = 1, \text{ where } \tilde{\chi}_\epsilon(y) = 1 \text{ if}$$

$\text{dist}(y, \, \partial \tilde{X}) < \epsilon$ and $\tilde{\chi}_\epsilon(y) = 0$ otherwise.

Proof. This follows from the relations $\tilde{\chi}_\epsilon(\tilde{\pi}(x, t))$ $= \chi_\epsilon(p(\tilde{\pi}(x, t))) = \chi_\epsilon(\pi(p(x), t))$, where $\chi_\epsilon(y) = 1$ if $\text{dist}(y, \, \partial X) < \epsilon$ and $\chi_\epsilon(y) = 0$ otherwise; and $M(p(x)) \subset \partial X$.

3.3 LEMMA. For every x in $\tilde{X}$, $\lim\limits_{T \to \infty} \left[\tilde{\pi}(x, T)\right]_3 = \infty$.

Proof. Let $\mu > 0$ be such that $[\tilde{\pi}(x, t_0)]_3 - [x]_3 \geq 1$ if $\text{dist}(x, \, \partial \tilde{X}) < \mu$. Let $m = \min \left\{ [\tilde{\pi}(x, t)]_3 - [x]_3 \, | \, x \in \tilde{X}, \, 0 \leq t \leq t_0 \right\}$. We have

$$\left[\tilde{\pi}(x, T)\right]_3 - [x]_3$$

$$= \frac{1}{t_0} \int_0^{t_0} \left[\tilde{\pi}(x, T)\right]_3 - \left[\tilde{\pi}(x, T + t)\right]_3 \, dt$$

$$+ \frac{T}{t_0} \left(\frac{1}{T} \int_0^T \left[\tilde{\pi}(x, t + t_0)\right]_3 - \left[\tilde{\pi}(x, t)\right]_3 \right.$$

$$+ \frac{1}{t_0} \int_0^{t_0} \left[\tilde{\pi}(x, t)\right]_3 - [x]_3 \, dt$$

$$\geq -2|m| + \frac{T}{t_0} \left[\frac{1}{T} \int_0^T \tilde{\chi}_\epsilon(\tilde{\pi}(x, t)) \, dt \right.$$

$$+ m\left(1 - \frac{1}{T} \int_0^T \tilde{\chi}_\epsilon(\tilde{\pi}(x, t)) \, dt\right)\right] \to \infty$$

3.4 LEMMA.   There exists a number t_1 such that for x in $\widetilde{X}$, $[\widetilde{\pi}(x, t_1)]_3 - [x]_3 > 1$.

<u>Proof</u>.   The lemma follows from 3.3, the compactness of $\{x \in \widetilde{X} \mid 0 \leq [x]_3 \leq 1\}$, and the upper semicontinuity of $f(x) = \max\{t \in R \mid [\widetilde{\pi}(x, t)]_3 - [x]_3 \leq 1\}$.

3.5 LEMMA.   There exists a continuous function $W : \widetilde{X} \to R$ such that for $s \geq 0$, $W(\widetilde{\pi}(x, s)) - W(x) \geq s$.

<u>Proof</u>.   Set $W(x) = \displaystyle\int_o^{t_1} [\widetilde{\pi}(x, t)]_3 \, dt$.   Then for $s \geq 0$,

$$W(\widetilde{\pi}(x, s)) - W(x) = \int_s^{t_1+s} - \int_o^{t_1} [\widetilde{\pi}(x, t)]_3 \, dt$$

$$= \int_{t_1}^{t_1+s} - \int_o^{s} [\widetilde{\pi}(x, t)]_3 \, dt$$

$$= \int_o^{s} [\widetilde{\pi}(x, t + t_1)]_3$$

$$- [\widetilde{\pi}(x, t)]_3 \, dt \geq s$$

3.6 LEMMA. $\Sigma = \{x \in \widetilde{X} \mid W(x) = 0\}$ is compact and has the fixed point property.

<u>Proof</u>.   This follows from the fact that for sufficiently large R, Σ is a retract of

$\{x \mid \mid [x]_3 \mid \leq R\}$.   See $[4, 3.8, 3.9]$.

3.7 LEMMA. There exists a point $\widetilde{x}_0 = (d, r)$ in $\widetilde{X}$, an integer n, and a real number $\tau > 0$ such that $\widetilde{\pi}(\widetilde{x}_0, \tau) = (d, r + n)$.

Proof. Let n be an integer such that
$$n \geq \max\{[x]_3 \mid x \in \Sigma\} - \min\{[x]_3 \mid x \in \Sigma\}.$$
Let $\Sigma' = \{(d, r + n) \mid (d, r) \in \Sigma\}$. Now let $\sigma : \Sigma \to \Sigma'$ be defined by $\{\sigma(x)\} = \widetilde{\pi}(x, (0, \infty)) \cap \Sigma'$.

It may be shown that σ is well defined and continuous. See $[4, 3.8]$.

The map $h : \Sigma \to \Sigma$, defined by $h(x) = (d, r - n)$ where $(d, r) = \sigma(x)$, must, according to 3.6, have a fixed point $\widetilde{x}_0$, and the lemma follows.

We now complete the proof of the theorem. Let $x_0 = p(\widetilde{x}_0)$. Then $\pi(x_0, \tau) = \pi(p(\widetilde{x}_0), \tau)$ $= p(\widetilde{\pi}(\widetilde{x}_0, \tau)) = x_0$. Thus the orbit O through x_0 is closed. But $O = M(x_0)$, since it is closed, and therefore, by assumption, $O \subset \partial X$. Thus we arrive at a contradiction and the theorem is proved.

REFERENCES

1. Birkhoff, G. D., Über gewisse Zentralbewegungen

dynamischer Systeme, G̈öttinger Nachr., 1926, pp.
81-82.

2.   Fuller, F. B., Note on Trajectories in a Solid
Torus, Ann. Math., 2nd Series, 56 (1952), pp. 438-
439.

3.   Nemytskii, V. V., and Stepanov, V. V.,
Qualitative Theory of Differential Equations,
Princeton University Press, Princeton, New Jersey,
1960.

4.   Schwartz, A. J., Flows on the Solid Torus
Asymptotic to the Boundary, J. Diff. Eq. (to be
published).

5.   Seifert, H., Closed Integral Curves in 3-Space
and Isotopic Two-Dimensional Deformations, Proc.
Am. Math. Soc., 1 (1950), pp. 287-302.

A CONCEPT OF STABILITY IN

DYNAMICAL SYSTEMS

P. Seibert

(Instituto Politecnico Nacional,

Mexico City)

1. INTRODUCTION

The idea of "stability under persistent perturbations" or "total stability" may be summarized as follows: A class of dynamical systems is given, one of which, S_o, is distinguished as being "unperturbed," while the others are considered as "perturbed" relative to S_o. One usually assumes that a distance between a perturbed system and S_o is defined. A set M (for instance an orbit of S_o) is called totally stable if all orbits of systems sufficiently close to S_o, with initial points sufficiently near M, remain in a given neighborhood of M.

In the case of autonomous differential

423

equations,[1] it follows easily by Liapunov's second
method that asymptotic stability implies total
stability.[2] The converse of this theorem is true
only in special cases.[3] In the present note we
announce the following necessary and sufficient
condition for total stability:

THEOREM A. A compact set is totally stable if and
only if it is either asymptotically stable or
possesses a fundamental system of asymptotically
stable neighborhoods.[4]

   Since, for asymptotical stability, there are
very simple and well-known criteria available,
Theorem A completely settles the problem of total

---

[1]The development of the theory of total stability
for differential equations up to 1958 is outlined
in the book of W. Hahn [4, Section 28]. See also
the paper [11] by I. Vrcoč, where a necessary and
sufficient condition for total stability in terms
of a Liapunov function is given.

[2]Malkin [5, 6] and Gorsin [3]; in the case of
continuous flows and more general systems in
locally compact metric spaces, this result is
contained in [9, Theorem 2].

[3]Compare with Massera [7].

[4]Sufficiency of this condition was proved in [8].

stability for autonomous differential systems. The only question which it leaves open is under what additional conditions total stability implies asymptotic stability. An answer to this is given by the following theorem.

THEOREM B. A totally stable compact set is asymptotically stable if and only if it is isolated from invariant sets.[5]

This is an immediate corollary of a theorem by Ura and Kimura which states that a closed invariant set which is stable and isolated from closed invariant sets, is asymptotically stable.[6]

In the proof of Theorem A we use a concept of "contracting sets." A set A is said to be contracting if, for every boundary point x of A, the positive semiorbit through x, except for its initial point x, is contained in the interior of A. Now an equivalent definition of total stability can

---

[5]A set M is called "isolated from invariant sets" if there exists a neighborhood U of M such that every invariant set contained in U is contained in M.

[6]Compare with [10, Propositions 1 and 2].

be formulated in terms of contracting neighborhoods.
Being entirely topological, the new definition can
be applied to continuous flows in locally compact
spaces. In this case we speak of P*-stability.
Moreover, Theorem A can be extended to P*-stabili-
ty, thus providing the basis for a generalized
theory of total stability in continuous flows.

2. TOTAL STABILITY IN DIFFERENTIABLE FLOWS

Consider a differentiable flow (X, R, π),
where X denotes a differentiable manifold, R the
real line, and $\pi = \pi(x, t)$ a function from X x R
onto X which is continuous in x and differentiable
in t and satisfies the usual axioms of a transformation group.

By a δ-solution (or δ-approximate solution)
of (X, R, π) we mean an absolutely continuous
function g: $R^+ \to X$ [R^+: nonnegative real numbers]
which satisfies the differential inequality

$$\left| \frac{dg(t)}{dt} - \frac{\partial}{\partial \tau} \pi(g(t), \tau)_{\tau=0} \right| < \delta$$

for almost all values of t.

We introduce the following notations:

$$P_\delta(x) = \cup \left\{ g(R^+) : g \in \Gamma_\delta(x) \right\} \qquad P(x) = \cap \left\{ P_\delta(x) : \delta > 0 \right\}$$

Here $\Gamma_\delta(x)$ denotes the set of all δ-solutions satisfying the initial condition $g(0) = x$. $P(x)$ is the set of all points which can be reached from x by δ-solutions with δ arbitrarily small.

If $M \subset X$, we define $P_\delta(M) = \cup \left\{ P(x) : x \in M \right\}$. Now there are two possible ways of defining $P(M)$, namely, (a) as the intersection of all sets $P_\delta(M)$ with $\delta > 0$, and (b) as the union of all sets $P(x)$ with $x \in M$. However, it follows from Lemma 7 in [2] that both definitions are equivalent if M is compact. In what follows, we will apply P only to compact sets.

A set M is called <u>totally</u> <u>stable</u> if, given $\epsilon > 0$, there exists $\delta > 0$ such that $d(x, M) < \delta$ implies $P_\delta(x) \subset S_\epsilon(M)$. Here $d(x, M) = \inf \left\{ d(x, y) : y \in M \right\}$ and $S_\epsilon(M) = \left\{ x \in X : d(x, M) < \epsilon \right\}$.

The following theorem was proved as Theorem 15 in [2].[7]

THEOREM 1. A compact set M is totally stable if

and only if $P(M) = M$.

The replacement of the sets $P_\delta(M)$ by contracting neighborhoods is possible due to the following lemma.

LEMMA 1.   If $\delta > 0$ and $A \subset X$, the set $P_\delta(A)$ is contracting.

Now we denote by $P^*(x)$ the intersection of all contracting neighborhoods of x. Again, there are two possible ways of defining $P^*(M)$, and again it can be shown that they are equivalent if M is compact. If $P^*(M) = M$, we call M P^*-stable.

THEOREM 2.   A compact set is totally stable if and only if it is P^*-stable.

This is an immediate consequence of Theorem 1 and of the following lemma:

LEMMA 2.   If M is compact, then $P(M) = P^*(M)$.

---

[7]For the proofs on total stability in [2] it is immaterial whether the space is a differentiable manifold or Euclidean, because they depend only on local considerations.

3. P*-STABILITY IN CONTINUOUS FLOWS

Consider now a continuous flow in a locally compact metric space X. Since the concept of P^*-stability depends only on the purely topological notion of "contracting," it can be applied to sets in X with respect to the flow under consideration.

A set B ⊂ X is called an attractor if it possesses a neighborhood A, its "region of attraction," such that all positive limit points (or "ω-limit points") of orbits in A are contained in B. An attractor which is stable in the sense of Liapunov is called asymptotically stable.

We can now state our principal result:

THEOREM 3. Given a continuous flow in a locally compact metric space X and a compact set M ⊂ X. Then M is P^*-stable if and only if it possesses a fundamental system of asymptotically stable neighborhoods.

Note 1. If M is asymptotically stable, it obviously possesses a fundamental system of asymptotically stable neighborhoods. Let, for instance, V be a continuous, strictly decreasing Liapunov function

for M (the existence of which is proved in [2]),
then the sets $\{x : V(x) < 1/n\}$, n = 1, 2,..., have
the required property.

Note 2. In the case of a differentiable flow,
Theorem 3 reduces to Theorem A of the introduction,
taking into account Theorem 2.

The proof of Theorem 3 is based on the two
following lemmas.

LEMMA 3.   Compact contracting sets are asymptotically stable.

LEMMA 4.   If M is compact and P^*-stable, each of
its neighborhoods contains a contracting neighborhood of M.

In a special case, a slightly stronger condition can be proved using Theorem 1 of [1]:

THEOREM 4.   Suppose M is compact and P^*-stable and
contains no positive limit points of orbits outside
M.   Then M possesses a fundamental system of
asymptotically stable invariant neighborhoods.

4.   TWO SIMPLE EXAMPLES

(a)   Consider the differential equation (due to Massera [7])

$$\frac{dx}{dt} = \begin{cases} - x \sin^2 \frac{\pi}{X} & \text{for} \quad x \neq 0 \\ 0 & \text{for} \quad x = 0 \end{cases}$$

which has critical points at 0, ± 1, $+\frac{1}{-2}$, $+\frac{1}{3}$, ... The origin satisfies the hypothesis of Theorem 4 and, indeed, the neighborhoods

$$\left[-\frac{1}{k}, \frac{1}{k} \right] \qquad k = 1, 2, ... \qquad (1)$$

are invariant and asymptotically stable.

(b)   In the case of the differential equation

$$\frac{dx}{dt} = \begin{cases} -x & \text{for} \quad x \leq 0 \\ -x \sin^2 \frac{\pi}{X} & \text{for} \quad x > 0 \end{cases}$$

the origin is totally stable without being asymptotically stable; however, it is the limit point of the orbit to the left. The neighborhoods (1) are again stable attractors, but fail to be negatively invariant.

REFERENCES

1. Auslander, J., Bhatia, N. P., and Seibert, P.,
Attractors in Dynamical Systems, Bol. Soc. Mat.
Mexicana, (2) 9 (1964), pp. 55-66.

2. Auslander, J., and Seibert, P., Prolongations
and Stability in Dynamical Systems, Ann. Inst.
Fourier, Grenoble, 14 (1964), pp. 237-268.

3. Goršin, S. I., Ob ustoĭcivosti dvizhenia s
postoianno deistvuiuscimi vozmuščeniami, Izv. Akad.
Nauk Kazakh. SSR (Ser. mat. mekh), 2 (1948), pp. 46-
73.

4. Hahn, W., Theory and Application of Liapunov's
Direct Method, Prentice-Hall, Englewood Cliffs, New
Jersey, 1963.

5. Malkin, I. G., On Stability under Constantly
Acting Disturbances [Russian with English summary],
Prikl. Mat. Mekh., 8 (1944), pp. 241-245.
[Translated in Am. Math. Soc. Transl., Ser. 1, Vol.
5 (1962)].

6. Malkin, I. G., Theory of Stability of Motion,
Gos. Izdat. Tekh.-Teoret. Lit. 1952; translated as
A. E. C. - transl. No. 3352.

7. Massera, J. L. Contributions to Stability

Theory, Ann. Math., 64 (1956), pp. 182-206. --
Correction, Ann. Math., 68 (1958), p. 202.

8.   Seibert, P., Prolongations and Generalized
Liapunov Functions, Proc. Intern. Symp. Nonlin.
Vibrations, Kiev (1961), Vol. II, pp. 332-341 (1963).

9.   Seibert, P., Stability under Perturbations in
Generalized Dynamical Systems, Proc. Intern. Symp.
Nonlin. Diff. Eq. and Nonlin. Mech., Colorado
Springs (1961), pp. 463-473 (1963).

10.   Ura, T., and Kimura, I., Sur le courant
extérieur à une région invariante, Theorème de
Bandixson, Comm. Math. Univ. Sancti Pauli, 8 (1960),
pp. 23-39.

11.   Vrkoč, I., Stability under Persistent Disturbances Russian with Czech and English summaries ,
Časopis pro pestovani mat., 87 (1962), pp. 326-358.

INVARIANT MEASURES AND POISSON STABILITY[1]

George R. Sell

(University of Minnesota and
University of Southern California)

1. INTRODUCTION

Liouville has shown that the solutions of the differential equation

$$x' = f(x) \qquad x' = \frac{dx}{dt} \qquad \text{(A)}$$

on Euclidean space R^n preserves the Lebesgue measure μ when div $f = 0$ on R^n. This means that if A is a measurable set in R^n and

$$A_t = \{\phi(x, t) : x \in A\}$$

where $\phi(x, t)$ is the solution of (A) satisfying

_____

[1]This research was supported in part by the National Science Foundation under Grant No. GP-7041X and U. S. Army Contract DA-31-124-ARO-D-265.

$\phi(x, 0) = x$, then $\mu(A) = \mu(A_t)$. Using this result, E. Hopf, compare with [3] and [5, pp. 448 ff], has derived the following results concerning the Poisson stability of solutions of (A):

(H-1) On R^n, for almost every point x, the solution $\phi(x, t)$ is either Poisson stable or departing.

(H-2) If K is a compact invariant set in R^n, then for almost every point x in K, the solution $\phi(x, t)$ is Poisson stable.

If one allows the vector field f to change with time t, that is, if the differential equation is nonautonomous, or of the form

$$x' = f(x, t) \qquad\qquad\qquad\qquad (NA)$$

then Liouville's theorem is still valid when $div_x f = 0$ for all (x, t). One might ask whether Hopf's theorems are still valid. If one tries to change (NA) into an autonomous equation by setting $t' = 1$, then the question is trivial because every solution of the system

$$x' = f(x, t) \qquad t' = 1$$

is departing.

The question of Poisson stability for the solutions of (NA), nevertheless, is reasonable and it actually arises in some applications. For example, the motion of a satellite (with no gravitational mass) in the gravitational field of n-bodies would satisfy (NA) with $\text{div}_x f = 0$.

It is the primary purpose of this paper to derive an appropriate form of Hopf's theorems for (NA). Our theory will use, in an essential way, the way f depends on t. In particular, certain aspects of the topological-dynamical theory of non-autonomous differential equations, as developed in [7, 8], will be used.

In Section 2 we shall discuss the question of the existence of invariant measures for the flow generated by (NA). In Section 3 we shall apply the theorems of Hopf for general flows to the study of Poisson stability of (NA). Our main result, Theorem 2, is given there. In Section 4 we show how the ergodic theorems of G. D. Birkhoff can be generalized to (NA).

2. INVARIANT MEASURES

Let W be an open set in Euclidean space R^n and let R denote the real numbers. Let $f(x, t) : R^n \times R$ be a continuous function and define the translate f_τ by $f_\tau(x, t) = f(x, \tau + t)$. We define the hull of f (denoted by F^*_{co} in [7, 8]) by

$$H(f) = C\ell\{f_\tau : \tau \in R\}$$

where $C\ell$ denotes the closure operation in the topology of uniform convergence on compact sets, and we assume that H(f) is given with this topology. We shall assume throughout that f is regular on W x R in the sense defined in [7, 8]. This means that for every f^* in H(f) the differential equation

$$x' = f^*(x, t) \tag{NA*}$$

has unique solutions. We shall let $\Phi(x, f, t)$ denote the solution of

$$x' = f(x, t) \tag{NA}$$

that satisfies $\Phi(x, f, 0) = 0$. We define a mapping (π), see [7], by

$$\pi(x, f, t) = (\Phi(x, f, t), f_t) \tag{π}$$

It was shown in $[7]$ that (π) is a local flow, or local dynamical system, on $W \times H(f)$. We refer the reader to $[7]$ for the precise definition of a local flow, but we note here that it differs from a flow in the sense that the motion $\pi(x, f, t)$ may not be defined for all time t. In the sequel, we shall assume, without explicitly stating it, that all measures are positive. We shall say that a measure on W is invariant with respect to f--or (NA)--if for every measurable set $A \subset W$ one has

$$\mu(A) = \mu(\phi(A, f, \tau))$$

for all τ with the property that <u>every</u> solution $\phi(x, f, .t)$, $x \in A$, can be continued up to $t = \tau$. We shall say that a measure μ is <u>bounded</u> if the measure of every compact set is finite. We have already noted that the Lebesgue measure on W is invariant with respect to f when $\mathrm{div}_x f = 0$ for all (x, t).

The next lemma, in addition to being a cornerstone of our theory, has some analytical significance. It is a generalization of Liouville's theorem.

LEMMA 1. Let $f(x, t)$ be a regular function on

W x R. Let μ be a bounded measure on W that is
invariant with respect to f. Then μ is invariant
with respect to each f^* in H(f).

Proof. It is elementary to verify that μ is invariant with respect to each translate f_τ, and we
omit these details. Now let f^* be any function in
the hull H(f) and let A be a measurable set in W.
Let $\tau \in R$ be fixed and assume that every solution
of (NA*) can be continued up to t = τ. We then
want to show that

$$\mu(A) \; = \; \mu(B) \tag{1}$$

where B = $\phi(A, \; f^*, \; \tau)$. Since W is locally compact
and since the measure μ is additive it will suffice
to prove (1) whenever A is compact.

Because of the definition of H(f) we can find
a sequence of translates $\{f_{\tau_n}\}$ with $f_{\tau_n} \to f^*$.
Define B_n by $B_n = \phi(A, \; f_{\tau_n}, \; \tau)$. Since A is compact,
it follows that for all n sufficiently large, every
solution $\phi(x, \; f_{\tau_n}, \; t)$, $x \in A$, can be continued up
to t = τ. Thus B_n is compact, say for $n \geq N$, and
because μ is invariant with respect to each translate f_{τ_n} one has

$$\mu(A) = \mu(B_n) \tag{2}$$

for all $n \geq N$. Furthermore, it follows (see [6]) from the continuity of solutions $\phi(x, f^*, t)$ that $B_n \to B$ in the Hausdorff sense, that is, for every $\epsilon > 0$ there is an $M \geq 0$ such that

$$B_n \subset S(B, \epsilon) \quad \text{and} \quad B \subset S(B_n, \epsilon) \quad (n \geq M)$$

where $S(B, \epsilon)$ is the ϵ-neighborhood about B. But this implies that $\mu(B_n) \leq (S(B, \epsilon))$ for all $n \geq M$. Since μ is bounded one has $\mu(S(B, \epsilon)) \to \mu(B)$ as $\epsilon \to 0$. From (2) one then has

$$\mu(A) \leq \mu(B)$$

We have thus shown that for every compact set A one has

$$\mu(A) \leq \mu(\phi(A, f^*, \tau)) \tag{3}$$

for every f^* in $H(f)$ and every τ satisfying the continuability condition. Since

$$A = \phi(\phi(A, f^*, \tau), f_\tau^*, -\tau)$$

it follows from (3) that

$$\mu(\phi(A, f^*, \tau)) \leq \mu(A)$$

which completes the proof of the lemma.

The mapping $(f, t) \to f_t$ defines a flow on H(f), see [7]. If the hull H(f) is compact, then it is a consequence of the theorem of Krylov and Bogoliubov, see [4 and 5, p. 493], that there exists a nontrivial invariant measure ν for this flow. For example, if $f(x, t)$ is uniformly almost periodic (see Corollary 2 below for a definition) then H(f) is a compact, Abelian, topological group, and the invariant measure ν is the Haar measure.

THEOREM 1. Let f be regular on W x R and let μ be a bounded measure on W that is invariant with respect to f. Assume that the hull H(f) is compact and let ν be any invariant measure for the flow on H(f). Then the product measure $m = \mu \times \nu$ on W x H(f) is invariant for the local flow (π).

Proof. Since the measure m is additive, it will suffice to show that for every compact set A in W x H(f) of the form A = B x C, where B $\subset$ W and C $\subset$ H(f), one has $m(A) = m(\pi(A, \tau))$ provided every motion $\pi(x, f^*, t)$, $(x, f^*) \in$ B x C, can be continued up to $t = \tau$. We define

$$A_\tau = \pi(A, \ \tau) \quad \text{and} \quad C_\tau = \{f_\tau^* : f^* \in C\}$$

then

$$A_\tau = \{(\phi(x, \ f^*, \ \tau), \ f_\tau^*) : (x, \ f^*) \in B \times C\}$$

The section of A_τ found by fixing f_τ^* is $\phi(B, \ f^*, \ \tau)$. Since μ is invariant with respect to f^*, by Lemma 1, it follows that

$$\mu(B) = \mu(\phi(B, \ f^*, \ \tau))$$

for all f^* in C. That is, every section $\phi(B, \ f^*, \ \tau)$ has the same μ-measure. By Fubini's theorem [2] one has

$$m(A_\tau) = \int_{A_\tau} 1 \ dm = \int_{C_\tau} \left(\int_{\phi(B, \ f^*, \ \tau)} 1 \ d\mu \right) d\nu$$

$$= \int_{C_\tau} \mu(B) \ d\nu = \mu(B)\nu(C_\tau)$$

However ν is invariant on H(f) so $\nu(C_\tau) = \nu(C)$, and therefore

$$m(A_\tau) = \mu(B)\nu(C) = m(A)$$

which completes the proof.

In the two corollaries to this theorem we shall assume that f is smooth enough so that $\text{div}_x f$ is defined and so that Liouville's theorem is valid.

COROLLARY 1.   Let f(x, t) be a regular function on
W x R.   Assume the following:

(i) $\text{div}_x f = 0$ for all   (x, t)

(ii)   f(x, t) is uniformly almost periodic in
t; that is, f(x, t) is bounded and uniformly
continuous on sets of the form K x R, where K
is compact in W, and for each x, f(x, t) is
almost periodic in t.

Then the measure m = μ x ν on W x H(f), where
μ is the Lebesgue measure on W and ν the Haar
measure on H(f), is invariant for the local flow
(π).

Proof.   First we note that the Lebesgue measure μ
is invariant with respect to f by Liouville's
theorem.   One can show, see [9], that H(f) is a
compact, Abelian, topological group and therefore
the Haar measure on H(f) is translation invariant.
We now apply Theorem 1.

One can weaken the almost periodicity condition (ii) as we show in the next result.   However,
in this case one should note that the measure ν on
H(f) may fail to be unique.

COROLLARY 2. Let $f(x, t)$ be given as in Corollary
1 satisfying (i) and:

(iii) $f(x, t)$ is bounded and uniformly
continuous on sets of the form K x R, where K
is compact in W.

Then there is a nontrivial measure ν on $H(f)$
such that the measure $m = \mu \times \nu$ on $W \times H(f)$, where
μ is the Lebesgue measure on W, is invariant for
the local flow (π).

Proof. It was shown in [7] that condition (iii)
is equivalent to the condition that $H(f)$ be compact.
Then by the Krylov-Bogoliubov theorem there exists
a nontrivial translation invariant measure ν on
$H(f)$. The corollary now follows from Theorem 1.

Remark. Theorem 1 and its corollaries are "local"
results in the sense that the open set W can be
replaced by any C^{∞}-manifold M^n. The divergence
condition on f would then be interpreted in terms
of a Riemannian metric on M^n.

3. POISSON STABILITY

Throughout this section we shall make the
following assumptions:

(G-1)   f(x, t) is regular on W x R and μ is
a bounded measure on W that is invariant with
respect to f.

(G-2)   H(f) is compact and ν is an invariant
measure on H(f).

Under these assumptions we then proceed to
investigate the Poisson stability of the solutions
of

$$x' = f(x, t) \qquad\qquad\qquad (NA)$$

We shall use the following definition of Poisson
stability which applies either to solutions of (NA)
or for motions of a flow.

DEFINITION.   Let f : R $\rightarrow$ X be a continuous function,
where X is a topological space. We shall say that
f is <u>Poisson stable</u> if for every τ in R and every
neighborhood U of f(τ) the sets

$$\{t \geq 0 : f(t) \in U\} \quad \text{and} \quad \{t \leq 0 : f(t) \in U\}$$

are unbounded in R.

In the introductory section we referred to
two theorems of Hopf. We shall restrict our attention here to generalizing statement (H-2).

Statement (H-1) can be similarly generalized. The corresponding theorem and proof should be evident from what follows, and we will say nothing more about it.

Before we proceed, it will be convenient to recall Hopf's theorem for a general flow, see [5, p. 448].

HOPF'S THEOREM. Let π be a flow on a compact metric space X and let λ be a finite measure on X that is invariant with respect to π. Then except for a set of λ-measure zero, every point $x \in X$ has the property that the motion $\pi(x, t)$ is Poisson stable.

Since we have restricted our attention to generalizing (H-2), we shall make the following assumption:

(G-3)   There is a compact set $K \subset W$ such that $\phi(x, f, t) \in K$ for all t in R, whenever $x \in K$.

One should note, see [8], that if f is regular on W x R and (G-3) is satisfied, then for every f^* in H(f) one has $\phi(x, f^*, t) \in K$ for all t in R, whenever $x \in K$.

THEOREM 2. Assume that hypotheses (G-1), (G-2),
and (G-3) are satisfied. Then except for a set E
in H(f) of ν-measure zero, the set

$$\{x \in K : \phi(x, f^*, t) \quad \text{is not Poisson stable}\}$$

has μ-measure zero, where $f^* \in H(f)$ - E. Furthermore, if μ is the Lebesgue measure, then for f^* in
H(f) - E the set

$$\{x \in K : \phi(x, f^*, t) \quad \text{is Poisson stable}\}$$

is everywhere dense in K.

Proof. We can normalize the measures so that $\mu(K)$
= 1 and $\nu(H(f)) = 1$. (If either measure is the
zero measure, the result is trivial.) Since the
measure $m = \mu \times \nu$ on K x H(f) is invariant for the
flow (π) on K x H(f) it follows from Hopf's theorem
that the set

$$A = \{(x, f^*) : \pi(x, f^*, t) \quad \text{is Poisson stable}\}$$

has m-measure one, that is, $m(A) = m(K \times H(f))$.
Define the set E in H(f) as the collection of all
f^* such that the section

$$\{x \in K : \pi(x, f^*, t) \quad \text{is Poisson stable}\}$$

has μ-measure less than one. It follows from
Fubini's theorem, see [2], that $\nu(E) = 0$. Also,
for every f^* in $H(f)$ - E the set

$$B = \left\{ x \in K : \pi(x, f^*, t) \quad \text{is Poisson stable} \right\}$$
$$\subset \left\{ x \in K : \Phi(x, f^*, t) \quad \text{is Poisson} \right.$$
$$\left. \text{stable} \right\}$$

has μ-measure one and its complement has μ-measure
zero, which proves the first assertion.

Since every nonempty open set in W has positive Lebesgue measure it follows that the set B is
everywhere dense in K, which completes the proof.

Remarks. (1) If $f(x, t)$ is uniformly almost
periodic in t, then the measure ν on $H(f)$ is the
Haar measure. For the special case where $f(x, t)$
is periodic in t, the set E is necessarily empty.
One might ask whether the set E can be nonempty
when $f(x, t)$ is uniformly almost periodic, but not
periodic. The author does not know the answer, but
it seems like an interesting question, not only
because of its mathematical content, but also
because of some physical implications.

(2) The conclusion of Theorem 2 can be

reformulated as follows, where μ is the Lebesgue measure. We refer to a differential equation (NA*) for f* in H(f) as a <u>world</u>, and we say that a world f* is <u>good</u> if the set

$$\{x \in K : \phi(x, f^*, t) \quad \text{is Poisson stable}\}$$

is everywhere dense in K. Then Theorem 2 asserts that "except for a set of ν-measure zero, every world is good." But again, the reader should note that the question of whether a <u>given</u> world (NA) is good is not resolved, except for the special case noted above.

4. ERGODIC THEORY

The ergodic theorems of G. D. Birkhoff, see [1 and 5, pp. 459 ff.], can be extended to the non-autonomous equation (NA) using the analysis of Section 2. For this section we shall make the following assumptions:

(K-1) f is regular on W x R.

(K-2) μ is a measure on W with $\mu(W) = 1$ and such that μ is invariant with respect to f.

(K-3) H(f) is compact and ν is an invariant

measure on H(f) with $\nu(H(f)) = 1$.

(K-4) For every f^* in H(f) and x in W, the solution $\phi(x, f^*, t)$ remains in W for all t in R.

THEOREM 3. Under hypotheses (K-1) - (K-4), for every g in $L_1(W, \mu)$ there is a G in $L_1(W \times H(f), m)$ such that

$$\lim_{T \to \infty} \frac{1}{T} \int_0^T g(\phi(x, f, t)) \, dt$$

$$= \lim_{T \to \infty} \frac{1}{2T} \int_{-T}^T g(\phi(x, f, t)) \, dt = G(x, f)$$

$$G(\pi(x, f, t)) = G(x, f)$$

$$\int_W g(x) \, d\mu = \int_{W \times H(f)} G(x, f) \, dm$$

where $m = \mu \times \nu$ and the first two equalities hold m almost everywhere.

The proof of Theorem 3 is a direct application of the standard ergodic theorem. We refer the reader to [9] for the details.

An interesting problem is to decide whether the function G in Theorem 3 is actually independent of f, which would mean that one could view G as an element of $L_1(W, \mu)$. The only result we can prove

has hypotheses which are so strong that the function
G is a constant function.

A set $A \subset W$ is said to be <u>invariant</u> for (NA)
if $\phi(x, f, t) \in A$ for all t in R whenever $x \in A$.
We shall say that the solutions $\phi(x, f, t)$ are
μ-<u>mixing</u> if for every measurable invariant set $A \subset W$
one has

$$\mu(A)\mu(W - A) = 0$$

that is either A, or its complement has μ-measure
zero.

THEOREM 4.   Assume that hypotheses (K-1) - (K-4)
are satisfied and also assume that for every f^*
in H(f) the solutions $\phi(x, f^*, t)$ are μ-mixing.
Then the function G(x, f) given in Theorem 3 is
the constant function

$$G(x, f) = \int_W g(x) \, d\mu$$

We refer the reader to [9] for a proof of this
result.

REFERENCES

1. Birkhoff, G. D., Dynamical Systems, Am. Math. Soc. Coll. Publ., 9, Rev. ed. (1966).

2. Dunford, N., and Schwartz, J. T., Linear Operators, Part I, Interscience, New York, 1958.

3. Gottschalk, W. H., and Hedlund, G. A., Topological Dynamics, Am. Math. Soc. Colloq. Publ., 36 (1955).

4. Krylov, N. M., and Bogol'ubov, N. N., La theorie generale de la mesure et son application a l'etude des systemes dynamique de la mecanique non lineaire, Ann. Math.(2), 38 (1937), pp. 65-113.

5. Nemytskii, V. V., and Stepanov, V. V., Qualitative Theory of Differential Equations, Princeton University Press, Princeton, New Jersey, 1960.

6. Sell, G. R., On the Fundamental Theory of Ordinary Differential Equations, J. Diff. Eq., 1 (1965), pp. 370-392.

7. Sell, G. R., Nonautonomous Differential Equations and Topological Dynamics I, The Basic Theory, Trans. Am. Math. Soc., 127 (1967), pp. 241-262.

8.   Sell, G. R., Nonautonomous Differential
Equations and Topological Dynamics II, Limiting
Equations, Trans. Am. Math. Soc., 127 (1967), pp.
263-283.

9.   Sell, G. R., Topological Dynamics and Ordinary
Differential Equations, Lecture Notes, University
of Minnesota, 1967.

TOPOLOGICAL PROPERTIES OF WEAK
ATTRACTORS

G. P. Szegö

(Universita di Milano, Italy)

It has been recently shown [1, 2] that the concept of weak attractor, introduced by N. P. Bhatia [2] can be effectively used as a fundamental concept in the stability theory of dynamical systems. For instance, since it has been proved [1, Theorem 2.6.12; 2] that all compact sets which are stable and weakly attracting are asymptotically stable, the concept of weak attraction can replace that of attraction in the usual definition of symptotic stability. In what follows we shall prove some topological properties of the weak attractor and of the regions of weak attraction.

1. NOTATIONS AND DEFINITIONS

X denotes a locally compact Hausdorff space, R^n the n-dimensional Euclidean space, R the set of real numbers, R^+ and R^- the set of nonnegative and nonpositive real numbers, respectively.

A dynamical system, or continuous flow on X, is the triplet (X, R, π) where the continuous map π: X x R → X satisfies the two following conditions

(i) $\pi(x, 0) = x$ for all $x \in X$

(ii) $\pi(\pi(x, t_1), t_2) = \pi(x, t_1 + t_2)$ for all $t_1, t_2 \in R$, $x \in X$

If, for each $x \in X$, $\varphi(x) \subset X$, for any $M \subset X$,

$$\varphi(M) = \bigcup_{x \in M} \varphi(x).$$

For any $x \in X$, the trajectory, positive semi-trajectory, the sets $\gamma(x) = \pi(x, R)$, $\gamma^+(x) = \pi(x, R^+)$, $\gamma^-(x) = \pi(x, R^-)$.

$M \subset X$ is called invariant, positively invariant, negatively invariant if, respectively, $\gamma(M) = M$, $\gamma^+(M) = M$, $\gamma^-(M) = M$.

If $x \in X$ is invariant, it is called a rest point.

If $M \subset X$ is closed and invariant and does not contain any closed and invariant proper subset, then it is called minimal.

The set $\Lambda^+(x) = \cap\{\overline{\gamma^+(y)}: y \in \gamma^+(x)\}$ is called the positive limit set of the point $x \in X$, while the set $\Lambda^-(x) = \cap\{\overline{\gamma^-(y)}: y \in \gamma^-(x)\}$ is called the negative limit set of x.

The set $D^+(x) = \cap\{\gamma^+(V): V$ is a neighborhood of $x\}$ is called the first positive prolongation of the point $x \in X$.

The set $J^+(x) = \cap\{D^+(y): y \in \gamma^+(x)\}$ is called the (first positive) prolongational limit set.

$\Lambda^+(x)$ and $J^+(x)$ are closed and invariant sets while $\overline{\gamma^+(x)}$ and $D^+(x)$ are closed and positively invariant. A compact set $M \subset X$, is said to be:

(i)   a (positive) weak attractor if the set

$$A_\omega(M) = \{x \in X: \Lambda^+(x) \cap M \neq \phi\} \tag{1.1}$$

is a neighborhood of M;

(ii)   a (positive) attractor if the set

$$A(M) = \{x \in X: \Lambda^+(x) \neq \phi, \ \Lambda^+(x) \subset M\} \tag{1.2}$$

is a neighborhood of M;

(iii)   a (positive) attractor relative to a set $B \subset X$ if $B \neq \phi$ and $B \subset A(M)$;

(iv)   a (positive) uniform attractor if the

set

$$A_u(M) = \left\{ x \in M: J^+(x) \neq \phi, \ J^+(x) \subset M \right\} \quad (1.3)$$

is a neighborhood of M;

(v) (positively) stable, if for every neighborhood V of M there is a neighborhood V of M such that $\gamma^+(V) = U$;

(vi) (positively) asymptotically stable [or (positive) stable attractor] if it is stable and weakly attracting; and

(vii) unstable if it is not stable. The sets $A_\omega(M)$, $A(M)$, and $A_u(M)$ are called the regions of weak attraction, attraction, and uniform attraction of M, respectively. Similarly, by using the sets $\Lambda^-(x)$ one can define negative weak attractors, negative attractors, negatively asymptotically stable sets, etc.

2.   STATEMENT OF THE PROBLEM

The strongest possible stability property of the ones listed above is asymptotic stability. In fact, asymptotic stability implies uniform attraction [1, Theorems 1.5.6, 1.5.28, 2.6.13; 3] and the

existence of a continuous real-valued function $\Phi(x)$
which characterizes M as shown in the following
lemma.

2.1 LEMMA [1, Theorem 2.21; 4]. Let X be a locally
compact metric space. Let $M \subset X$ be a compact
asymptotically stable set. Let $v = \Phi(x)$ be any
continuous function defined on some neighborhood
N of M and having the properties

$$\Phi(x) = 0 \quad \text{for} \quad x \in M, \ \Phi(x) > 0 \quad \text{for}$$
$$x \notin M$$
$$\Phi(xt) < \Phi(x) \quad \text{for} \quad x \notin M, \ t > 0, \quad \text{and}$$
$$x[0, \ t] \subset N$$

[such functions can always be defined on A(M)].
Let $\epsilon > 0$ be such that $S[M, \ \epsilon]$ is a compact subset
of N. Let α, $0 < \alpha < m(\epsilon)$, where

$$m(\epsilon) = \min\{\Phi(x) : x \in H(M, \ \epsilon)\} \tag{2.2}$$

Then the set

$$P_\alpha = K_\alpha \cap S[M, \ \epsilon] \tag{2.3}$$

where

$$K_\alpha = \left\{ x \in N: \Phi(x) \leq \alpha \right\} \tag{2.4}$$

is a compact positively invariant set, with
$P_\alpha \subset A(M)$.

Moreover, P_α is a retract of $A(M)$.

Also weak attractors and their regions can be shown to have strong properties in spite of the generality of the concept of weak attraction. These strong properties are essentially due to the fact that there exists an asymptotically stable set associated with each compact weak attractor.

2.5 THEOREM [1, Theorem 2.6.15; 2]. Let M be a compact weak attractor. Then:

(i) the set $D^+(M)$ is compact and asymptotically stable;

(ii) $A(D^+(M)) = A_\omega(M)$;

(iii) $D^+(M)$ is the smallest asymptotically stable set containing M.

Similarly associated with each compact positively (or negatively) invariant set M there exists an invariant set $M^* \subset M$ which is positively (or negatively) asymptotically stable. In fact

2.6 THEOREM [1, Theorem 1.5.40; 5]. Let M be a positively invariant compact set and $M^* \subset M$ be the largest invariant set contained in M. Then M^* is asymptotically stable relative to M.

Notice that the set M^* is never empty because, since M is compact such that $\gamma^+(M) \subset M$, it follows that $\Lambda^+(M) \subset M$ and $\Lambda^+(M) \subset M^*$. Thus again, we can prove rather strong properties of a compact positively (negatively) invariant set M by considering the properties of M^*.

In this paper, we shall discuss results on the topological properties of weak attractors. These results have proved to be quite useful in the solution of various problems [6] and it is hoped that when completed they will provide a classification of the possible "canonical regions" defined by dynamical systems in the space X. Most of the results that we shall present are proved in the space R^n.

3. TOPOLOGICAL PROPERTIES OF WEAK ATTRACTORS

Our main result is:

3.1 THEOREM [1, Theorem 2.8.6; 7]. Let $M \subset R^n$ be a compact weak attractor. Let $A_\omega(M)$ be homeomorphic to R^n. Then M contains a rest point.

The proof of this theorem is based upon the following lemma, whose proof is omitted.

3.2 LEMMA [1, Theorem 1.9.5; 3]. Let $M \subset X$ be compact. Let $\{\gamma_n\} \subset M$ be a sequence of periodic trajectories with periods $t_n \to 0$. Then M contains a rest point.

3.3 PROOF OF THEOREM 3.1.

<u>Proof</u>. By Theorem 2.5, $D^+(M)$ is an asymptotically stable compact set with $A(D^+(M)) = A(M)$. Let $\Phi(x)$ be any function for the asymptotically stable set $D^+(M)$ as in Lemma 2.1 and consider a set P_a for $\Phi(x)$. Then P_a is compact, positively invariant, and a retract of $A(M)$. As $A(M)$ is homeomorphic to E we can choose a compact set B, $P_a \subset B \subset A(M)$, where B is homeomorphic to the unit ball in R^n. Then P_a is a retract of B. Thus P_a has the fixed point property, as B has by the Brouwer fixed point theorem. Since P_a is positively invariant, the

transition π^τ maps P_a into P_a for each $\tau \geq 0$. Thus for each fixed $\tau > 0$, π^τ has a fixed point in P_a, that is, corresponding to any $\tau > 0$ there is an $x_\tau \in P_a$ such that $\pi^\tau(x_\tau) = \pi(x_\tau, \tau) = x_\tau$. Thus the orbit $\gamma(x_\tau)$ is closed and has a period τ, moreover $\gamma(x_\tau) \subset P_a$, because $\gamma(x_\tau) = \gamma^+(x_\tau) \subset P_a$. We have thus shown that, corresponding to any sequence $\{\tau_n\}$, $\tau_n > 0$, $\tau_n \to 0$, there is a sequence of closed orbits $\{\gamma_n\}$, $\gamma_n = \gamma(x_{\tau_n})$, with γ_n having a period τ_n. This sequence being in P_a, P_a contains a rest point $x*$, say (Lemma 3.2). However, $M \subset D^+(M) \subset P_a \subset A(M)$. As M is a weak attractor we have $\Lambda^+(x) \cap M \neq \phi$ for each $x \in A(M)$. Thus $\Lambda^+(x^*) \cap M \neq \phi$. But $\Lambda^+(x^*) = \{x^*\}$, as x^* is a rest point. Hence $x^* \in M$ and the theorem is proved.

3.4 COROLLARY. Let $M \subset R^n$ be a compact positively invariant set, which is homeomorphic to R^n; then M contains a rest point.

3.5 COROLLARY. Let $M \subset R^n$ be a compact minimal global weak attractor; then M is a rest point.

4. TOPOLOGICAL PROPERTIES OF STABLE ATTRACTORS

By using a theorem on the properties of uniform attractors [1, Theorems 1.5.28, 1.5.6, 2.6.13] (Lemma 4.1) and a theorem due to M. Brown [8] (Lemma 4.2), we shall be able to prove an interesting result on the topological properties of the region of attraction of an asymptotically stable rest point.

4.1 LEMMA [1, Theorems 1.5.6, 1.5.28, 2.6.13]. Let M be a compact stable attractor, then it is a uniform attractor, and there is a neighborhood U of M such that for each compact set $K \subset U$ and $\alpha > 0$ there exists a $t \in R^+$, $z = z(K, \alpha)$, such that $\gamma^+(\pi(x, \tau)) \subset S(M, \alpha)$ for each $x \in K$.

4.2 LEMMA. Let $\{V_n\}$ be a monotone sequence of open n-cells in R^n, that is, $V_n \subset V_{n+1}$, $n = 1, 2, \ldots$. Then $\{\bigcup_{n=1,2,\ldots} V_n\}$ is an open n-cell.

4.3 THEOREM. If a rest point $p \in E$ is asymptotically stable, then A(p) is homeomorphic to R^n.

Proof. Since A(p) is a neighborhood of p, there is

an $\epsilon > 0$ such that the closed ball $S[p, \epsilon] \subset A(p)$. For each $t \in R$, the transition π^t being a homeomorphism of R^n onto R^n, the image $S(p, \epsilon)t$ of the open ball $S(p, \epsilon)$ by π^t is an open n-cell. We claim now that for any given t_1 there exists a t_2, $t_2 < t_1$, such that $S(p, \epsilon)t_1 \subset S(p, \epsilon)t_2$. This is so because $\overline{S(p, \epsilon)t_1}$ being a subset of the compact set $S[P, \epsilon]t_1$, is itself compact. Further, $S[p, \epsilon]t_1 \subset A(p)$, and $A(p)$ is open. Since p is a stable attractor (Lemma 4.1) there exists a $T > 0$ such that $S[p, \epsilon](t_1 + t) \subset S(p\ \epsilon)t_1$ for $t \geq T$. In particular,

$$S[p, \epsilon](t_1 + T) \subset S(p, \epsilon)t_1 \subset S[p, \epsilon]t_1$$

Hence

$$S[p, \epsilon]t_1 \subset S(p, \epsilon)(t_1 - T) \subset S[p, \epsilon](t_1 - T)$$

Setting $t_2 = t_1 - T$, we get $S[p, \epsilon]t_1 \subset S(p, \epsilon)t_2$. The above analysis shows that we can choose a sequence $\{t_n\}$, $t_n \rightarrow -\infty$, such that $\{S(p, \epsilon)t_n\}$ is a monotone sequence of open n-cells. By Lemma 4.2 $\cup \{S(p, \epsilon)t_n; n = 1, 2., ...\}$ is an open n-cell. But this last union is $A(p)$, so that $A(p)$ is an open n-cell and hence homeomorphic to E.

4.5 COROLLARY. If p is an asymptotically stable
rest point, then $A(p)\backslash\{p\}$ is homeomorphic to $R^n\backslash\{0\}$,
where 0 is the origin in R^n.

We can now prove the following result.

4.6 THEOREM. Let $M \subset R^n$ be a compact globally
asymptotically stable set. Then $R^n\backslash M = C(M)$ is
homeomorphic to $R^n\backslash\{0\}$.

Proof. By Theorem 2.1, M contains a rest point. We
may assume without loss of generality that M contains
the origin 0 and 0 is a rest point. Consider now
the homeomorphism $\hbar: R^n\backslash\{0\} \to E\backslash\{0\}$ defined by
$h(x) = \dfrac{x}{\|x\|^2}$ where $\|x\|$ is the Euclidean norm of x.
$\hbar$ maps the given dynamical system into a dynamical
system on E, with 0 becoming a negatively asymptotically stable rest point, and $R^n\backslash M$ is mapped onto
$A(0)\backslash\{0\}$, where $A(0)$ is now the region of negative
attraction of 0. By the Corollary 4.5, $A(0)\backslash\{0\}$ is
homeomorphic to $R^n\backslash\{0\}$. Hence the result follows.

Lemma 4.2 is due to Morton Brown [8]. The
results contained in this section, and in particular Theorem 4.3 and the natural conjecture which
generalizes this theorem to sets $M \subset R^n$ such that
$R^n\backslash M$ is homeomorphic to $R^n\backslash\{0\}$, are rather useful.

In particular they may have a strong influence on the solution of one of the most important still open problems in the stability theory of dynamical systems, namely, the problem of local properties and the related theory of separatrices.

A separatrix, according to S. Lefschetz [9, p. 223] is, in R^2, "a trajectory (not a critical point) behaving topologically abnormally in comparison with neighboring paths."

A theory of separatrices in R^2 was formally suggested by Markus [10] who gives a definition of separatrix and concludes that the union σ (separating set) of all separatrices of a differential system in R^2 is closed.

Each component of the set $C(\sigma)$ is called a canonical region by Markus. Markus proves that in each canonical region the flow is "parallel," that is, either parallelizable or homeomorphic to a family of concentric cycles.

Clearly since the flow is parallel in each canonical region it admits a transversal section there. The results presented in this section are helpful in generalizing some of these results to

flows in R^n. For instance, one can show (after a
suitable generalization of the concept of separatrix) that the number of canonical regions homeomorphic to balls cannot exceed the number of
equilibrium points of the flow. If, in addition,
one defines the separating set in such a way that
in the corresponding canonical regions the flow has
only strong stability properties, then the
characterization of the separating set above (which
may have a very complicated structure) would be
enough for the complete global description of the
stability properties of the flow.

REFERENCES

1. Bhatia, N. P., and Szegö, G. P., Dynamical
Systems: Stability Theory, Lecture Notes in
Mathematics, Vol. 35, Springer-Verlag, Berlin-
Heidelberg-New York, 1967
2. Bhatia, N. P., Weak Attractors in Dynamical
Systems, Bol. Soc. Mat. Mex., 11 (1966), pp. 56-64.
3. Bhatia, N. P., Lazer, A. C., and Szegö, G. P.,
On Global Weak Attractors in Dynamical Systems, J.
Math. Anal. App., 16 (1966), pp. 544-552.

4. Bhatia, N. P., On Asymptotic Stability in Dynamical Systems, Math. Systems Th., 1 (1967), pp. 113-127.

5. Lefschetz, S., Liapunov and Stability in Dynamical Systems, Bol. Soc. Mat. Mex., 3 (1958), pp. 25-39.

6. Szegö, G. P., Olech, C., and Cellina, A., On the Stability Properties of a Third-Order System, Ann. Mat. Pura Appl. (to appear).

7. Bhatia, N. P., and Szegö, G. P., Weak Attractors in R^n, Math. Systems Th., 1 (1967), pp. 129-133.

8. Brown, M., The Monotone Union of Open n-Cells Is an Open n-Cell, Proc. Am. Math. Soc., 12 (1961), pp. 812-814.

9. Lefschetz, S., Differential Equations: Geometric Theory, Interscience, New York, 1962.

10. Markus, L., Global Structure of Ordinary Differential Equations in the Plane, Trans. Am. Math. Soc., 76 (1954), pp. 127-148.

TOTALLY PARALLELIZABLE 3-MANIFOLDS

David Tischler

(The City University of New York)

A considerable amount of study has been done on the following questions:

(1)   For what k does a differentiable n-manifold M_n have k linearly independent vector fields?

(2)   For what k does M_n admit a field of k planes?

Less is known about corresponding nonlinear questions such as:

(1')   If there are k linearly independent vector fields on M_n, do there exist k linearly independent vector fields on M_n which pairwise commute?

(2')   If there is a field of k planes on M_n, is there a k-dimensional foliation of M_n?

Having k pairwise commuting vector fields X_i on M_n means that $[X_i, X_j] = 0$ for i, j = 1, ..., k. The largest k for which there are k linearly independent, pairwise commuting vector fields on M_n is called the rank of M_n. That M_n has a k-foliation means that there is a field of k planes on M_n which is given locally by k independent vector fields X_i such that $[X_i, X_j] = \sum_{\ell=1}^{k} f_{i,j}^{\ell} X_\ell$, where i, j = 1, ..., k and the $f_{i,j}^{\ell}$ are real-valued functions on M_n. Here we shall be concerned with questions which in a sense fall between (1') and (2').

If M_n has k independent vector fields one can ask whether there exist k independent vector fields X_i which are pairwise integrable as well. That the X_i are pairwise integrable means $[X_i, X_j] = f_{i,j}X_i + g_{i,j}X_j$ where i, j = 1, ..., k and the $f_{i,j}$ and $g_{i,j}$ are real-valued functions on M_n. It is clear that pairwise commuting implies pairwise integrable and that k linearly independent, pairwise integrable vector fields define a k-foliation.

DEFINITION. A C^∞ n-manifold M_n is totally paral-lelizable if there exist n independent C^∞ vector fields on M_n which are pairwise integrable.

It is clear that each subset of (n - 1) vector fields of the (n) totally parallelizing vector fields gives rise to an (n - 1)-foliation. These n foliations clearly meet transversally [that is, the n (n - 1) planes in the tangent space of M_n at each point meet transversally].

Before going into detail I would like to thank Richard Sacksteder for his advice.

Since, as is well known, all compact orientable 3-manifolds are parallelizable and, by [1], they all admit a 2-foliation, we propose the question: Which compact orientable 3-manifolds are totally parallelizable? It was shown in [2, 3] that there are compact orientable 3-manifolds including S^3 and $S^1 \times S^2$ which have rank one. In this paper it is shown that compact orientable 3-manifolds which are principal circle bundles over orientable 2-manifolds are totally parallelizable. The precise statement is given in Section 1 below. These bundles include S^3 and $S^1 \times S^2$. I believe the total parallelizability of the other compact orientable 3-manifolds is not known. In particular, it would be instructive to know the answer for the lens spaces L (p, q), where q $\neq$ 1. A more general

question which also seems to be unanswered is: If
M_n is parallelizable, is it totally parallelizable?

1.   PRELIMINARIES AND STATEMENT OF RESULT

All mappings and manifolds that are used will
be understood to be differentiable of class C^∞.

DEFINITION.   A k-foliation F of M_n is a collection
of disjoint k-dimensional connected submanifolds of
M_n (not necessarily regular) which are called leaves
of F, and have the following properties:

(i) M_n = union of the leaves of F;

(ii)   each point of M_n lies in an open
neighborhood U of M_n such that there is a
diffeomorphism from U to R^n which carries the
intersection of any leaf with U (nonempty) onto
a union of k planes in R^n of the form
$$\{(x_1, \ldots, x_n) \,|\, x_j = \text{constant}, \, j \geq k + 1\}.$$
To see that this definition of a foliation
agrees with the definition given above see [4].
The correspondence between the two definitions is
that the leaves of F are the integral manifolds for
the field of k planes.   Denote the leaf of F through

the point p by F_p. An $(n - 1)$-dimensional foliation F is called oriented if there is a nonzero vector field on M_n which is nowhere tangent to the leaves of F. It was mentioned above that if M_n is totally parallelizable then there are n codimension 1 foliations on M_n which are transversal; these foliations are oriented by taking the kth vector field as the transversal field to the foliation which is tangent to the other $(n - 1)$ vector fields. There is a converse: if M_n has n oriented transversal foliations, then M_n is totally parallelizable. We show this converse for the case $n = 3$. Suppose that F^1 and F^2 are orientable transversal 2-foliations on M_3. Then it is straightforward to show that there exists a nonzero vector field on M_3, each of whose integral curves is the intersection of a leaf of F^1 with a leaf of F^2. So if we have oriented foliations F^i, $i = 1, 2, 3$ on M_3, which are transversal, they will yield three nonzero vector fields $X_{i,j}$, $i \neq j$, $i, j = 1, 2, 3$, where $X_{i,j}$ is gotten from F^i and F^j. The $X_{i,j}$ are independent because the F^i are transversal. The $X_{i,j}$ are pairwise integrable since for i, j, k distinct indices, $X_{i,j}$ and $X_{i,k}$ span a field of

2=planes whose integral manifolds are the leaves
of F^i.

In this paper we consider principal circle
bundles which are differentiable bundles in the
sense of [5].

THEOREM 1.0. If (M, B_K, S^1) is a principal circle
bundle with:

(i)   total space, a compact orientable 3-
manifold;

(ii)   base space B_K, a compact orientable
2-manifold of genus K, $K \geq 0$;

(iii) fiber the circle S^1;

then M is totally parallelizable.

Theorem 1.0 will follow from a series of
lemmas. By the above remark, to show Theorem 1.0
it suffices to find three oriented transversal
2-foliations on M.

2. INITIAL CONSTRUCTIONS

DEFINITION 2.0. $D_K = \{(x, y) \in R^2 \mid (x^2 + y^2)^{1/2}$
$\leq 10K + 9\frac{1}{2}, ((x - a_i)^2 + y^2)^{1/2} \geq \frac{1}{2}\}$ where a_i
$= 10(-K - 1 + 2i)$, $i = 1, \ldots, K$. Let $a_0 = 0$ for

notational convenience. (R denotes the real numbers and the circle S^1 is identified with R mod 2π.)

D_K is a closed 2-disk with K holes. The boundary of D_K, denoted ∂D_K, consists of K + 1 circles C_i centered at $(a_i, 0)$, i = 0, 1, ..., K. The radius of C_0 is $10K + 9\frac{1}{2}$ and that of C_i, i $\neq$ 0, is $\frac{1}{2}$. For each i, let (τ_i, θ_i) be polar coordinates centered at $(a_i, 0)$. The sets

$$\beta^i = \{(\tau_i, \theta_i) \in D_K \mid \tau_i \in [\tfrac{1}{2}, 9\tfrac{1}{2}]\} \quad i \neq 0$$

and

$$\beta^0 = \{(\tau_0, \theta_0) \in D_K \mid \tau_0 \in [10K + \tfrac{1}{2}, 10K + 9\tfrac{1}{2}]\}$$

form collar neighborhoods of the C_i, which are pairwise disjoint. Letting $t_i = 9\frac{1}{2} - \tau_i$, i $\neq$ 0, and $t_0 = \tau_0 - 10K - \frac{1}{2}$ we have

$$\beta^i = \{(t_i, \theta_i) \in [0, 9] \times S^1\}$$

We set $\beta = \cup_{i=0}^K \beta^i$. If T is a subset of $[0, 9]$, define

$$\beta_T^{\ i} = \{(t_i, \theta_i) \mid t_i \in T\} \quad \text{and} \quad \beta_T = \cup_{i=0}^K \beta_T^{\ i}$$

The compact orientable 2-manifold of genus K, B_K (K $\geq$ 0), is the double of the manifold D_K.

We use $D_K{}^j$, $j = 1$, 2, to denote the two copies of
D_K whose union is B_K. We will also sometimes use
the notation $\partial D_K{}^j = \cup_{i=0}^{K} C_i{}^j$.

We begin by finding three transversal foliations on $D_K \times S^1$.

LEMMA 2.1. There exist foliations G^i, $i = 1$, 2, 3,
on $D_K \times S^1$ with the following properties:

(i)   the G^i are oriented $i = 1$, 2, 3;

(ii) the G^i, $i = 1$, 2, 3 are transversal;

(iii) G^1 on $\beta_{[3,9]} \times S^1$ consists of the
leaves $\{(t, \theta) \times S^1 \mid t = \text{constant}\}$;

(iv) with the usual Euclidean metric, the
leaves of G^i, $i = 2$, 3, are normal to the leaves
of G^1 on $\beta_{[3,9]} \times S^1$.

First we find foliations F^i, $i = 1$, 2, 3, on
$D_K \times R$ satisfying conditions analogous to (i) and
(ii). The F^i will be modified on $\beta \times R$ to E^i,
which will satisfy conditions analogous to (iii)
and (iv) in addition. Finally the E^i will be
transferred to $D_K \times S^1$ as the G^i satisfying the
lemma.

Denote points in R by z and the corresponding
points in S^1 by $\bar{z}$. The leaves of the foliation F^1

will be given on $(D_K - \beta_{[2,9]}) \times R$ by the graphs of
the family of functions $A_1{}^\rho : D_K - \beta_{[2,9]} \to R$, $\rho \in R$.
In order to define $A_1{}^\rho$ we note the existence of a
real-valued function g on $(-\infty, 1)$ with the properties:

   (i) $g(t) = 0$ for $t \le \frac{1}{2}$

   (ii) $g'(t) > 0$ for $t \in (\frac{1}{2}, 1)$

   (iii) $g'(t)$ is a monotonically

           increasing function

   (iv)   the graph of g in the plane

           asymptotically approaches the

           vertical at one. Furthermore,

           the graphs of the family of   (2.2)

           functions $g^\rho(t) = g(t) + \rho$,

           $\rho \in R$, along with the vertical

           lines in the plane with equations,

           $t = $ constant, $t \ge 1$, form a one-

           dimensional foliation of the

           plane.

For details on the construction of g and a
proof that F^1 to be defined is a foliation, see [1].
For each $\rho \in R$ define $A_1{}^\rho$ by

$$A_1^\rho (x, y) = \rho \quad (x, y) \in D_K - \beta \qquad \text{(i)}$$

$$A_1^\rho (t_i, \theta_i) = g(t_i - 1) + \rho$$
$$(t_i, \theta_i) \in \beta_{[0,2]}^i \quad i \neq 0 \qquad \text{(ii)}$$

$$A_1^\rho (t_0, \theta_0) = -g(t_0 - 1) + \rho$$
$$(t_0, \theta_0) \in \beta_{[0,2]}^0 \qquad \text{(iii)}$$

It remains to define F^1 on $\beta_{[2,9]}$ x R. For each
i, $0 \leq i \leq K$, $\beta_{[2,9]}^i$ x R is foliated by the leaves

$$\{(t_i, \theta_i, z) \mid t_i = \text{constant}\}$$
$$t_i \in [2,9] \qquad \qquad (2.3)$$

To define F^2 we again utilize families of
functions. On the (x, y) plane minus the strip
$H = \{(x, y) \mid \ |y| \leq \epsilon\}$, $\epsilon < \dfrac{1}{2}$, define for $\rho \in R$,

$$A_2^\rho (x, y) = -g(-\frac{1}{2} \cdot \frac{|y|}{10(K + 1)}$$

$$+ 1 + \frac{1}{2} \cdot \frac{\epsilon}{10(K + 1)}) + \rho$$

Define the foliation of H x R given by the leaves

$$N_\gamma = \{(x, y, z) \in R^2 \text{ x R} \mid y = \gamma\}$$
$$|\gamma| \leq \epsilon \qquad \qquad (2.4)$$

The graphs of the family of functions A_2^ρ, $\rho \in R$, and the family of planes N_γ, $|\gamma| \leq \epsilon$ form a foliation of $R^2 \times R$ which we simply restrict to $D_K \times R$ to form the foliation F^2; F^2 is a foliation by (2.2), property (iv).

To define F_3, along with g we need an auxiliary function h. There exists a real-valued function h on (0, 1) such that:

(i) $h(t) \leq 0$ for $t \leq \frac{1}{2}$

(ii) $h(t) \geq 0$ for $t \geq \frac{1}{2}$

(iii) $h'(t) \geq \delta > 0$ where $\delta > 0$ is sufficiently large

(iv) the graph of h in the plane asymptotically approaches the vertical at $t = 0$ and $t = 1$. The graphs of the family $h^\rho(t) = h(t) + \rho$ and the vertical lines given by t = constant, $|t| \geq 1$, form a foliation of the plane.

(2.5)

The construction of h satisfying (2.5) is essentially the same as that of g and will not be included here either.

Let $b_i = 10(-K - 1 + i)$, $1 \leq i \leq 2K + 1$.

Note that $a_i = b_{2i}$ and $a_i < b_{2i+1}$ for $i = 1, \ldots, K$
and $b_{2i+1} < a_{i+1}$ for $i = 0, \ldots, K - 1$. On the
(x, y) plane minus the strips

$$V_i = \{(x, y) \mid b_i - \epsilon \leq x \leq b_i + \epsilon\}$$
$$1 \leq i \leq 2K + 1$$

define the family of functions $A_3{}^\rho$, $\rho \in R$,

$$A_3{}^\rho(x, y) = \begin{cases} -h\left(\dfrac{x - (b_i + \epsilon)}{10 - 2\epsilon}\right) + \rho & i \text{ odd} \\ \\ h\left(\dfrac{x - (b_i + \epsilon)}{10 - 2\epsilon}\right) + \rho & i \text{ even} \end{cases}$$

for $x \in (b_i + \epsilon, b_{i+1} - \epsilon)$, $1 \leq i \leq 2K$,

$$A_3{}^\rho(x, y) = -g\left(\frac{x}{20} + 1 + \frac{(10K + \epsilon)}{20}\right) + \rho$$
$$x < b_1 - \epsilon$$

$$A_3{}^\rho(x, y) = -g\left(\frac{-x}{20} + 1 + \frac{(10K + \epsilon)}{20}\right) + \rho$$
$$x > b_{2K+1} + \epsilon$$

On the space $V \times R$, where $V = \cup_{i=1}^{2K+1} V_i$, define the
foliation consisting of the planes

$$M_\gamma = \{(x, y, z) \mid x = \gamma\}$$
$$\gamma \in \cup_{i=1}^{2K+1} [b_i - \epsilon, b_i + \epsilon] \qquad (2.6)$$

The graphs of the functions $A_3{}^\rho$, $\rho \in R$, along with
the foliation of $V \times R$ given by the M_γ, form a
foliation of $R^2 \times R$ by properties (iv) of (2.5) and
(2.2). We restrict this foliation to $D_K \times R$ to get
F^3. The F^i, $i = 1, 2, 3$, can be shown to be transversal on $D_K \times R$, but we include only an outline
of the proof since the details are tedious but
straightforward. One sees immediately that since
the gradients of $A_2{}^\rho$ and $A_3{}^\rho$, $\rho \in R$, are nonzero
on D_K, F^2 and F^3 are transversal. The curves gotten
by intersecting the leaves of F^2 with the leaves
of F^3 can then be shown transversal to the leaves
of F^1; on $(D_K - \beta_{[1,9]}) \times R$ clearly; on $\beta^i \times R$,
$i \neq 0$, by (2.2) and $h' > 0$; on $\beta^0 \times R$ by (2.2) and
property (iii) of (2.5). The δ of property (iii)
of (2.5) depends only on g, ϵ, and K.

We now restrict our attention to $\beta_{[3,9]} \times R$
where we modify F^2 and F^3 to E^2 and E^3 so that E^2
and E^3 will be normal to F^1 on $\beta_{[6,9]} \times R$. For
each i, $\beta^i_{[3,9]} \times R$ will have the coordinates
(t_i, θ_i, z), $t_i \in [3, 9]$, $\theta_i \in S^1$, $z \in R$. The
intersection γ_p of $F_p{}^2$ and $F_p{}^3$ for $p \in \beta_{[3,9]} \times R$
will be a curve which meets each leaf of F^1 once
and only once. Thus we can write γ_p as a function

of t_i: $\gamma_p(t_i) = (t_i, \theta_p(t_i), z_p(t_i))$. To complete
Lemma 2.1 we need another lemma.

LEMMA 2.7. There exists a z-invariant diffeomorphism J of $\beta_{[3,9]}$ x R such that:

(i) $\beta_{[3,4]}$ x R and $\beta_{[9,9]}$ x R are left
pointwise fixed;

(ii) the leaves of F^1 are invariant under J;

(iii) J sends lines orthogonal to the (x, y)
plane into such lines;

(iv) $\overline{\gamma}_p(t_i)$ induced from $\gamma_p(t_i)$ by J,
$0 \le i \le K$, is such that

$$\overline{\gamma}_p(t_i) = \gamma_p(t_i) \quad t_i \in [3, 4]; \quad \overline{\gamma}_p(t_i)$$
$$= (t_i, \theta_p(9), z_p(9)), \quad t_i \in [5, 9]$$

(v) the foliations E^i induced from F^i,
$i = 2, 3$, are normal to F^1 on $\beta_{[5,9]}$ x R.

Let Ψ be a function from $[0, 1]$ to itself
such that $\Psi([0, \frac{1}{3}]) = 0$ and $\Psi([\frac{2}{3}, 1]) = 1$. Define
J by

$$p = (t_i, \theta_i, z) \to (t_i, (1 - \Psi(t'_i)) \cdot \theta_i$$
$$+ \Psi(t'_i) \cdot \theta_p(9), (1 - \Psi(t'_i)) \cdot z$$
$$+ \Psi(t'_i) \cdot Z_p(9))$$

where $t'_i = \dfrac{t_i - 3}{6}$

Using the fact that θ_p is not a function of z and that Z_p is z-invariant (that is,

$$\theta(t_i, \theta_i, z_1) = \theta(t_i, \theta_i, z_2) \quad \text{and}$$

$$Z(t_i, \theta_i, z_1 + z_2) = Z(t_i, \theta_i, z_i) + z_2$$

where $z_1, z_2 \in \mathbb{R}$), it is easy to see that J is a diffeomorphism. By the definition of Ψ, (i) is true. By (2.3) and the form of J, (ii) is true. Since θ_p is not a function of z, (iii) follows, and (iv) is clear and implies (v). Thus Lemma 2.7 is true.

Note. For use in Lemma 4.2 the leaves of E^2 and E^3 are like those of F^2 and F^3; either a union of "fibers" (lines orthogonal to the (x, y) plane) or the graphs of a family of functions on $\beta_{[3,9]}$. Note follows from (iii) of Lemma (2.7).

Since F^i on $(D_K - \beta_{[4,9]}) \times \mathbb{R}$ and E^i on $\beta_{[3,9]} \times \mathbb{R}$ agree on $\beta_{[3,4]} \times \mathbb{R}$ and are both z-invariant, they induce foliations G^i on $D_K \times S^1$ (set $E^1 = F^1$). The G^i are clearly oriented by construction [or note that the F^i, i = 1, 2, 3, are invariant under $y \to -y$ and $(D_K \times R)$ $\cap \{(x, y, z) \mid y \geq 0\}$ is simply connected]. Thus the G^i satisfy Lemma 2.1.

3.   DECOMPOSITION OF THE BUNDLE M

Let (M, B_K, S^1) be the bundle in the statement of Theorem 1.0. We denote by $(M^j, D_K{}^j, S^1)$ the bundle M restricted to $D_K{}^j$, $j = 1, 2$.

LEMMA 3.0.   There exists a fiber bundle diffeomorphism $\chi_j : M^j \to D_K{}^j \times S^1$, $j = 1, 2$, where $D_K{}^j \times S^1$ is the trivial principal circle bundle (that is, the restriction of the bundle M to $D_K{}^j$ is trivial).

$D_K{}^j$ is contractible for $K = 0$. For $K > 0$ there is a deformation retraction of $D_K{}^j$ onto the one point union of K circles. Since the only principal S^1 bundle over S^1 is the trivial bundle, we conclude that M^j has a continuous cross section. According to [5] there is then a differentiable cross section and this implies the lemma.

The map Φ defined by

$$\Phi = \chi_2 \circ \chi_1^{-1} : \partial D_K{}^1 \times S^1 \to \partial D_K{}^2 \times S^1$$

is a fiber-preserving, orientation-preserving diffeomorphism. Here $\partial D_K{}^1 = \cup_{i=0}^{K} C_i{}^1$

is identified with $\partial D_K^2 = \cup_{i=0}^K C_i^2$ in B_K by the
identity map. Each connected component of the do-
main of Φ is the product bundle $C_i \times S^1$. Denote Φ
restricted to the ith component of its domain by
Φ_i, $i = 0, \ldots, K$. Then $\Phi_i(\theta_i, \bar{z}) = (\theta_i, \varphi_i(\theta_i, \bar{z}))$.
Consider $(\theta, z) \in [0, 2\pi] \times R$ as a subset of the
universal covering space of $C_i \times S^1$. The universal
covering space is $R \times R$ and the covering map is
given by $\theta_i = \theta \mod 2\pi$, $\bar{z} = z \mod 2\pi$. We use Φ_i,
φ_i to denote their respective liftings to $[0, 2\pi] \times R$.
We let the integer $N_i = \varphi_i(2\pi, 0) - \varphi_i(0, 0)$ and
note that for all $z \in R$, $\varphi_i(2\pi, z) = \varphi_i(0, z)$
$+ 2\pi N_i$.

LEMMA 3.1.   Let $\Phi^{N_i}: C_i \times S^1 \to C_i \times S^1$ be given by
$\Phi^{N_i}(\theta_i, \bar{z}) = (\theta_i, \bar{z} + N_i \theta_i)$. Then for each i,
$i = 0, \ldots, K$, we have that Φ_i is isotopic to Φ^{N_i}.
     Consider the map

$$I: [0, 1] \times [0, 2\pi] \times R \to [0, 2\pi] \times R:$$
$$I(t, \theta, z) = (\theta, (1 - \Psi(t))(z + N_i \theta)$$
$$+ (\Psi(t))(\varphi_i(\theta, z))$$

where Ψ is as in the last section. Since, for a
fixed θ, $z + N_i \theta$ and $\varphi_i(\theta, z)$ are strictly

monotonically increasing functions of z, it follows

for each fixed t that $I(t, \theta, z)$ is a diffeomorphism

of $[0, 2\pi] \times R$. Thus I is an isotopy of the lift-

ings of Φ_i and Φ^{N_i}. It is clear that $I(t, \theta, z + 2\pi n)$

$= I(t, \theta, z) + 2\pi n$, n an integer, and that

$I(t, 2\pi, z) = I(t, 0, z) + 2\pi N_i$. Thus I covers an

isotopy on $C_i \times S^1$ of Φ_i and Φ^{N_i}.

Thus, without loss of generality, we assume

from now on that $\Phi_i = \Phi^{N_i}$. That is, we can assume

$M = (D_K^{\,1} \times S^1) \cup (D_K^{\,2} \times S^1)$ with the identifications

$\Phi^{N_i}: C_i^{\,1} \times S^1 \to C_i^{\,2} \times S^1$ for $i = 0, \ldots, K$. The

maps Φ^{N_i} define the map $\Phi: \partial D_K^{\,1} \times S^1 \to \partial D_K^{\,2} \times S^1$.

Although we have three transversal foliations on

$D_K^{\,1} \times S^1$ and $D_K^{\,2} \times S^1$ by Lemma 2.1, they are not

compatible with the identifications given by Φ.

In the next section we adjust the foliations on

$D_K^{\,2} \times S^1$ so that those on $D_K^{\,2} \times S^1$ and those on

$D_K^{\,1} \times S^1$ do match up along $\partial D_K^{\,1} \times S^1 = \partial D_K^{\,2} \times S^1$.

4. A "HOMOTOPY" OF FOLIATIONS

Consider $[6, 9] \times [0, 2\pi] \times R$ as a subset of

the universal covering space of $[6, 9] \times C_i \times S^1$,

$i = 0, \ldots, K$. Define the diffeomorphism $I_2^{\,i}$ from

$[6, 9]$ x $[0, 2\pi]$ x R to itself:

$$I_2{}^i(t, \theta, z)$$

$$= (t, \theta, z + \eta^i(\theta) \cdot \Psi(\frac{t}{3} - 2) \cdot N_i \cdot \theta) \qquad (4.0)$$

where

$$\eta^i(\theta) = \begin{cases} \Psi\left(\dfrac{\theta}{e^i}\right) & \theta \in [0, e^i] \\[2mm] \Psi\left(\dfrac{\theta - (2\pi - e^i)}{e^i}\right) & \theta \in [2\pi - e^i, 2\pi] \\[2mm] 1 & \text{otherwise} \end{cases}$$

where $e^0 = \sin^{-1}\left(\dfrac{\epsilon}{10K + 9\frac{1}{2}}\right)$; $e^i = \sin^{-1}(2\epsilon)$, $i \neq 0$,

where N_i and Ψ are as in the preceding sections. $I_2{}^i$ covers a diffeomorphism, also denoted $I_2{}^i$, of $[6, 9]$ x C_i x S^1 because $\eta^i(0) = 0 = \eta^i(2\pi)$.

In a similar fashion we define the diffeomorphism $I_3{}^i$ from $[6, 9]$ x $[\frac{\pi}{2}, \frac{5}{2}\pi]$ x R to itself:

$$I_3{}^i(t, \theta, z)$$

$$= (t, \theta, z + \eta^i(\theta - \frac{\pi}{2}) \cdot \Psi(\frac{t}{3} - 2) \cdot N_i \cdot (\theta - \frac{\pi}{2})) \qquad (4.1)$$

$I_3{}^i$ also covers a diffeomorphism of $[6, 9]$ x C_i x S^1. The $I_j{}^i$, $i = 0, \ldots, K$; $j = 2, 3$, define diffeomorphisms I_j of $\beta_{[6,9]}$ x S^1. Let H^j be the foliation of $\beta_{[6,9]}$ x S^1 induced from G^j by I_j,

$j = 2, 3.$

LEMMA 4.2.   (i) I_j, $j = 2, 3$, leaves G^1 invariant on $\beta_{[6,9]} \times S^1$.

(ii) H^j coincides with G^j on $\beta_{[6,7]} \times S^1$, $j = 2, 3$.

(iii)   The diffeomorphism of $\beta_{[8,9]} \times S^1$ to itself given by $(t, \theta_i, \bar{z}_i) \rightarrow (t, \Phi^{N_i}(\theta_i, \bar{z}_i))$, $i = 0, \ldots, K$, takes the foliation G^j into H^j on $\beta_{[8,9]} \times S^1$.

(iv) G^1, H^2, H^3 form a transversal set of foliations on $\beta_{[6,9]} \times S^1$.

Since I_j is fiber preserving, (i) follows. On $\beta_{[6,7]} \times S^1$, I_j, $j = 2, 3$, is the identity, so that (ii) follows. For $t_i \in [8, 9]$ and $\theta_i \notin [0, e^i] \cup [2\pi - e^i, 2\pi]$ we have that $I_2^i(t_i, \theta_i, \bar{z}_i) = (t_i, \theta_i, \Phi^{N_i}(\theta_i, \bar{z}_i))$. Thus, using that I_2^i is fiber preserving and (2.4), we have (iii) when $j = 2$. A similar argument holds for I_3^i, and using (2.6) and $b_{K+1} = 0$, we see that (iii) holds for $j = 3$. In showing (iv) we consider L^j to be the lifting of H^j to $\beta_{[6,9]} \times R$, $j = 2, 3$. $\beta_{[6,9]}$ is the union of two disjoint sets P_1 and P_2; P_1 is the region where in Lemma 2.1 both G^2 and G^3

are given as the graphs of families of functions.
On P_2, one and only one of G^2 and G^3 is given as
the graph of the family of functions; the leaves of
the other are a union of fibers. Hence, since I_j
is fiber preserving, in order to show (iv), it
suffices to check the transversality of E^1, L^2, L^3
on $P_1 \times R$. If P is an arbitrary connected component
of $P_i \cap \beta^i_{[6,9]}$, then $P = \{(t_i, \theta_i) | \theta_i \in (p_1, p_2),$
$t_i \in [6, 9]\}$ for some $(p_1, p_2) \subset (e^i, 2\pi - e^i)$.
For each $q = (\hat{t}_i, \hat{\theta}_i, \hat{z})$ in P x R we conclude from
Lemma 2.1 that $E_q^1 \cap E_q^2$ and $E_q^1 \cap E_q^3$ are the
graphs of the functions $f_2: \{\hat{t}_i\} \times (p_1, p_2) \to R$ and
$f_3: \{\hat{t}_i\} \times (p_1, p_2) \to R$, respectively, where either
$f_2'(\theta_i) > f_3'(\theta_i)$ or $f_3'(\theta_i) > f_2'(\theta_i)$ for $\theta_i \in (p_1, p_2)$.
Assume the latter for concreteness. Now, by (4.0)
and (4.1), it is clear that $E_q^1 \cap L_q^2$ and $E_q^1 \cap L_q^3$
are the graphs of the functions $h_2(\theta_i) = f_2(\theta_i)$
$+ \Psi(\frac{\hat{t}_i}{3} - 2) \cdot N_i \cdot \theta_i$ and $h_3(\theta_i) = f_3(\theta_i) + \Psi(\frac{\hat{t}_i}{3} - 2)$
$\cdot N_i \cdot (\theta_i - \frac{\pi}{2})$, respectively. Thus $h_3'(\theta_i) > h_2'(\theta_i)$,
$\theta_i \in (p_1, p_2)$, and (iv) is true.

We are now in a position to define foliations
F_i, $i = 1, 2, 3$, on all of M. Let $\beta_{[6,9]}$ refer to
D_K^2. Then for $i = 1, 2, 3$ define F_i on $D_K^1 \times S^1$
by G^i, on $(D_K^2 - \beta_{[6,9]}) \times S^1$ by G^i, on $\beta_{[6,9]} \times S^1$

by H^i, where $H^1 = G^1$. It follows from Lemma 4.2
(i), (ii), (iii), and the form of M given at the
end of Section 3, that the F_i are well-defined
foliations. The F_i, i = 1, 2, 3, are transversal
foliations by Lemmas 2.1 and 4.2 (iv). The F_i are
clearly oriented and thus Theorem 1.0 follows.

REFERENCES

1. Lickorish, W. B. R., A Foliation for 3-Mani-
folds, Ann. Math., 82 (1965), pp. 414-420.

2. Lima, E. L., Commuting Vector Fields on S^3, Ann.
Math., 81 (1965), pp. 70-81.

3. Rosenberg, H., The Rank of S^2 x S^1, Am. J. Math.,
87 (1965), pp. 11-24.

4. Palais, R. S., A Global Formulation of the Lie
Theory of Transformation Groups, Mem. Am. Math. Soc.,
No. 22 (1957).

5. Steenrod, N. E., The Topology of Fibre Bundles,
Princeton University Press, Princeton, New Jersey,
1951.

LOCAL ISOMORPHISMS AND LOCAL

PARALLELIZABILITY OF

DYNAMICAL SYSTEMS[1]

Taro Ura

(Kobe University and

Case Western Reserve University)

1. INTRODUCTION

The motivation of this paper is the same as
the paper of O. Hajek in this proceedings. But the
subject to which I will apply categorial considerations is only the parallelizability of flows.
The main purpose of the paper is to introduce local
parallelizability corresponding to various notions
of local isomorphisms, and to establish a necessary
and sufficient condition for each notion of
parallelizability thus considered, with emphasis
on the mutual relations of these notions. Some of

---

[1]This work was partly supported by the National
Science Foundation under Grant No. NSF-GP-7447.

493

them are essentially new as far as the author
knows, and the others are modifications of known
results. Proofs and further detailed discussions
will appear elsewhere.

2. DYNAMICAL SYSTEMS AND THEIR ISOMORPHISMS

   Let (X, π) be a continuous flow or a dynamical system on X, that is, X is a topological space
and π is a mapping of X x R onto X satisfying the
following axioms:

   (1) Identity axiom: $\pi(x, 0) = x$ for $x \in X$

   (2) Homomorphism axiom: $\pi(\pi(x, t), s)$
$= \pi(x, t + s)$ for $x \in X$ $t, s \in R$.

   (3) Continuity axiom: π is continuous on
X x R, where R denotes the set of real numbers.

   Let (X', π') be another flow on X'. An
isomorphism of (X, π) onto (X', π'), which we shall
consider, is a pair of mappings (h, φ) which
satisfies one of the conditions explained later.
An isomorphism which satisfies the condition of
type n will be called a type-n-isomorphism. If
there exists a type-n-isomorphism of (X, π) onto
(X', π'), then we shall say that (X, π) and (X', π')

are type-n-isomorphic. The notion "type-n-isomorphic" for each n defines an equivalence relation
on the family of all dynamical systems.

TYPE 1.   (Topological isomorphisms, [4].)

    (1)   h is a <u>homeomorphism</u> of X onto X'.

    (2) φ is a <u>homeomorphic</u> <u>group</u> <u>isomorphism</u> of
the real additive group R onto itself.

    (3)   (<u>Homomorphism</u> <u>condition</u>)

$$h \ (\pi(x, \ t) = \pi'(h(x), \ \varphi(t)) \tag{α}$$
$$\text{for all} \quad x \in X \quad \text{and for all}$$
$$t \in R$$

This definition is the restriction to dynamical systems of the same definition for continuous
transformation groups given in [4].

    We may note that if φ is a homeomorphic group
isomorphism of R onto R, then there exists $c \neq 0$
such that $\varphi(t) = ct$. We shall say that if $c > 0$,
then (h, φ) is <u>proper</u> and if $c < 0$, then (h, φ) is
<u>dual</u>.

TYPE 2.   (Phase-map with reparametrization [6].)

    (1)   h is a <u>homeomorphism</u> of X onto X'.

(2) φ is a mapping of X x R onto R such that

(a) φ is <u>continuous</u> on X x R,

(b)   for every fixed x $\in$ X, $\varphi(x, t)$
= $\varphi_x(t)$ is an <u>homeomorphism</u> of R onto R
such that $\varphi_x(0) = 0$.

(3)   (<u>Homomorphism condition</u>)

$$h(\pi(x, t)) = \pi'(h(x), \varphi(x, t))$$
$$\text{for all} \quad x \in X \quad \text{and for all} \quad (\alpha')$$
$$t \in R$$

If X is connected, then $\varphi_x(t)$ is strictly
increasing for every x or strictly decreasing for
every x. Therefore, in this case, the distinction
"proper" and "dual" still has meaning.

TYPE 3. In type 2, replace (2) and (3) by the
following (2) and (3).

(2)   For every x $\in$ X, let there be given
two open (finite) or (infinite) intervals J_x
and $J'_{h(x)}$ containing 0. Let $\varphi(x, t)$ be a
continuous function defined on $\cup_{x \in X}\{x\} \times J_x$
and suppose that the mapping $(h(x), \varphi(x, t))$
maps $\cup_{x \in X}\{x\} \times J_x$ homeomorphically onto
$\cup_{x \in X}\{h(x)\} \times J'_{h(x)}$.

(3) $h(\pi(x, t) = \pi'(h(x), \varphi(x, t))$

for all   (x, t)   in (α')

$\cup_{x \in X} \{x\} \times J_x$

(Nonextendability)

If x, x' $\in$ X   and $\pi(x, J_x)$

$\cap \pi(x', J_{x'}) \neq \phi$, then   ($\beta$)

$\pi(x, J_x) = \pi(x', J_{x'})$

Remark. It is clear that type 1 $\subset$ type 2 $\subset$ type 3. We can prove type 2 $\supset$ type 3. This means that the introduction of type-3-isomorphisms is of no use in dynamical systems. But, as we shall see later, they will play a certain role in local dynamical systems.

3. LOCAL DYNAMICAL SYSTEMS

    Before going into local dynamical systems, we would like to explain a theorem concerning dynamical systems.

THEOREM A [11]. Let (X, π) be a given dynamical system and U be an open subset of X. Let x $\in$ U and $I_x \equiv (a_x, b_x)(\ni 0)$ be the maximal open interval such that $(x, I_x) \subset U$. Then:

(1) a_x, b_x are upper and lower semicontinuous functions on U;

(2) if a_x (or b_x) is finite, then $\pi(x, a_2)$ [or $\pi(x, b_2)$] is contained in boundary U.

Condition 1 is equivalent to

(1') the set $U^* = \cup_{x \in U}\{x\} \times I_x$ is open in X x R.

This theorem motivates the following definition of a local dynamical system.[2]

DEFINITION 1 (see [5, 9, 10]). Let X be a topological space, and let an <u>open</u> interval I_x $\equiv (a_x, b_x)(\ni 0)$ be defined for every x $\in$ X such that $X^* \equiv \cup_{x \in X}\{x\} \times I_x$ is <u>open</u> in X x R. Let π be a mapping of X^* into X. (X, π) is called a <u>local dynamical system</u> if

(1) <u>Identity axiom</u>: $\pi(x, 0) = x$ for x $\in$ X.

(2) <u>Homomorphism axiom</u>: $\pi(\pi(x, t), s)$ $= \pi(x, t + s)$ if and only if $\pi(x, t)$ and either side have meaning.

_____

[2] For another motivation, see [9].

(3) <u>Continuity</u> axiom: $\pi(x, t)$ is continuous
on X^*.

(4) <u>Nonextendability</u> axiom: If a_x (or b_x)
is finite, then the cluster set of the mapping
$\pi(x, t)$ (x: fixed; t: considered as the variable)
as $t \rightarrow a_x + 0$ (or $b_x - 0$) is empty.

A dynamical system defined in Section 2,
which will be called a global system from now on,
is a local dynamical system (abbreviated as local
system).

COROALLARY. Let (X, π) be a local system and U be
an open subset of X. Define U^* as in Theorem A,
and let π^* be the restriction of π to U^*. Then
(U, π^*) is again a local system on U.

We are now in a position to define three
types of isomorphisms of local systems corresponding
to those of global systems. To do this, we make
the following changes in the definition of each
type for global systems [11] :

In each of types 1 and 2, the condition (3)
is replaced by

(3') The equality (α) or (α') is satisfied
for all $x \in X$ and for all $t \in I_x$.

In type 3, the condition $(3\alpha')$ is replaced by:

$(3')$ $I_x \subset J_x$ and $I'_{h(x)} \subset J'_{h(x)}$;

and (α') is satisfied on X^*.

DEFINITION 2.   Let (X, π) and (X', π') be two local systems.   Let M be a point or a subset of X. If there exist an open subset U of X containing M and an open subset U' of X' such that there exists a type-n-isomorphism of $(U, \pi*)$ onto $(U', \pi'*)$, n = 1, 2, 3, then we shall say that (X, π) and (X', π') are locally type-n-isomorphic locally at M [and at h(M)].   If, in particular, $(U, \pi*)$ or $(U', \pi'*)$ is a global system, then (X, π) and (X', π') are said to be globally type-n-isomorphic locally at M [and at h(M)].

Remark.   In [8], Definition 3.21 and Theorem 3.22 (R. E. Vinograd) are considered to have type-3-isomorphisms for local dynamical systems as their background of arguments.

4.   PARALLELIZABILITY

DEFINITION 3.   Let X_p be a topological space which

can be written in the form $X_p = Y_p \times R$. Let π_p be the mapping of $X_p \times R$ into X_p defined by $\pi_p((y, t), s) = (y, t + s)$, $y \in Y_p$, $t, s \in R$. Then the global system (X_p, π_p) is called a parallel flow.

DEFINITION 4. Let (X, π) be a global system. If there exists a parallel flow (X_p, π_p) which is type-n-isomorphic to (X, π), then (X, π) is said to be globally type-n-parallelizable (globally on X).

Let (X, π) be a local system and M a point or a subset of X. If there exists a parallel flow (X_p, π_p) such that (X, π) and (X_p, π_p) are globally (or locally) type-n-isomorphic locally at M, then (X, π) is said to be globally (or locally) type-n-parallelizable locally at M.

In the following, we shall always suppose, for simplicity, that the phase space X of a given local system is locally compact and metrizable.

THEOREM 1. Let (X, π) be a local system and $x \in X$. Then

(X, π) is locally type-1-or-2-

parallelizable locally at x

$\Longleftarrow$ (X, π) is globally type-3-

parallelizable locally at x

$\Longleftarrow$ x is regular

$\Longleftrightarrow$ x $\notin$ S

where S denotes the set of all singular points.

For type-1-parallelizability, this is known as the theorem of Whitney and Bebutov (see [8]).

THEOREM 2 [11]. Let (X, π) be a local system and x $\in$ X. Then

(X, π) is locally type-1-or-2-

parallelizable locally at C(x)

$\Longleftarrow$ (X, π) is globally type-3-

parallelizable locally at C(x)

$\Longleftrightarrow$ x is positively and negatively Poisson

unstable

$\Longleftrightarrow$ x $\notin$ L$^+$(x) $\cup$ L$^-$(x)

where L$^+$(x) and L$^-$(x) denote the ω- and α-limit sets of x, and C(x) denotes the whole trajectory through x.

As far as the author knows, this theorem is

essentially new.

THEOREM 3. Let (X, π) be a global system, and let $x \in X$. Then

> (X, π) is globally type-1 or-2
>
> parallelizable locally at x
>
> $\Longleftrightarrow (X, \pi)$ is globally type-1 or 2
>
> parallelizable locally at $C(x)$
>
> $\Longleftrightarrow x$ is a wandering point
>
> $\Longleftrightarrow x \notin J^+(x) \cup J^-(x)$
>
> $\Longleftrightarrow x \notin J^+(x)$
>
> $\Longleftrightarrow x \notin J^-(x)$

where $J^+(x)$, $J^-(x)$ denote the positive and negative prolongational limit sets of x, that is, for example, $J^+(x)$ is the cluster set of the filter base

$$\{ \pi(U, [a, \infty)) \mid U \in \mathcal{U}(x), a \in R \}^3$$

($\mathcal{U}(x)$ is the neighborhood filter of x).

    For type-1-parallelizability, this is known

---

^{3}See [1, 2, 10].

(see [3]).

THEOREM 4. Let (X, π) be a global system and suppose that X is separable. Then

$\quad\quad (X, \pi)$ is globally type-1-or-2-

$\quad\quad\quad$ parallelizable, globally on X

$\Longleftarrow\Longrightarrow (X, \pi)$ is dispersive

$\Longleftarrow\Longrightarrow$ for every $x \in X$, $\quad J^+(x) = \phi$, $\quad J^-(x) = \phi$

$\Longleftarrow\Longrightarrow$ for every $x \in X$, $\quad J^+(x) = \phi$

For type-1-parallelizability the theorem is
essentially proved in [7] and [3], and is given
this form in [2].

Remark. We defined "proper isomorphism" and "dual
isomorphism." But as far as parallelizability is
concerned, the distinctions "proper" and "dual"
do not play any role, since a parallel flow is
type-1-dual isomorphic to itself.

REFERENCES

1. Auslander, J., Generalized Recurrence in Dynamical Systems, Contr. Diff. Eq., III (1964), pp. 65-
74.

2. Bhatia, N. P., Criteria for Dispersive Flows, Math. Nachr., 32 (1966), pp. 89-93.

3. Dugundji, J., and Antosiewicz, H. A., Parallelizable Flows and Liapunov's Second Method, Ann. Math. (2), 73 (1961), pp. 543-555.

4. Gottschalk, W. H., and Hedlund, G. A., Topological Dynamics, Am. Math. Soc. Colloq. Publ, 36 (1955).

5. Hájek, O., Structure of Dynamical Systems, Comment. Math. Univ. Carol., 6 (1965), pp. 53-72.

6. Hájek, O., Categorial Concepts in Dynamical System Theory, this volume.

7. Nemyckiĭ, V. V., Topological Problems of the Theory of Dynamical Systems, Usp. Math. Nauk (N.S.), 4, No. 6 (34) (1949), pp. 91-153; English Translation, Am. Math. Soc. Transl., No. 103 (1954), pp. 1-85.

8. Nemitskii, V. V., and Stepanov, V. V., Qualitative Theory of Differential Equations, Princeton University Press, Princeton, New Jersey, 1960.

9. Ura, T., Sur le courant extérieur à une région invariante, Prolongements d'une caractéristique et l'ordre de stabilite, Funkc. Ekvac., 2 (1959), pp. 143-200.

10. Ura, T., On the Flow Outside a Closed Invariant Set; Stability, Relative Stability and Saddle Sets, Contr. Diff. Eq., III (1964), pp. 249-294.

11. Ura, T., Lecture Notes on Dynamical Systems (unpublished), 1966-67.

NOTES ON COSET TRANSFORMATION GROUPS[1]

Ta-Sun Wu

(Case Western Reserve University)

Let G be a topological group, and let H be a closed subgroup of G, H\G the right coset space. Define the function π: H\G x G → H by (Hg, f)π = Hgf. Then (H\G, G, π) is a coset transformation group [3]. In this note, we shall consider only those coset transformation groups whose phase space is compact: that is, H\G is compact. Let (X, T, π) be a transformation group. An endomorphism ϕ of a transformation group (X, T, π) is a continuous map from X → X which commutes with the action, that is,

$$(x,\ t)\pi\ \phi = (x\phi,\ t)\pi \quad \text{for all} \quad x \in X \quad t \in T$$

[1]Partially supported by the National Science Foundation.

507

When ϕ is an onto homeomorphism, we say ϕ is an isomorphism. In this note, we shall prove that every endomorphism of a coset transformation group is an isomorphism. When G is locally compact and metrizable, we shall characterize distal coset transformation groups in terms of some subgroup of G.

PROPOSITION 1. Let $(H\backslash G, G, \pi)$ be a coset transformation group with compact phase space. Then every endomorphism of $(H\backslash G, G, \pi)$ is an isomorphism.

Proof. It is clear that $(H\backslash G, G, \pi)$ is a minimal set. Every endomorphism of $(H\backslash G, G, \pi)$ is completely determined by its image at any point. Denote the semigroup of endomorphisms of $(H\backslash G, G, \pi)$ by E. Suppose $\theta \in E$ and $H\theta = Ha$. Then $Hg\theta = Hag$, $g \in G$. In particular, $Hh\theta = H\theta = Ha = H\theta h = Hah$, $h \in H$, a fortiori, $aHa^{-1} \subseteq H$, $aH \subseteq Ha$. Conversely, suppose $aHa^{-1} \subseteq H$, define $\phi : H\backslash G \to H\backslash G$ by $Hg\phi = Hag$. Then ϕ is an endomorphism of $(H\backslash G, G, \pi)$. Let A $= \{a: a \in G, aHa^{-1} \subseteq H\}$. As a subset of G, A forms a closed semigroup. Since $H \subseteq A$, $\pi(A) = HA$ is a compact subset of $H\backslash G$, π the natural projection from

G onto H\G. In fact, HaHa' ⊆ Haa', $\pi(A)$ is a
compact topological semigroup. Suppose HaHa = Ha,
Ha^2 = Ha, Ha = H. This shows $\pi(A)$ has only one
idempotent, $\pi(A)$ is a topological group. For each
$\theta \in E$ with $H\theta$ = Ha, we associate θ with the element
Ha $\in \pi(A)$. It is easy to see this defines an onto
isomorphism between E and $\pi(A)$. It is easy to see
this defines an onto isomorphism between E and $\pi(A)$,
a fortiori, E is a group, and θ is an isomorphism
for $\theta \in E$.

Remark. One might ask the question: Let T be a
subgroup of G such that (H\G, T, $\pi|T$) is minimal.
Is then every endomorphism of (H\G, T, $\pi|T$) an
isomorphism? The answer is negative. Witness:
The example given by J. Auslander [1] is a
homogeneous minimal set which has nonisomorphic
endomorphisms. The proof of homogeneity of that
example is quite long and shall not be given here.

DEFINITION 1. Let H be a closed subgroup of G
such that H\G is compact. We say that H satisfies
the distal condition if there is an ordinal number
γ and a collection of closed subgroups $\{H_i : i \leq r\}$

of G such that

$$H_o = G \quad H_r = H \tag{1}$$

$$H_i \supseteq H_{i+1} \quad \text{and} \quad (H_{i+1}\backslash H_i, H_i) \quad \text{is an}$$
$$\text{almost periodic transformation} \tag{2}$$
$$\text{group for each} \quad i \leq \gamma$$

$$\text{if } i \text{ is a limit ordinal, then}$$
$$H_i = \bigcap_{j<i} H_j \tag{3}$$

DEFINITION 2. A transformation group (X, T, π) is distal if $x, y \in X$, and $\lim xt_\mu = \lim yt_\mu$, then $x = y$.

PROPOSITION 2. Suppose G is locally compact and metrizable. Then $(H\backslash G, G, \pi)$ is distal if and only if H satisfies the distal condition.

Proof. (1) Assume $(H\backslash G, G)$ is distal. Let $H_o = G$. If $(H\backslash G, G)$ is almost periodic, then $r = 1$ and $H = H_1$. If $(H\backslash G, G)$ is not almost periodic, then it has nontrivial structure group. Since G acts transitively on $H\backslash G$, it is clear that the structure group of $(H\backslash G, G)$ is of the form $(H_1 G, G)$ where H_1

is a closed subgroup of G, $H \subset H_1$. Suppose we have already defined H_i such that: (a) $H \subset H_i$, H_i is a closed subgroup of H_{i-1}; (b) $(H_i\backslash H_{i-1}, H_{i-1})$ is almost periodic. If $(H\backslash H_i, H_i)$ is almost periodic, then $\gamma = i + 1$. Otherwise, we have the nontrivial structure group $(H_{i+1}\backslash H_i, H_i)$ of $(H\backslash H_i, H_i)$, $H \subset H_{i+1}$, and H_{i+1} is some closed subgroup of H_i. Let i be a limit ordinal. Assume $\{H_j\}$ has been defined for all $j < i$. We define $H_i = \cap_{j<i} H_j$. Then $H \subset H_i$, H_i is a closed subgroup of H_j for $j < i$. It is clear that such a process will be terminated for some ordinal γ, a fortiori, H satisfies the distal condition.

(2) Conversely, assume that H satisfies the distal condition. We show that $(H\backslash G, G)$ is distal. Since $(H_1\backslash H_0, H_0) = (H_1\backslash G, G)$ is almost periodic, $(H_1\backslash G, G)$ is distal. Suppose we have shown that $(H_i\backslash G, G)$ is distal. Since $(H_{i+1}\backslash H_i, H_i)$ is almost periodic, by a theorem in [3], $(H_{i+1}\backslash G, G)$ is distal. Now let i be a limit ordinal, and assume $(H_j\backslash G, G)$ is distal for all $j < i$. Consider the following map: $(H_i\backslash G, G) \overset{\Pi'}{\to} \underset{j<i}{\Pi} (H_j\backslash G, G)$, $(H_i g \pi)_j = H_j g$. Since $H_i = \cap_{j<i} H_j$, π is an isomorphism (into), a fortiori, $(H_i\backslash G, G)$ is distal, $(H\backslash G, G)$ is distal.

Remark. It is known that there are nondistal

coset transformation groups. We shall give a

general method to construct such examples. Let

K be a compact group and let H be a group of

automorphisms of K such that there is an element

k $\in$ K and a net $\{h_\nu\}$ in H with the property

$h_\nu(k) \to e$, identity of K. For instance, let K be

a compact group which admits either an ergodic or

expansive automorphism θ. Let H be the group

generated by θ. Now form the semidirect product

K $\circledS$ H. Then (H$\backslash$K $\circledS$ H, K $\circledS$ H) is not distal.

REFERENCES

1.   Auslander, J., Endormorphisms of Minimal Sets,
Duke Math. J., 30 (1963), pp. 605-614.
2.   Furstenberg, H., The Structure of Distal Flows,
Am. J. Math., 85 (1963), pp. 477-515.
3.   Keynes, H. B., A Study of the Proximal Relations
in Coset Transformation Groups (To be published).

PROBLEMS

J. AUSLANDER

1. <u>Totally</u> <u>minimal</u> <u>flows</u>. Let (X, φ_t) be
a totally minimal dynamical system (that is,
minimal under every nontrivial subgroup of the
real line). If r and s are nonzero real numbers,
the homeomorphisms φ_r and φ_s generate minimal
cascades on X. Are these cascades isomorphic? If
not (as seems likely) in what sense are they
equivalent? Which totally minimal cascades can be
embedded in totally minimal flows?

  In addition to their intrinsic interest,
the analysis of totally minimal flows is important
in connection with the unsolved problem of whether
an odd dimensional sphere can support a minimal

flow. (It is known that if such a flow exists, it
must be totally minimal.)

2. Recurrence. It is known that if the
real line acts as a transformation group on the
plane, then every recurrent orbit is periodic.
Does the same conclusion hold if R^n acts as a
transformation group on R^{n+1}?

3. Distal transformation groups. If (X, T)
is a distal transformation group, then it is pointwise almost periodic (a union of minimal sets).
The study of distal transformation groups is not
thereby reduced to the study of distal minimal
sets, however, since it is not known how the
minimal sets "fit together." What can be said about
the decomposition space (where each minimal set is
collapsed to a point)? Does (X, T) admit a
continuous nonconstant eigenfunction? If (X, T)
is not minimal, can it always be mapped homo-
morphically onto a nonminimal equicontinuous
transformation group?

4. Minimal sets. Let f be a continuous map
of a compact metric space X onto itself. If f is

not one-to-one, can X be minimal under the semigroup generated by f?

E. EFFROS

1. For which cardinals n can a minimal flow
have precisely n=ergodic invariant probability
measures? It is known that n can be 1 and $2^{\aleph_0}$.

O. HÁJEK

1. Conjecture. Euclidean n-space, $n > 2$, is
never minimal. (Remarks: false for $n = 1$, proof
known for $n = 2$.)

2. Conjecture. Let P be compact Hausdorff,
locally path-connected, with two points at least,
and minimal under a continuous dynamical system;
then P is not simply connected. (Corollary: S^3
is never minimal.)

H. KEYNES

1. Let (X, φ) be a discrete flow where X is
a compact metric space. If (X, φ) is distal, is
the topological entropy zero?

TA-SUN WU

Reference: Numbers refer to Bibliography for
              Topological Dynamics, Gottschalk, 1967.

1.   Expansive homeomorphisms and automorphisms.

(1)   Let X be a compact metric space, and
let θ and φ be homeomorphisms on X such that
θ and φ are isotopic.   If θ is expansive,
then is φ also expansive?   (Reddy and
Hemmingsen: Lifting, to appear.)

(2)   If θ is an expansive homeomorphism
at each point of a compact metric space, then
is θ expansive [376]?

(3)   Does there exist an expansive automorphism on an infinite dimensional torus
group?   Other infinite dimensional groups
[947, 283, 284]?

2.   Almost periodic functions (in the sense
of Gottschalk and Hedlund).

(1)   Let G be the affine group (in
particular R ⓢ R, semidirect product of reals
by reals).   Does there exist a nonconstant
almost periodic function on G [946]?

(2)   Can one produce some sort of structure theorem as Freuenthal's, using uniform almost periodic functions (something like this: Let G be a locally compact group. If it has enough uniformly almost periodic functions, then it is a semidirect product of a group with a compact group).

(3)   Discuss the uniformly almost periodic functions on semisimple Lie groups.

3.   Classification problem.   Classify almost periodic minimal sets.

4.   Lifting.   Generalize the method of R. Ellis on lifting of the action (R. Ellis, Am. J. Math., 1965).   Is there some sort of obstruction theory around [297]?

5.   Coset transformation groups.

(1)   Let X be a compact homogeneous space.   Is X a coset space (T. S. Wu: Homogeneous spaces, Manuscript)?

(2)   Let (H\G, G) be a coset transformation group with H\G compact.   Suppose the proximal relation of (H\G, G) is an

equivalence relation.   Is it closed [557]?

6. Locally almost periodic minimal sets.
Does there exist a compact locally almost periodic
minimal set (X, T, π) such that there exists $x \in X$
such that $P_X(x)$ is countable but not finite; P_X is
the proximal relation of (X, T, π) [948].

7. Proximal relation.   If (X, T, π) is a
compact minimal set such that the least closed
equivalence relation containing P_X is $X \times X$, then
is P_X dense in $X \times X$?   Is the least equivalence
relation containing P_X dense in $X \times X$?

8. Dense orbits.

(1) Let G be a locally compact totally
disconnected group.   Suppose θ is an auto-
morphism on G such that there is an element
g in G such that $[\theta^n(g) | n \in I]$ is dense in
G.   Then is G compact (T. S. Wu: Continuous
Automorphisms on Locally Compact Groups,
Math. Z., 1967)?

(2) Let θ be an automorphism on a
locally compact group which is measure
preserving with respect to Haar measure on G.

Assume θ has a dense orbit.   Then is θ
ergodic?

Symposium Participants

Roy Adler
I.B.M., T. J. Watson Research Center

Richard D. Anderson
Louisiana State University

Joseph Auslander
University of Maryland

Andrew Avez
University of Paris

Prem N. Bajaj
Case-Western Reserve University

Anatole Beck
University of Wisconsin

Kenneth R. Berg
University of Maryland

Nam P. Bhatia
Case-Western Reserve University

Leonard Bidwell
Rutgers, the State University

Julius R. Blum
University of New Mexico

Robert B. Brook
Wesleyan University

John Brookes

Hsin Chu
University of Maryland

Jesse Paul Clay
Rutgers, the State University

John Michael Cole
Academic Industrial Epistemology

Courtney Coleman
Harvey Mudd College

Charles C. Conley
University of Wisconsin

Ubiratan D'Ambrosio
University of Rhode Island

Edward G. Effros
University of Pennsylvania

Murray Eisenberg
University of Massachusetts

Robert Ellis
University of Minnesota

James W. England
University of Virginia

Neal E. Foland
Southern Illinois University

Richard Freiman
University of Maryland

F. Brock Fuller
California Institute of Technology

Harry Furstenberg
Hebrew University

Lew W. Goodwyn
University of Maryland

Walter H. Gottschalk
Wesleyan University

Leon W. Green
University of Minnesota

Glenn Haddock
University of Missouri

Frank J. Hahn
Yale University

Arshag Hajian
Northeastern University

Otomar Hájek
Case-Western Reserve University

William B. Heard
United States Air Force

Alan J. Heckenbach
Iowa State University

G. W. Hedlund
Yale University

Brindell Horelick
University of Maryland

J. G. Horne, Jr.
University of Georgia

Ter-Jenq Huang
Wesleyan University

John Huneke
University of Minnesota

Ralph Hughes
University of North Carolina

Yuji Ito
Brown University

Shizuo Kakutani
Yale University

Michael S. Keane
Mathematisches Institut
der Universität Erlangen-Nurnberg

Joseph F. Kent
University of Virginia

Harvey Keynes
University of California

Adam Kleppner
University of Maryland

Anthony W. Knapp
Cornell University

V. Lakshmikantham
University of Rhode Island

Ping-Fun Lam
Wesleyan University

G. W. Mackey
Harvard University

Vojislav S. Maric
University of Kentucky

Nelson G. Markley
University of Maryland

Lawrence Markus
University of Minnesota

Jerrold E. Marsden
Princeton University

William Parry
University of Warwick

Carlos Perello
Instituto Politécnico Nacional

Stephen E. Puckette
University of Kentucky

Coke S. Reed
Auburn University

Frank Rhodes
University of Southampton

James P. Ryan
Yale University

Richard Sacksteder
City University of New York

Arthur J. Schwartz
University of Michigan

Sol Schwartzman
University of Washington

Peter Seibert
Instituto Politécnico Nacional

George Sell
University of Minnesota

George Seifert
Iowa State University

Leonard D. Shapiro
Yale University

G. P. Szego
University of Milan

Walter Tape

David Tischler
City University of New York

Taro Ura
Case-Western Reserve University

W. Roy Utz, Jr.
University of Missouri

William A. Veech
University of California

Peter Walters
University of California

Benjamin Weiss
I.B.M., T. J. Watson Research Center

Rosamond Welchman
City University of New York

Robert F. Williams
Northwestern University

Ta-Sun Wu
Case-Western Reserve University